PERGAMON INTERNATIONAL LIBRARY
of Science, Technology, Engineering and Social Studies
*The 1000-volume original paperback library in aid of education, industrial
training and the enjoyment of leisure*
Publisher: Robert Maxwell, M.C.

ELECTRIC CIRCUIT
THEORY

THE PERGAMON TEXTBOOK
INSPECTION COPY SERVICE

An inspection copy of any book published in the Pergamon International Library will
gladly be sent to academic staff without obligation for their consideration for course
adoption or recommendation. Copies may be retained for a period of 60 days from receipt
and returned if not suitable. When a particular title is adopted or recommended for
adoption for class use and the recommendation results in a sale of 12 or more copies, the
inspection copy may be retained with our compliments. The Publishers will be pleased
to receive suggestions for revised editions and new titles to be published in this important
International Library.

APPLIED ELECTRICITY AND ELECTRONICS

General Editor: P. HAMMOND

Other titles of interest in the

PERGAMON INTERNATIONAL LIBRARY

ELECTRIC CIRCUIT THEORY

By

R. YORKE,
B.Eng., B.Sc., Ph.D., M.I.E.E.
Department of Electrical Engineering,
The University of Southampton

PERGAMON PRESS

OXFORD · NEW YORK · TORONTO · SYDNEY
PARIS · FRANKFURT

U.K.	Pergamon Press Ltd., Headington Hill Hall, Oxford OX3 0BW, England
U.S.A.	Pergamon Press Inc., Maxwell House, Fairview Park, Elmsford, New York 10523, U.S.A.
CANADA	Pergamon Press Canada Ltd., Suite 104, 150 Consumers Road, Willowdale, Ontario M2J 1P9, Canada
AUSTRALIA	Pergamon Press (Aust.) Pty. Ltd., P.O. Box 544, Potts Point, N.S.W. 2011, Australia
FRANCE	Pergamon Press SARL, 24 rue des Ecoles, 75240 Paris, Cedex 05, France
FEDERAL REPUBLIC OF GERMANY	Pergamon Press GmbH, 6242 Kronberg-Taunus, Hammerweg 6, Federal Republic of Germany

Copyright © 1981 R. Yorke

First edition 1981
British Library Cataloguing in Publication Data

Yorke, R
Electric circuit theory.
– (Applied electricity and electronics). – (Pergamon international library).
1. Electric circuits
I. Title II. Series
621.319.2   TK454   80-41323

ISBN 0-08-026133-7 (Hard)
0-08-026132-9 (Flexi)

Computer typeset by Page Bros (Norwich) Ltd.
Printed in Great Britain by A. Wheaton & Co. Ltd., Exeter

TO MY WIFE

PREFACE

THE aim of this book is to provide the first-year student of Electrical, Electronic or Control Engineering with a Circuit Theory text of modest complexity and length, which nevertheless does not shrink from introducing him to some of the relatively sophisticated concepts which are essential, ultimately, for a complete understanding of the subject. The only prerequisites are Mathematics to A-level (or possibly Scholarship) standard, some slight background knowledge of Engineering and a desire to learn.

Some of the concepts involved in the modern approach to Electrical Engineering have to be pondered upon for a considerable length of time before their full significance becomes apparent, and for this reason the author believes that the sooner the student is made aware of them the better. This is not to say that, on first acquaintance, an exhaustive study should be undertaken, but merely that he should "rub shoulders" with the ideas so as to be prepared for deeper study at a later stage.

An example is the distinction between the time- and frequency-domain descriptions of signals, and, accordingly, this has been introduced at an early stage in the book. This helps, later, in understanding the Laplace Transformation—which itself has been included because it is so widely used now in the study of all linear systems that a student would feel inadequate without some knowledge of it. Notwithstanding this, however, it may be omitted on first reading, if the reader so wishes, with no loss of continuity. The simpler exponential transform is dealt with first and is considered by many to be an adequate introduction to the transform technique.

Likewise, network topology is touched upon without delving too far into its complexities, and several techniques for discovering the frequency characteristics of networks should provide a useful insight for those going on, in later years, to study communications or control engineering.

The book is based on a 1 hour per week, first-year Circuits course for Electrical Engineers which has been taught for many years at Southampton University, although several of the topics have been expanded to provide enough material for use in other universities and colleges where such courses might occupy 2 hours per week.

There is no substitute, in the author's view, for worked examples as a teaching aid and so they appear in abundance both in the text, where full solutions are given, and at the end of each chapter, where they are graded in order of difficulty, in the main, and for which answers only are provided. Well over 200 problems are used altogether—most of them original—though the scope for exhibiting originality in a problem based on Ohm's Law is somewhat limited!

S.I. units have been used throughout and standard symbols and abbreviations strictly adhered to—with one exception. The author felt that the recommended abbreviation for the second—the single lower-case s—would be too readily confused with the complex variable associated with the exponential and Laplace transformations. Consequently he has preferred to use the abbreviation sec. His apologies to the purists. Finally, his sincere thanks are offered, with enthusiasm, to Miss Gina Lott, Miss Joan Sutton and Miss Susan Makin for their accurate and painstaking typing from the manuscript, and with respect to the Senate of Southampton University for their permission to use problems from some past examination papers.

EDITOR'S PREFACE

ELECTRIC circuit theory provides the framework of electrical engineering and is therefore central to all courses for future electrical engineers. Such a central subject makes great demands on the teacher, particularly in laying foundations which can give adequate support to later advanced work. No amount of computational skill, useful though it is, can compensate for a lack of physical understanding of circuit parameters, circuit response and circuit topology. In this book Dr. Yorke, out of his long experience as a university teacher, lays a foundation which will serve his readers well. His emphasis throughout is on physical processes rather than on abstract mathematics and the book has a real engineering flavour, which sustains interest and meets the needs of those who want to apply their knowledge to the practice of the profession of electrical engineering.

P. HAMMOND

CONTENTS

SYMBOLS, UNITS AND ABBREVIATIONS

1. *Standard symbols for electrical parameters*

R	Resistance
X	Reactance
Z	Impedance
G	Conductance
B	Susceptance
Y	Admittance
C	Capacitance
L	Inductance (self)
M	Inductance (mutual)
P	Power
Q	Q-factor (of resonant circuit); Imaginary compt. of complex power
q	Electric charge
I, i	Current
V, v	Voltage
V_m, I_m	Peak voltage or current
V^*, I^*	Conjugate complex of V, I
p.d.	Potential difference
E, e	Electromotive force
e.m.f.	Electromotive force
VA	Volt-amperes
VAr	Reactive volt-amperes
P.F., p.f.	Power factor
$S = P + jQ$	Complex power = real + imaginary compts.

2. *Units*

A	Amperes $(pA, \mu A, mA)$
C	Coulomb $(mC, \mu C)$

F	Farad	(nF, μF, pF)
g	Gram	(mg, kg)
H	Henry	(mH, μH)
Hz	Hertz	(cycles per second) (kHz, MHz)
J	Joule	(kJ, MJ)
min		minute
m	Metre	(mm, cm, km)
rad		radian
S	Siemens	(reciprocal ohms)
sec	Second	(msec, μsec)
V	Volt	(μV, mV, kV, MV)
W	Watt	(μW, mW, kW, MW)
Ω	Ohm	(μΩ, mΩ, kΩ, MΩ)

3. General abbreviations

A, a	A constant
α, β	Constants
α	Damping constant, $\dfrac{R}{2L}$ in series $R, L, C,$ circuit
b	A constant
B	Number of branches (in a network)
α	Ratio of frequencies ⎫
β	Ratio of inductances ⎬ in a resonant circuit
δ	Ratio of capacitances ⎭
dB	Decibel
e	Base of Naperian logarithms (2.718 28)
η	$\dfrac{\omega}{\omega_0}$ (ratio of any radian frequency : resonant radian frequency)
η	Efficiency
$F(s), \mathscr{L}...$	Laplace transform of
f	Frequency (Hz)
f	Function
$G(s), \mathbf{G}(j\omega)$	Gain function
$\mathscr{I}m$	Imaginary part
j	$=\sqrt{-1}$
K, k	Constant

λ	$-\frac{1}{2} + j\dfrac{\sqrt{3}}{2}$
λ^2	$-\frac{1}{2} - j\dfrac{\sqrt{3}}{2}$
log	Logarithm to base 10
ln	Logarithm to base e
L	Number of link branches in a network
N	Number of nodes in a network
P	Phasor
$\left.\begin{array}{c}P(s) \\ Q(s)\end{array}\right\}$	Polynomial in s
r	Ratio of wattmeter readings
$\mathscr{R}e$, Re	Real part
r.m.s.	Root-mean-square
s	Complex variable
σ	Real part of s
T, t	Time
$T(s)$, $\mathbf{T}(j\omega)$	Transfer function
$t(0^-)$	Instant just before $t = 0$
$t(0^+)$	Instant just after $t = 0$
τ	Time constant
$U(t)$	Unit step function
W, w	Energy
ω_0	Undamped natural frequency
y	$\left(\dfrac{\omega}{\omega_0} - \dfrac{\omega_0}{\omega}\right)$ for a resonant circuit
a	$= yQ$ ($Q = Q$-factor)
ω	Any frequency; imaginary part of s
Φ, ϕ	Function
ϕ	Phase angle
$Y(s)$, $\mathbf{Y}(j\omega)$	Admittance function
$Z(s)$, $\mathbf{Z}(j\omega)$	Impedance function
ζ	Damping ratio $\left(= \dfrac{\text{damping constant } \alpha}{\text{critical damping constant } \alpha_c}\right)$

CHAPTER 1

FIELDS, CIRCUITS AND CIRCUIT PARAMETERS

1.1 FUNDAMENTAL CONCEPTS

1.1.1 Potential and potential difference

Electric charge is as fundamental a constituent of our Universe as are mass and energy. Indeed, present physical theory supposes that all matter consists of particles, the principal attributes of which are mass and electric charge.

Two kinds of charge are known, arbitrarily designated positive and negative, which are characterised by the experimental observation that, under static conditions, separated like charges exert a mutual force of repulsion, whilst unlike charges, under similar conditions, exert a force of attraction. Under these conditions the field of force associated with charge is referred to as an *electric field*.

The smallest known charge is that of a single electron, and, since this is much too small to adopt as a unit for all but a few special purposes, a unit, the COULOMB, equal to 6.24×10^{18} electrons, has been chosen as the practical (S.I.) unit.

As a consequence of their mutual forces, any system of charges possesses potential energy, since, unless constrained, the individual charges will move and energy will be released. As part of the theoretical structure this energy is ascribed to the electric field, and so it is possible to identify with every point in the field a level of energy, the magnitude of which is dependent upon the charges and their relative positions.

When one of the charges is of unit magnitude, and positive, the energy

1

at the point defining its position is referred to as the POTENTIAL at that point, and hence is measured (in S.I. units) in JOULES per COULOMB (J/C) or VOLTS. The POTENTIAL DIFFERENCE between two points in a field is therefore the difference in energy, per unit charge, at the two points.

Observation shows that the force experienced by a charge—a measure of the electric field strength—varies with distance and diminishes to zero only at an infinite distance from the source charge(s). Therefore a point at infinity may be considered to be at zero potential.

In practice, however, we are generally concerned with a datum of potential which is not zero—the most common being the earth's surface considered as an equipotential. Since most of our experiments are earth-bound there is no need to take into account the potential of the earth with respect to the *true* zero datum.

PROBLEM 1.1

The potential energy of a charge of $+4\,C$ at a point A in a field is $24\,J$, and at a point B, $36\,J$. Determine, in volts, the potential difference V_{AB}.

Solution

$$\text{Energy difference } W_{AB} = 24 - 36$$
$$= -12\,J.$$

But this is for a charge of $4\,C$. Hence, the potential difference (p.d.) or energy difference per unit charge

$$= \frac{-12}{4} = \underline{-3\,V}\ (J/C).$$

The negative sign means that energy is required from an external source to move the charge from A to B. This energy is recoverable when the charge moves from B to A. Point B is said to be at a higher potential than point A. Hence, $V_{BA} = +3\,V$.

Note that, since energy is scalar, it is not necessary to know the path followed by the charge in passing from A to B (or from B to A) nor the law of variation of force with distance over this range.

If, however, the data were in terms of force at each point of the field, the potential difference would be given by integrating the scalar product of the force (per unit charge) and displacement vectors over the distance AB: or

$$V = \frac{1}{q} \int_{A}^{B} \mathbf{F} \cdot \mathbf{ds} \qquad (1.1)$$

1.1.2 Electric current

When a charge is in motion relative to a "fixed" frame of reference, an additional force appears to an observer (equipped with a suitable detector) in the fixed frame, this force being referred to as a magnetic force. Analogously, the region of magnetic influence associated with the moving charge is called a *magnetic field*, because it has similar characteristics to the field of force of a magnet. It is usual to refer to moving charge by the term ELECTRIC CURRENT, the intensity of which is equal to the time rate of charge transference between two points in a field.

In consequence, the relation connecting charge and current is:

$$i(t) = \frac{dq}{dt} \qquad (1.2)$$

where i = current, and q = charge.

Unit current, therefore, flows when charge is transferred at the rate of 1 C/sec,* i.e. 6.24×10^{18} electronic charges/sec, this current being designated 1 ampere (1 A). It is important to appreciate, however, that when a current flows from A to B it is not necessary for every individual charge to move the whole distance AB, but only that the *average* rate of charge transference should conform to eqn. (1.2).

1.2 THE ELECTRIC CIRCUIT

These and all other aspects of stationary, moving and accelerating charges are truly encompassed by Maxwell's electromagnetic theory, but, accepting certain restrictions, it is possible to apply a much simplified theory which is sufficiently accurate to describe a wide range of electrical

---

* The abbreviation "sec" is used for second throughout the text in order to avoid possible confusion with s (the recommended S.I. abbreviation) since s is used later as the complex variable.

phenomena and applications. Such a theory is referred to as CIRCUIT THEORY and is concerned with the transmission of energy from one point to another through the use of real devices such as generators, wires, batteries, motors and transformers. In this process, interest is focused less upon electric and magnetic fields than upon their circuit equivalents, potential differences and currents. As section 1.1 indicates, the field and circuit concepts are inseparably related, so it is a matter for philosophical argument whether energy transfer is effected by fields or by voltages and currents. Nevertheless, the usefulness of the circuit concept lies in the relatively simple solution of such problems which it permits.

The transformation from field to circuit conceptualisation consists in regarding currents as flowing from one physical device to another only through wires, which connect them together, and the characteristics of each device as being purely local; that is to say, the currents may be constant or time-dependent but not dependent on space coordinates in the circuit. Such a circuit is said to consist of lumped (rather than distributed) elements, and the restrictions imply that only conduction currents are considered and that displacement currents are not. Conduction currents flow particularly easily in most metals, this property being due to the extremely large number of free electrons available as charge carriers in the crystal lattice. Thus, at normal temperatures, silver is the best of all conductors, with copper and aluminium only slightly inferior.

PROBLEM 1.2

Given that a typical metal contains 10^{28} free (conduction) electrons per m^3, calculate the *average* velocity of these electrons when a wire of cross-sectional area $1\,mm^2$ carries a current of $1\,A$.

Solution

The number of charge carriers/m length of wire $= 10^{28} \times 10^{-6}$
$$= 10^{22}$$

for $1\,A$ to flow (i.e. for 6.24×10^{18} electrons/sec to pass a given point in the wire); the average velocity is given by:

$$v = \frac{6.24 \times 10^{18}}{10^{22}}\ m/sec$$

or

$$v = 0.624 \, \text{mm/sec.}$$

Superimposed upon this slow, drift velocity is, under normal conditions of temperature, a much larger but random thermal agitation velocity which, since it does not contribute to the net transference of charge, is of no concern in the macroscopic view of current adopted here.

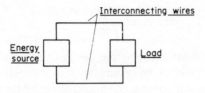

FIG. 1.1. The electric circuit in its simplest form.

The diagram of Fig. 1.1 illustrates the essential parts of an electric circuit, which consists, in its simplest form, of an energy source and an interconnected energy dissipation or conversion device, known as the load.

1.2.1 Energy sources

A practical energy source may take one of many forms, depending, for example, on electro-chemical, electromagnetic, thermo-electric, photo-electric, etc., principles, but for the purpose of circuit analysis only two idealised forms are recognised, to one of which all practical sources approximate. These are: (i) the voltage source and (ii) the current source.

The *voltage source* maintains a constant terminal voltage irrespective of the current supplied to the load. It is important to appreciate that the voltage may be a function of, for example, time, temperature, pressure, etc.; it is constant only with respect to variations of load.

The *current source* maintains a constant current in the load irrespective of the terminal voltage—which, in this case, is determined by the magnitude of the load. As with the voltage source, the generated current may depend on many other factors, but its one essential attribute is its independence of load.

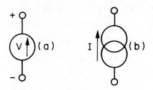

FIG. 1.2. (a) A voltage source.
(b) A current source.

The symbols used for these active devices are illustrated in Fig. 1.2 (a) and (b). Also shown on the figure are the arbitrarily chosen positive directions of voltage and current. It should be noted that, conventionally, current flows through the source from the negative to the positive terminal.

The transformation from these idealised sources to simulate the characteristics of real sources can be simply effected, as shown in Problem 1.5.

1.2.2 Power and energy

The definitions of potential and potential difference given in section 1.1.1 lead to the following relationships: the energy, w, expanded in moving a charge q through a potential difference (p.d.) v is given by:

$$w = qv$$

hence

$$\frac{\mathrm{d}w}{\mathrm{d}t} = v\frac{\mathrm{d}q}{\mathrm{d}t} = vi.$$

The rate of expenditure of energy is defined as the power p. Hence, in general the power is given by

$$p(t) = v(t)\, i(t) \tag{1.3}$$

and is measured in WATTS when v and i are in volts and amperes, respectively.

If power $p(t)$ is expended for time T, the total energy expended (or stored) is:

$$W = \int_0^T p(t)\, dt. \tag{1.4}$$

1.2.3 The load

By a method similar to that adopted for energy sources, the load— or passive element of a circuit—may be idealised and defined by its terminal voltage/current relationship. All practical passive devices possess energy dissipative properties, often accompanied by energy-storage properties so that three distinct idealised types are possible.

(a) *The resistance parameter*

A circuit which dissipates energy but stores none is said to consist solely of *resistance*. The property is defined by the relationship:

$$R = \frac{v(t)}{i(t)} \tag{1.5}$$

where R is the resistance in OHMS if $v(t)$ and $i(t)$ are in volts and amperes, respectively, and eqn. (1.5) is known as OHM'S LAW.

The corresponding diagrammatic representation is shown in Fig. 1.3(a) which also shows the positive directions of p.d. and current. It should be noted that, unlike an active element, a passive element develops a potential difference in opposition to the current flow so that there is a fall of potential through the element in the direction of the current flow.

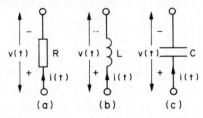

FIG. 1.3. Symbols for (a) resistance, (b) inductance, (c) capacitance.

For this reason the terminal p.d. is called a potential drop—or voltage drop. The element which possesses resistance is termed a *resistor*.

The reciprocal of resistance is *conductance* designated by the symbol G.

Thus,

$$G = \frac{1}{R} \qquad (1.6)$$

the units of G being siemens, or reciprocal ohms. Hence, an alternative form of Ohm's Law is:

$$i(t) = v(t)\,G. \qquad (1.7)$$

From eqn. (1.3) the power dissipated, $v(t)\,i(t)$, may be written in terms of resistance (or conductance) and voltage or current only; thus,

$$p(t) = i(t)R\,i(t) = R[i(t)]^2 \qquad (1.8)$$

$$= v(t)\frac{v(t)}{R} = G[v(t)]^2. \qquad (1.9)$$

If, for example, the voltage applied is constant, i.e. $v(t) = V$, then $i(t) = I$ and the power

$$P = I^2R = V^2G \qquad (1.10)$$

is also independent of time.

(b) *The inductance parameter*

A circuit is said to possess inductance if it is able to store magnetic field energy. The property is defined by the relationship

$$v(t) = L\frac{di(t)}{dt} \qquad (1.11)$$

where L is the *inductance*, the units of which are HENRYS if v and i are in volts and amperes, respectively, and t is in seconds. A p.d. of 1 V will, therefore, cause the current to change at the rate of 1 A/sec in an inductance of 1 H. The circuit representation of the inductance parameter is shown in Fig. 1.3(b).

Equation (1.11) may also be written in general integral form:

$$i(t) = \frac{1}{L} \int v(t)\,dt. \tag{1.12}$$

The element which possesses inductance is termed an *inductor*.
From eqn. (1.3) the power, $v(t)\,i(t)$, may be written:

$$p(t) = Li(t)\frac{di(t)}{dt}$$

and is non-zero only when $di(t)/dt$ has a value. Hence for a steady current $i(t) = I$, $p(t) = 0$, but for the current I to have been established, $p(t)$ has contributed to the stored energy:

$$W = \int_0^T p(t)\,dt$$

where T is the time taken for the current to build up to I.
Hence,

$$W = \int_0^T Li(t)\frac{di(t)}{dt}\,dt$$
$$= \int_0^I Li(t)\,di(t) = \tfrac{1}{2}LI^2. \tag{1.13}$$

(c) *The capacitance parameter*

A circuit which is able to store electrostatic field energy is said to possess *capacitance*. The property is defined in terms of the electric charge stored per unit of potential difference at its terminals, according to the equation:

$$q(t) = Cv(t) \tag{1.14}$$

where C is the *capacitance*, the units of which are FARADS when v and q are in volts and coulombs, respectively. Hence, a capacitance of 1 F stores a charge of 1 C for a terminal p.d. of 1 V. Combining eqns. (1.2) and (1.14) gives:

$$i(t) = C\frac{dv(t)}{dt} \tag{1.15}$$

with t in seconds.

Thus, a current of 1 A flows into a capacitance of 1 F when the terminal voltage changes at the rate of 1 V/sec.

Equation (1.15) may be rewritten in general integral form:

$$v(t) = \frac{1}{C} \int i(t)\, \mathrm{d}t. \qquad (1.16)$$

The element which possesses capacitance is termed a *capacitor*, and its circuit representation is illustrated in Fig. 1.3(c).

From eqn. (1.3) the power, $v(t)\,i(t)$, may be written:

$$p(t) = v(t)C\frac{\mathrm{d}v(t)}{\mathrm{d}t}$$

and is non-zero only when $\mathrm{d}v(t)/\mathrm{d}t$ has a value. Hence, for a steady voltage $v(t) = V$, say, $p(t) = 0$, but for the voltage V to have built up on the capacitor, $p(t)$ has contributed to the stored energy

$$W = \int_0^T p(t)\, \mathrm{d}t$$

where T is the time taken for the voltage to have built up to V.

Hence,

$$W = \int_0^T v(t)C\frac{\mathrm{d}v(t)}{\mathrm{d}t}\, \mathrm{d}t$$
$$= \int_0^V C\,v(t)\, \mathrm{d}v(t) = \tfrac{1}{2}CV^2. \qquad (1.17)$$

Equations (1.11) and (1.15) show that step discontinuities are not possible in the current through inductance nor in the voltage across capacitance, since such steps would require, respectively, infinite voltage and infinite current. The ideas implicit in these restrictions are important in the analysis of circuits containing inductance and capacitance since they enable the initial conditions to be defined.

1.2.4 Summary

The results of section 1.2.3 are summarised in Table 1.1, in which the circuit parameters are expressed in each case as the ratio between a voltage function (of time) and a current function.

Although the relationships of section 1.2.3 have been dealt with in a manner which could suggest that resistance, inductance and capacitance exist separately, this is never true in practice. For example, a common method of making an inductor is to wind a coil of wire on a rigid, circular former, but a moment's thought will show that, although the coil is predominantly inductive, the wire must have resistance and some capacitance must exist between the turns of the coil. Nevertheless a good approximation, in circuit analysis terms, to the real coil can be made by suitably combining the resistance, inductance and capacitance parameters. The properties of this *equivalent circuit* may then be determined by a suitable admixture of the relationships of Table 1.1. Problem 1.23 illustrates this principle quantitatively.

TABLE 1.1

$R = \dfrac{v(t)}{i(t)}$	$L = \dfrac{v(t)}{di(t)/dt}$	$C = \dfrac{i(t)}{dv(t)/dt}$
$G = \dfrac{i(t)}{v(t)}$	$L = \dfrac{\int v(t)\,dt}{i(t)}$	$C = \dfrac{\int i(t)\,dt}{v(t)}$

Similar considerations hold for real capacitors and resistors and much skill and expertise is needed in the design and manufacture of practical circuit components in which the desired property (resistance, inductance or capacitance, as the case may be) is predominant.

1.3 KIRCHHOFF'S LAWS

Although Ohm's Law and the laws expressed by eqns. (1.11) and (1.15) are generally true, two extensions of them are of great value in dealing with circuits having many interconnected circuit elements and energy sources. They were first suggested by Kirchhoff in 1848.

1.3.1 The first, or current, law

There is no storage—or depletion—of charge at a junction (a node) of a network, so that the algebraic sum of currents, meeting at a node is zero. Thus, in the circuit of Fig. 1.4(a), at node A,

$$i - i_1 - i_2 = 0. \tag{1.18}$$

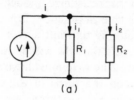

(a)

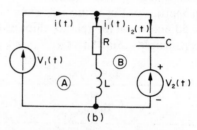

(b)

FIG. 1.4. Illustrating Kirchhoff's laws. (a)
The current law. (b) The voltage law.

1.3.2 The second, or voltage, law

In any closed mesh of a network, the algebraic sum of all the potential drops due to current flow is equal to the algebraic sum of all the e.m.f.s in the mesh, one direction round the mesh being arbitrarily taken to be positive. Thus, in the circuit of Fig. 1.4(b):
in mesh A

$$i_1(t)R + L\frac{\mathrm{d}i_1(t)}{\mathrm{d}t} = v_1(t) \tag{1.19}$$

and in mesh B

$$-i_1(t)R - L\frac{\mathrm{d}i_1(t)}{\mathrm{d}t} + \frac{1}{C}\int i_2(t)\,\mathrm{d}t = -v_2(t). \tag{1.20}$$

The clockwise direction in meshes A and B has been taken as positive.

It is usual, in such a circuit, for $v_1(t)$ and $v_2(t)$ as well as R, L and C to be known, so that eqns. (1.18), (1.19) and (1.20) contain only the three unknown currents i_1, i_2 and i. In principle, therefore, the three currents—and hence all potential differences—may be found by solving the three equations.

PROBLEM 1.3

A voltage source of e.m.f. 12 V is connected to a load consisting of two resistors in series, one of resistance 10 Ω and the other of 5 Ω. Determine the current and power in each resistor and the total energy supplied in 10 min.

Solution

(i) *Currents:* Referring to Fig. 1.5, by Ohm's Law,

$$i = \frac{12}{10 + 5} = \underline{0.8 \text{ A}},$$

and since the resistors are in series this is the current in each.

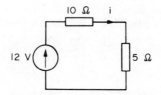

FIG. 1.5. The circuit for Problem 1.3.

(ii) *Powers:* Voltage across the 10-Ω resistor $= 10 \times 0.8$
$$= \underline{8 \text{ V}},$$

$$\therefore \quad P_{10} = 8 \times 0.8 = \underline{6.4 \text{ W}}.$$

Voltage across the 5-Ω resistor is either $12 - 8 = 4$ V
or $5 \times 0.8 = 4$ V,

$$\therefore \quad P_5 = 4 \times 0.8 = \underline{3.2 \text{ W}}.$$

Note that the power is proportional to the resistance when the current is constant.

(iii) *Energy:*

$$W = \int_0^T v(t)\,i(t)\,\mathrm{d}t = 12 \times 0.8 \int_0^{600} \mathrm{d}t,$$

since both V and I are constant.

$$\therefore \quad W = 9.6 \times 600 \text{ J}$$
$$= \underline{5760 \text{ J.}}$$

This energy is dissipated as heat in the two resistors.

PROBLEM 1.4

Three resistors of resistances $3\,\Omega$, $5\,\Omega$ and $8\,\Omega$ are connected in parallel across a 20-V source. Determine the equivalent resistance of the combination.

Solution

Referring to Fig. 1.6, applying Kirchhoff's first Law,

$$I = I_1 + I_2 + I_3 = \frac{20}{3} + \frac{20}{5} + \frac{20}{8} = \underline{13.1667 \text{ A.}}$$

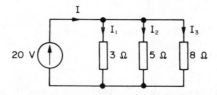

FIG. 1.6. The circuit for Problem 1.4.

Hence, R, the equivalent resistance, is

$$R = \frac{20}{13.1667} = \underline{1.52\ \Omega.}$$

In general, therefore, if the resistances are R_1, R_2 and R_3

$$R = \frac{1}{(1/R_1) + (1/R_2) + (1/R_3)}, \quad \text{or} \quad G = G_1 + G_2 + G_3$$

where $G = 1/R$ and $G_n = 1/R_n$.

PROBLEM 1.5

A certain car battery had an open-circuit p.d. of 13.4 V and would supply 2000 A when short-circuited. Determine equivalent circuits in terms of (a) a voltage source and (b) a current source. In each case use the equivalent circuit to determine the current and power in an external load of 0.1 Ω, and the corresponding terminal p.d.

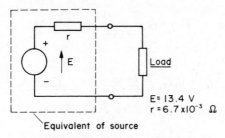

E= 13.4 V
r = 6.7 x 10⁻³ Ω

Equivalent of source

FIG. 1.7. Voltage-source equivalent circuit, Problem 1.5.

Solution

(a) On short circuit the terminal p.d. = 0 so that the e.m.f. of 13.4 V is used in circulating 2000 A through the internal resistance. The equivalent circuit in terms of a voltage source is therefore as shown in Fig. 1.7.

$$\therefore \quad r = \frac{13.4}{2000} = \underline{6.7 \times 10^{-3} \, \Omega}.$$

Current in a load of 0.1 Ω $= \dfrac{13.4}{0.1 + 0.0067} = \underline{125.5 \text{ A}}.$

Power in the load $= I^2 R = 125.5^2 \times 0.1 = \underline{1.57 \text{ kW}}.$

Voltage across the load (= terminal p.d. of battery)
$$= 125.5 \times 0.1 = \underline{12.55 \text{ V}}.$$

(b) On open circuit the generated current of 2000 A produces a terminal p.d. of 13.4 V, hence the current source must already be shunted by resistance r, where

$$r = \frac{13.4}{2000} = 6.7 \times 10^{-3} \, \Omega,$$

or by conductance

$$G = \frac{2000}{13.4} = 149.3 \text{ S (reciprocal ohms)}.$$

The equivalent circuit of the source in terms of a current generator is therefore as shown in Fig. 1.8. The load conductance = 10 S, so the total conductance $= 149.3 + 10 = 159.3 \text{ S} = G_T$. Now,

$$V = I/G_T = \frac{2000}{159.3} = \underline{12.55 \text{ V}}$$

and

$$I_L = V.G_L = 12.55 \times 10 = \underline{125.5 \text{ A}}.$$

$$\text{Power} = V^2.G_L = 12.55^2 \times 10 = \underline{1.57 \text{ kW}}.$$

Circuits in parallel, i.e. those to which a common voltage is applied, are often most quickly dealt with using the conductance concept.

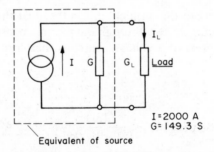

Fig. 1.8. Current-source equivalent circuit, Problem 1.5.

PROBLEM 1.6

A certain generator is represented by a voltage source of e.m.f. E in series with resistance R. Determine the maximum power which may be drawn from the generator and the resistance of the load which achieves this result.

Solution

Referring to the diagram of Fig. 1.9, the power in the load,

$$P_L = I_L^2 R_L$$

$$= \frac{E^2 R_L}{(R + R_L)^2}.$$

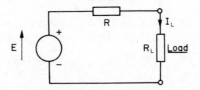

FIG. 1.9. Circuit for determining the power delivered to a load, Problem 1.6.

For maximum P_L,

$$\frac{dP_L}{dR_L} = 0$$

or

$$\frac{E^2[(R + R_L)^2 - 2R_L(R + R_L)]}{(R + R_L)^4} = 0$$

or

$$(R + R_L)^2 = 2R_L(R + R_L), \quad \text{giving } \underline{R_L = R}.$$

And

$$P_L(\text{max}) = \frac{E^2}{4R}.$$

Of the total generated power, one-half is available for the load and one-half is lost in the generator. Thus, although the power supplied to the load is a maximum the electrical efficiency is poor (only 50%).

PROBLEM 1.7

A galvanometer, of resistance $40\,\Omega$, is to be used to measure the voltage between two terminals, A and B. It is known that the voltage is approximately 10 times larger than would give full-scale deflection of the galvanometer, so a resistance potential divider is used to step it down by a factor of 10. At the same time the divider must be designed to present to the galvanometer a resistance of $300\,\Omega$ to provide correct damping conditions. Determine suitable values for the resistances of the divider.

Solution

The diagram of Fig. 1.10 shows a possible circuit arrangement to achieve the desired result.

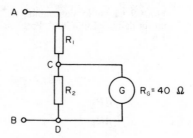

FIG. 1.10. Reducing the sensitivity of a galvanometer, Problem 1.7.

Let R be the combined resistance of R_2 and R_G in parallel. The voltage ratio of the divider is equal to the resistance ratio (cf. Problem 1.3). Hence,

$$\frac{R}{R_1 + R} = 0.1.$$

But

$$R = \frac{40R_2}{40 + R_2},$$

$$\therefore \quad 0.1R_1 + \frac{4R_2}{40 + R_2} = \frac{40R_2}{40 + R_2}. \tag{1.21}$$

Also, the effective resistance shunting the galvanometer is equal to the parallel combination of R_1 and R_2 (since terminals AB are effectively short-circuited when calculating the resistance looking into CD). This must be $= 300\ \Omega$. Hence,

$$300 = \frac{R_1 R_2}{R_1 + R_2}. \tag{1.22}$$

Equations (1.21) and (1.22) may be solved to give

$$\underline{R_1 = 353\ \Omega} \quad \text{and} \quad \underline{R_2 = 2000\ \Omega}.$$

PROBLEM 1.8

In the circuit of Fig. 1.11, known as the Wheatstone bridge, the resistances R_1, R_2, R_3 and R_4 are adjusted until the galvanometer indicates null (i.e. that the points A and C are at the same potential). Determine the relationship between the resistances.

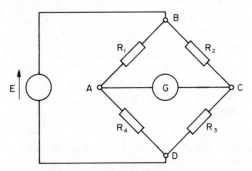

FIG. 1.11. The Wheatstone bridge.

Solution

Potential B to D $= E$ (determined by the e.m.f. of the voltage source). Hence,

$$\text{potential A to D} = E \cdot \frac{R_4}{R_1 + R_4},$$

and

$$\text{potential C to D} = E \cdot \frac{R_3}{R_2 + R_3}.$$

But these are equal since the potential A to C $=$ zero.

Hence,

$$\frac{R_4}{R_1 + R_4} = \frac{R_3}{R_2 + R_3} \quad \text{or} \quad \frac{R_1}{R_4} + 1 = \frac{R_2}{R_3} + 1,$$

giving

$$R_1 R_3 = R_2 R_4. \tag{1.23}$$

PROBLEM 1.9

In communication circuits it is sometimes necessary to insert a four-terminal network between a generator and a load in order to achieve resistance matching. Such a network is the "L-pad" shown in the circuit of Fig. 1.12, inserted between the generator, of e.m.f. 10 V and internal

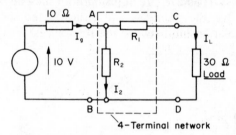

FIG. 1.12. Matching a load to a generator, Problem 1.9.

resistance 10 Ω, and the 30-Ω load. Determine R_1 and R_2 so that both generator and load are matched, i.e. that the generator looking into terminals AB sees 10 Ω and that the load looking back into terminals CD sees 30 Ω. Determine also the power transferred to the load and that lost in the L-pad.

Solution

The resistance looking into AB = 10 Ω. Hence,

$$10 = \frac{R_2 (30 + R_1)}{R_1 + R_2 + 30}$$

or,

$$10R_1 + 10R_2 + 300 = 30R_2 + R_1 R_2. \tag{1.24}$$

The resistance looking back into CD = 30 Ω. Hence,

$$30 = R_1 + \frac{10R_2}{10 + R_2}$$

or,

$$300 + 20R_2 = 10R_1 + R_1R_2. \qquad (1.25)$$

Adding eqns. (1.24) and (1.25) gives:

$$\underline{R_1 = 2R_2}.$$

Substituting this value of R_1 into (1.25) gives

$$R_2 = \sqrt{150} = \underline{12.25\ \Omega} \quad \text{and hence} \quad \underline{R_1 = 24.5\ \Omega}.$$

To calculate the power in the load, we first determine the current in it. The generator feeds, in effect, two 10-Ω resistors in series.
Hence

$$I_g = \frac{10}{2 \times 10} = \underline{0.5\ A}.$$

The current through the load,

$$I_L = \frac{R_2}{R_1 + R_2 + 30} \times 0.5 = \underline{0.0918\ A}.$$

So the power in the load $= I_L^2 \times 30 = \underline{0.252\ W}.$

Total power supplied by the generator $= V_{AB} \times I_g$
$$= 5 \times 0.5 = \underline{2.5\ W}.$$

Hence, the power lost in the L-pad $= 2.5 - 0.252$
$$= \underline{2.248\ W}.$$

The price of matching both the generator and the load is, in this case, the loss of 90% of the generated power.

PROBLEM 1.10
Determine the resistance of and the current taken by a 100-W, 240-V lamp.

Solution

$$\text{Power} = I^2 R = V^2/R, \quad \therefore 100 = \frac{240^2}{R}, \ \underline{R = 576 \ \Omega}.$$

And, by Ohm's Law,

$$I = \frac{240}{576} = \underline{0.417 \text{ A}}.$$

PROBLEM 1.11

An electric kettle absorbing 1250 W takes 4 min to boil its contents. Determine (a) the total energy supplied and (b) the cost of the energy at 3.125p per unit.

Solution

(a) Energy $= \displaystyle\int_0^T p(t) \, \mathrm{d}t = P \times T$ since $p(t) = $ constant

$$= 1250 \times 4 \times 60 \text{ J}$$
$$= \underline{300 \text{ kJ}}.$$

(b) 1 unit of electrical energy $\equiv 1 \text{ kWh} = 3.6 \times 10^6 \text{ J}$.

In this case, energy consumed $= \dfrac{3 \times 10^5}{3.6 \times 10^6}$ kWh

$$= \underline{0.0833 \text{ kWh}}.$$

$$\therefore \text{Cost} = 3.125 \times 0.0833 = \underline{0.26\text{p}}.$$

PROBLEM 1.12

The resistance R of a filament lamp is related to the current by the following equation:

$$R = 50 + 1200I \text{ ohm}, \quad \text{where } I \text{ is the current (A)}.$$

(a) Calculate the current and resistance when a voltage of 240 V is applied to the lamp.
(b) Determine also the voltage, current and resistance when the lamp is consuming 50 W.

Solution

(a) $V = IR = I(50 + 1200I)$, $\therefore 240 = 50I + 1200I^2$

$$\text{or } I = \frac{-5 \pm \sqrt{25 + 11{,}520}}{240} = \frac{-5 \pm 107.45}{240}.$$

Taking the positive root, $I = \dfrac{102.45}{240} = \underline{0.427 \text{ A}}$,

$$R = \frac{240}{0.427} = \underline{563 \ \Omega}.$$

(b) $I^2R = 50$ or $I^2(50 + 1200I) = 50$ or, $1200I^3 + 5I^2 - 5 = 0$, a cubic equation which is best solved by factorising. Thus:

$$(I - \tfrac{1}{3})(24I^2 + 9I + 3) = 0, \quad \text{which gives } \underline{I = \tfrac{1}{3}\text{A}}$$

and two complex roots which, in the present case, may be ignored.

$$\therefore R = 50 \times 3^2 = \underline{450 \ \Omega} \quad \text{and} \quad V = 450 \times \tfrac{1}{3} = \underline{150 \text{ V}}.$$

PROBLEM 1.13

A network covering the whole xy plane is made up of square meshes, each side of which has a resistance of 1Ω, as shown in Fig. 1.13.

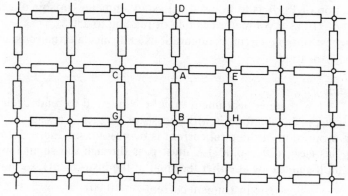

FIG. 1.13. A square-mesh network of resistors, Problem 1.13.

Determine the resistance between two adjacent nodes, such as A and B.

Solution

The problem may be solved by considering the network in two stages. First, assume a current I to be fed into node A and collected at infinity. Applying Kirchhoff's first Law at node A, I divides into four equal components flowing along AB, AC, AD and AE, since the infinite network is symmetrical about node A.

Second, assume that the current I returns from infinity and is drawn from the network at node B. By the same considerations of symmetry, and applying Kirchhoff's first Law at node B, the currents flowing along AB, HB, FB and GB are each $\frac{1}{4}I$.

The total current flowing along AB when the current I is fed into A and abstracted at B is, therefore,

$$2 \times \tfrac{1}{4}I = I/2.$$

Hence, the potential difference between A and B is, since $R_{AB} = 1\,\Omega$, $I/2$, and the effective resistance between A and B is

$$\frac{I}{2} \times \frac{1}{I} = \underline{0.5\,\Omega}.$$

PROBLEM 1.14

An indicating instrument having a resistance of $5\,\Omega$ and a full-scale deflection of $1\,\text{mA}$ is to be used (a) as an ammeter capable of reading to $20\,\text{A}$, (b) as a voltmeter capable of reading to $250\,\text{V}$.

Suggest suitable circuit configurations and calculate the resistance of the resistor used.

Solution

(a) A low-reading instrument may be converted to read a relatively high current by shunting it with a resistor of such a resistance that a large proportion of the total current is by-passed; see Fig. 1.14(a).

In this case, $(20 - 0.001)\,\text{A}$ must pass through the shunt (applying Kirchhoff's first Law at either terminal of the instrument), so the ratio:

$$\frac{I_i}{I_s} = \frac{\text{instrument current}}{\text{shunt current}} = \frac{0.001}{20 - 0.001}.$$

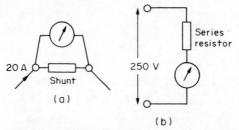

FIG. 1.14. Extension of instrument range. (a) Instrument shunted to indicate a large current. (b) Instrument connected in series with high resistance to indicate a high voltage.

If the voltage across the instrument and shunt is V, then

$$I_i = \frac{V}{R_i} \quad \text{and} \quad I_s = \frac{V}{R_s}.$$

Hence,

$$\frac{R_i}{R_s} = \frac{I_s}{I_i} = \frac{19.999}{0.001},$$

$$R_s = \frac{5 \times 0.001}{19.999} = \underline{0.250\,01 \times 10^{-3}\,\Omega}.$$

(b) For adaptation as a voltmeter, a relatively high resistance may be connected in series with the instrument, so that, for the maximum voltage reading required, only 1 mA flows through it; see Fig. 1.14(b).

For 1 mA at 250 V, the total resistance must be:

$$R_T = \frac{250}{0.001} = \underline{250\,k\Omega}.$$

Resistance of the instrument, R_i, is 5 Ω. Hence, the series resistance is:

$$(R_T - R_i) = (250{,}000 - 5)$$

$$= \underline{249{,}995\,\Omega}.$$

PROBLEM 1.15

Three resistors, of resistances R_1, R_2 and R_3, are arranged in a closed

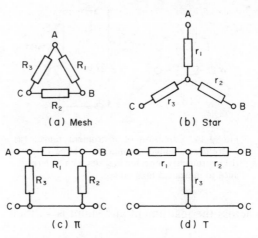

FIG. 1.15. Mesh, star, π and T circuits, Problem 1.15.

mesh as shown in Fig. 1.15(a). Determine the resistances r_1, r_2 and r_3 of three resistors which, arranged in a star configuration as shown in Fig. 1.15(b), will be the exact equivalent of the mesh arrangement.

Solution

By exact equivalence we mean that it is impossible, by electrical tests alone, to distinguish between the two circuits. In particular, the resistances between terminals A and B, B and C, C and A are identical for the two cases.

Taking first the resistance between A and B:

$$\frac{R_1 (R_2 + R_3)}{R_1 + R_2 + R_3} = r_1 + r_2. \tag{1.26}$$

Now that between B and C:

$$\frac{R_2 (R_1 + R_3)}{R_1 + R_2 + R_3} = r_2 + r_3 \tag{1.27}$$

and, finally, that between C and A:

$$\frac{R_3 (R_1 + R_2)}{R_1 + R_3 + R_3} = r_1 + r_3. \tag{1.28}$$

Subtracting eqn. (1.27) from eqn. (1.26) gives:

$$r_1 - r_3 = \frac{R_1(R_2 + R_3) - R_2(R_1 + R_3)}{R_1 + R_2 + R_3}. \tag{1.29}$$

Adding eqns. (1.28) and (1.29):

$$2r_1 = \frac{R_1(R_2 + R_3) - R_2(R_1 + R_3) + R_3(R_1 + R_2)}{R_1 + R_2 + R_3}$$

$$= \frac{2R_1R_3}{R_1 + R_2 + R_3},$$

$$\therefore \quad r_1 = \frac{R_1R_3}{R_1 + R_2 + R_3}.$$

And, by symmetry:

$$r_2 = \frac{R_2R_1}{R_1 + R_2 + R_3},$$

$$r_3 = \frac{R_3R_2}{R_1 + R_2 + R_3}. \tag{1.30}$$

This process is referred to as the mesh-to-star transformation, and is frequently of use in the simplification of more complicated networks.

When the mesh and star circuits of Figs. 1.15 (a) and (b) are redrawn in the forms of Figs. 1.15 (c) and (d) they are referred to as π- and T-sections, respectively, and eqns. (1.30) of course hold.

PROBLEM 1.16

For the circuits of Fig. 1.15, perform the converse transformation, i.e. determine R_1, R_2 and R_3 in terms of r_1, r_2 and r_3.

Solution

If terminals B and C are joined together and the resistance between A and B is calculated for each circuit, the values for circuits (a) and (b)—or (c) and (d)—must be identical.

Thus

$$\frac{R_1 R_3}{R_1 + R_3} = r_1 + \frac{r_2 r_3}{r_2 + r_3}$$

$$= \frac{r_1 r_2 + r_2 r_3 + r_3 r_1}{r_2 + r_3}$$

or

$$\frac{R_1 + R_3}{R_1 R_3} = \frac{r_2 + r_3}{r_1 r_2 + r_2 r_3 + r_3 r_1}. \tag{1.31}$$

By symmetry:

$$\frac{R_2 + R_1}{R_2 R_1} = \frac{r_3 + r_1}{r_1 r_2 + r_2 r_3 + r_3 r_1} \tag{1.32}$$

and

$$\frac{R_3 + R_2}{R_3 R_2} = \frac{r_1 + r_2}{r_1 r_2 + r_2 r_3 + r_3 r_1}. \tag{1.33}$$

Subtracting eqn. (1.32) from (1.31)

$$\frac{R_2 R_1 - R_3 R_1}{R_1 R_2 R_3} = \frac{r_2 - r_1}{r_1 r_2 + r_2 r_3 + r_3 r_1}$$

or

$$\frac{R_2 - R_3}{R_2 R_3} = \frac{r_2 - r_1}{r_1 r_2 + r_2 r_3 + r_3 r_1}. \tag{1.34}$$

Adding eqns. (1.33) and (1.34)

$$\frac{2}{R_3} = \frac{2 r_2}{r_1 r_2 + r_2 r_3 + r_3 r_1},$$

$$\therefore \quad R_3 = \frac{r_1 r_2 + r_2 r_3 + r_3 r_1}{r_2}$$

and by symmetry:

$$R_1 = \frac{r_1 r_2 + r_2 r_3 + r_3 r_1}{r_3}$$

and

$$R_2 = \frac{r_1 r_2 + r_2 r_3 + r_3 r_1}{r_1}. \tag{1.35}$$

The T- to π-transformation is, of course, identical with the star-to-mesh transformation of this problem.

Equations (1.35) may be written in a form identical with that of eqns. (1.30) by substituting conductances for resistance, as follows. Let

$$g_n = \frac{1}{r_n} \quad \text{and} \quad G_n = \frac{1}{R_n}.$$

Then it is easy to show that:

$$\left. \begin{array}{l} G_1 = \dfrac{g_1 g_2}{g_1 + g_2 + g_3}, \\[3mm] G_2 = \dfrac{g_2 g_3}{g_1 + g_2 + g_3}, \\[3mm] G_3 = \dfrac{g_3 g_1}{g_1 + g_2 + g_3}. \end{array} \right\} \qquad (1.35a)$$

and

PROBLEM 1.17

Determine the current, I, supplied to the Wheatstone bridge circuit represented in Fig. 1.16(a).

Solution

This problem reduces to one of determining the effective resistance between nodes A and C. If the bridge were balanced, i.e. the current through G, I_G, $= 0$, the resistance between A and C would be the parallel combination of $(10 + 6)$ and $(20 + 10)$, but in this case the solution is most readily found by applying the mesh-star transformation to either of the two meshes ABD or BCD.

Choosing BCD and transforming it to the star circuit BCDN of Fig. 1.16(b),

$$R_1 = \frac{6 \times 100}{6 + 10 + 100} = \underline{5.1724 \; \Omega},$$

$$R_2 = \frac{6 \times 10}{116} = \underline{0.517\,24 \; \Omega},$$

$$R_3 = \frac{10 \times 100}{116} = \underline{8.6207 \; \Omega}.$$

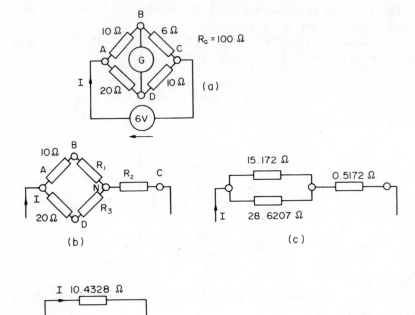

FIG. 1.16. The Wheatstone bridge and successive reductions.

Combining 10 and R_1, 20 and R_3 gives the circuit of Fig. 1.16(c), and combining 15.1724 Ω and 28.6207 Ω in parallel gives

$$R_4 = \frac{15.1724 \times 28.6207}{15.1724 + 28.6207} = \underline{9.9156\ \Omega}.$$

Thus,

$$R_T = 9.9156 + 0.51724 = \underline{10.4328\ \Omega}.$$

And, applying Ohm's Law,

$$I = \frac{6}{10.4328} = \underline{0.5751\ A}.$$

PROBLEM 1.18

A resistance of 12 Ω carries a current $i(t) = 10\,e^{-6t}$ A. Determine (a) the power, as a function of time, (b) the total energy dissipated from $t = 0$.

Solution

Using eqn. (1.3) $p(t) = v(t)\,i(t)$,

$$p(t) = 120\,e^{-6t}\,10\,e^{-6t} = \underline{1200\,e^{-12t}\,\text{W}}.$$

$$\text{The total energy} = \int_0^\infty p(t)\,dt = 1200 \int_0^\infty e^{-12t}\,dt$$

$$= 1200 \left[-\frac{1}{12}\,e^{-12t} \right]_0^\infty$$

$$= -100[0 - 1] = \underline{100\,\text{J}}.$$

PROBLEM 1.19

A steady voltage of 100 V is applied to a 2-H inductor. Determine the current flowing and the energy stored after 10 sec, given that the current at $t = 0$ was zero. Determine also the voltage which must be applied in order to reduce the current to zero in 2 sec. Sketch the current and voltage waveforms.

Solution

Equation (1.12) is used in definite integral form:

$$i(10) = \frac{1}{L} \int_0^{10} v(t)\,dt + i(0)$$

$$= \tfrac{1}{2} \int_0^{10} 100\,dt \quad \text{since } i(0) = 0$$

$$= \tfrac{1}{2}[100t]_0^{10} = \underline{500\,\text{A}}.$$

Alternatively, we know that for a steady applied voltage V, the current increases at a steady rate V/L. In this case

$$\frac{di(t)}{dt} = \frac{100}{2} = 50\,\text{A/sec}.$$

If this continues for 10 sec the final current (since the initial current was zero) is 50×10

$$= 500 \text{ A}.$$

$$p(t) = v(t)\, i(t) \quad \text{and} \quad W = \int_0^{10} v(t)\, i(t)\, \mathrm{d}t$$

$$= \int_0^{10} 100 \times 50t\, \mathrm{d}t$$

$$= \left[\frac{5000t^2}{2} \right]_0^{10} = 0.25 \text{ MJ}.$$

Alternatively, eqn. (1.13) may be used directly. Thus,

$$W = \tfrac{1}{2}LI^2$$

$$= \tfrac{1}{2} \times 2 \times 500^2 = 0.25 \text{ MJ}.$$

The use of eqn. (1.13) emphasises the fact that the stored energy depends only on the inductance and the current flowing and not on the manner in which the current has reached its final value nor on the elapsed time to reach it.

To reduce the current to zero in 2 sec

$$\frac{\mathrm{d}i(t)}{\mathrm{d}t} = - \frac{500}{2} = -250 \text{ A/sec}.$$

Hence, the applied voltage,

$$L\frac{\mathrm{d}i(t)}{\mathrm{d}t},$$

must be:

$$v(t) = -250 \times 2 = 500 \text{ V}$$

and this must be applied for 2 sec.

Alternatively,

$$i(12) = \frac{1}{L} \int_{10}^{12} v(t)\, \mathrm{d}t + 500$$

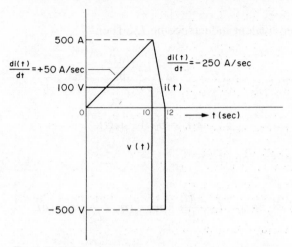

FIG. 1.17. Voltage and current waveforms for a 2-H inductor.

or

$$0 = \tfrac{1}{2}[Vt]_{10}^{12} + 500, \quad \text{since } v(t) = V$$

$$= V + 500.$$

Hence

$$\underline{V = -500 \text{ V}.}$$

The voltage and current waveforms are shown in Fig. 1.17.

PROBLEM 1.20

Determine the equivalent inductance of the three inductors connected as shown in the diagram of Fig. 1.18.

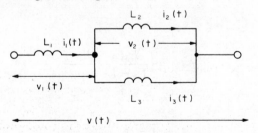

FIG. 1.18. Inductors in series and parallel.

Solution

Let the equivalent inductance be L_e. Then

$$v(t) = L_e \frac{di_1(t)}{dt}.$$

But,

$$v(t) = v_1(t) + v_2(t),$$

by Kirchhoff's second Law.

Now,

$$v_2(t) = L_2 \frac{di_2(t)}{dt} \quad \text{or} \quad i_2(t) = \frac{1}{L_2} \int v_2(t)\, dt.$$

Similarly,

$$i_3(t) = \frac{1}{L_3} \int v_2(t)\, dt,$$

and

$$i_1(t) = i_2(t) + i_3(t)$$

by Kirchhoff's Law

$$= \left(\frac{1}{L_2} + \frac{1}{L_3} \right) \int v_2(t)\, dt$$

$$= \frac{L_2 + L_3}{L_2 L_3} \int v_2(t)\, dt.$$

Thus,

$$v_2(t) = \left(\frac{L_2 L_3}{L_2 + L_3} \right) \frac{di_1(t)}{dt}.$$

Also

$$v_1(t) = L_1 \frac{di_1(t)}{dt}.$$

Hence,

$$v(t) = L_1 \frac{di_1(t)}{dt} + \left(\frac{L_2 L_3}{L_2 + L_3}\right) \frac{di_1(t)}{dt}$$

$$= \left[L_1 + \frac{L_2 L_3}{L_2 + L_3}\right] \frac{di_1(t)}{dt} = L_e \frac{di_1(t)}{dt}.$$

Thus,

$$L_e = L_1 + \frac{L_2 L_3}{L_2 + L_3}.$$

Hence, inductances combine as resistances do, viz. those in series have an equivalent inductance equal to the sum of their inductances, whilst those in parallel have an equivalent inductance equal to the reciprocal of the sum of their reciprocal inductances.

PROBLEM 1.21

Determine the equivalent capacitance of the three capacitors arranged as shown in the diagram of Fig. 1.19.

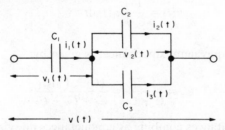

FIG. 1.19. Capacitors in series and parallel.

Solution

Using the symbols of the diagram:

$$i_2(t) = C_2 \frac{dv_2(t)}{dt} \quad \text{and} \quad i_3(t) = C_3 \frac{dv_2(t)}{dt}.$$

And, since

$$i_1(t) = i_2(t) + i_3(t)$$

by Kirchhoff's first Law, then

$$i_1(t) = (C_2 + C_3) \frac{dv_2(t)}{dt}$$

$$= C \frac{dv_2(t)}{dt},$$

where $C = C_2 + C_3$,

$$\therefore v_2(t) = \frac{1}{C} \int i_1(t) \, dt$$

and so

$$v(t) = v_1(t) + v_2(t)$$

by Kirchhoff's second Law

$$= \left(\frac{1}{C_1} + \frac{1}{C} \right) \int i_1(t) \, dt,$$

$$v(t) = \frac{1}{C_e} \int i_1(t) \, dt$$

where C_e, the equivalent capacitance, is given by:

$$C_e = \frac{CC_1}{C + C_1} = \frac{(C_2 + C_3)C_1}{C_1 + C_2 + C_3}.$$

Hence, capacitances combine as conductances do, viz. the equivalent capacitance of capacitors connected in parallel is equal to the sum of their capacitances and that of series-connected capacitors is equal to the reciprocal of the sum of their reciprocal capacitances.

PROBLEM 1.22

A steady current of 4 mA is fed into a 10-μF capacitor. Determine the voltage to which the capacitor is charged after 5 sec, and the corresponding stored energy. The capacitor was initially uncharged. Determine the current needed to discharge the capacitor completely in 20 sec. Sketch the voltage and current waveforms.

Solution

Equation (1.16) is used in definite integral form:

$$v(5) = \frac{1}{C} \int_0^5 i(t)\, \mathrm{d}t + v(0).$$

In this case $i(t)$ is constant at 4×10^{-3} A, and $v(0) = 0$,

$$\therefore v(5) = 10^5 \int_0^5 4 \times 10^{-3}\, \mathrm{d}t = \underline{2000\ \text{V}}.$$

$$v(t) = 10^5 \int 4 \times 10^{-3}\, \mathrm{d}t = 400t.$$

Hence

$$p(t) = v(t)\, i(t) = 400t \times 4 \times 10^{-3}$$

$$= 1.6t,$$

$$W_5 = \int_0^5 v(t)\, i(t)\, \mathrm{d}t = \int_0^5 1.6t\, \mathrm{d}t = \underline{20\ \text{J}}.$$

Alternatively, the stored energy can be calculated directly using eqn. (1.17),

$$W = \tfrac{1}{2}CV^2 = \tfrac{1}{2} \times 10^{-5} \times 4 \times 10^6 = \underline{20\ \text{J}}.$$

When C is discharging, the voltage is given by eqn. (1.16). The final voltage is zero. Hence,

$$0 = \frac{1}{C} \int_5^{25} i(t)\, \mathrm{d}t + v(5).$$

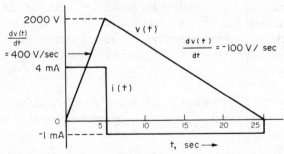

FIG. 1.20. Voltage and current waveforms for a 10-μF capacitor.

In this case $v(5) = 2000$ volts and $i(t) = I$.

Hence,

$$10^5 \left[It \right]_5^{25} + 2000 = 0 \quad \text{or} \quad 2 \times 10^6 I = -2000,$$

giving $\underline{I = -1 \text{ mA}}.$

The voltage and current waveforms are shown in the diagram of Fig. 1.20.

PROBLEM 1.23

A circuit consisting of inductance 0.5 H and resistance 10 Ω, in series, is fed from an ideal current source whose time-dependent current waveform is as shown in Fig. 1.21(a). Calculate the terminal voltage of the source and sketch the waveform for one complete cycle.

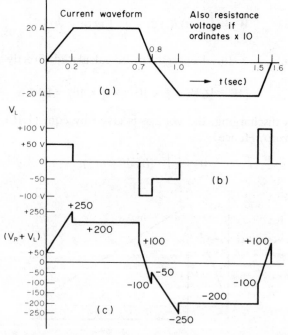

FIG. 1.21. Voltage and current waveforms for 10 Ω and 0.5 H in series, Problem 1.23.

Solution

The voltage developed across the source can be found by adding the voltages across the inductance and across the resistance, thus,

$$v_R(t) = i(t)R,$$

$$v_L(t) = L\frac{di(t)}{dt}.$$

Hence,

$$v(t) = Ri(t) + L\frac{di(t)}{dt}.$$

Each line segment of the current waveform is dealt with separately: time in seconds, current in amperes and voltage in volts.

$$0 < t < 0.2, i(t) = 100t,$$

$$\therefore \quad \frac{di(t)}{dt} = 100 \quad \text{and} \quad v(t) = (1000t + 50),$$

$$0.2 < t < 0.7, i(t) = 20,$$

$$\therefore \quad \frac{di(t)}{dt} = 0 \quad \text{and} \quad v(t) = 200,$$

$$0.7 < t < 0.8, i(t) = 20 - 200(t - 0.7),$$

$$\therefore \quad \frac{di(t)}{dt} = -200 \quad \text{and} \quad v(t) = (1500 - 2000t),$$

$$0.8 < t < 1.0, i(t) = -100(t - 0.8),$$

$$\therefore \quad \frac{di(t)}{dt} = -100 \quad \text{and} \quad v(t) = (750 - 1000t),$$

$$1.0 < t < 1.5, i(t) = -20,$$

$$\therefore \quad \frac{di(t)}{dt} = 0 \quad \text{and} \quad v(t) = -200,$$

$$1.5 < t < 1.6, i(t) = -20 + 200(t - 1.5),$$

$$\therefore \quad \frac{di(t)}{dt} = 200 \quad \text{and} \quad v(t) = (2000t - 3100).$$

The voltage waveform may be sketched from these expressions for $v(t)$ or by adding, graphically, the separate resistance and inductance voltage graphs. Figure 1.21 shows the waveforms of these voltages.

PROBLEMS I

1. A 60-V mains supply feeds a load having a resistance of $12\,\Omega$. Calculate (a) the current, (b) the power dissipated and (c) the energy converted into heat over a 2-hour period.
2. A voltage $v(t) = 100\,e^{-5t}$ volts is applied at $t = 0$ to a load resistance of $5\,\Omega$. Calculate the current, the power and the maximum energy that can be delivered to the load.
3. Determine the required power rating of an electric water-heater to maintain a flow of 10 litres/min at 60°C when the water inlet temperature is 15°C. Assume that the specific heat capacity of water is constant at 4180 J/kg/K.
4. Calculate the resistance at the operating temperature of a 150-W, 200-V tungsten-filament lamp.
5. A closed container, having a pair of external terminals, is known to contain an assortment of interconnected sources and resistors. When a 10-Ω load is applied to the terminals, a current of 2.5 A flows and when the load resistance is increased to $20\,\Omega$ the current drops to 2 A.

   Determine (a) the voltage-source and (b) the current-source equivalents of the contents of the box.
6. A certain cell has an e.m.f. of 2 V and an internal resistance of $0.1\,\Omega$. A battery of n such cells arranged (a) in series, (b) in parallel, (c) in a series/parallel array is used to supply a load of resistance $1\,\Omega$.

   Given that n is a perfect square, calculate the limiting current in each case as n increases without limit.
7. The electric charge passing a fixed point in a circuit is given by:

$$q(t) = 6t^3 + 5t^2 - 12t.$$

   Calculate and plot the current $i(t)$ over the interval $0 < t < 4\,\text{sec}$.

   Calculate also the work done over the 4-sec period in transferring this charge between two points in the circuit which have a difference of potential of 10 V.
8. The terminal voltage of a certain car battery falls linearly from 14.2 V to 11.0 V in 8 hours when supplying a load of equivalent resistance $2\,\Omega$.

   Calculate the energy delivered over the 8-hour period.
9. A power supply unit has an open-circuit terminal p.d. of 12 V and a load of 5 A causes this to drop to 11 V.

   Determine (a) the equivalent voltage source, (b) the equivalent current source and (c) the maximum power which the supply can deliver, assuming that its characteristics are constant.
10. A certain moving-coil instrument has a resistance of $15\,\Omega$ and gives full-scale deflection with a current of 20 mA.

    Determine the circuit to be used to enable the instrument to measure voltages up to 750 V and currents up to 100 A.
11. A certain 400-pF capacitor has no initial voltage. A current of 2 mA is suddenly applied and maintained for 2 msec.

Sketch the waveform of voltage across the capacitor and determine the voltage after 1 msec.

12. The voltage across a certain 0.5-µF capacitor increases linearly from zero to 200 V in 1 msec, remains at 200 V for 2 msec and then decreases linearly to zero in 0.25 msec.

Determine the current through the capacitor and sketch the current and voltage waveforms as functions of time.

13. A rectangular voltage pulse, of magnitude 50 V and duration 100 msec, is applied across a 2-H inductor. The initial current is zero. Calculate the current at the end of the 100-msec period.

It is desired to reduce the current to zero again in 5 msec. Determine the magnitude and polarity of the required voltage pulse.

14. A current given by:

$$i(t) = 3t^2 + 4t + 1, \quad t\,(\text{sec}) > 0 \text{ and}$$
$$i(t) \text{ in amps}$$

flows through a coil of resistance 2 Ω and inductance 10 H.

Determine (a) the power input to the coil at $t = 2$ sec, (b) the energy stored and the energy dissipated up to $t = 3$ sec, (c) the energy released if the current were to fall to zero after 5 sec.

15. A current given by:

$$i(t) = 3t^2 + 4t + 1, \quad t\,(\text{sec}) > 0 \text{ and}$$
$$i(t) \text{ in amps}$$

flows into a 10-µF capacitor.

Calculate the power and the energy stored at $t = 2$ sec.

16. A certain 0.5-H inductor carries a steady current of 5 A. Given that all the stored energy is discharged into a 10-µF capacitor, calculate the terminal voltage of the latter.

17. Calculate the resistance between the terminals AB of the network represented in Fig. P.I.1.

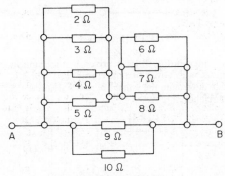

FIG. P.I.1 (Problem I.17).

18. The circuit represented by Fig. P.I.2 is used to test a 0–25-V voltmeter and a 0–100-mA ammeter simultaneously. By switching to positions 1, 2, 3 and 4, in turn, each instrument is tested for accuracy at $\frac{1}{4}$, $\frac{1}{2}$, $\frac{3}{4}$ and 1 times full-scale deflection.

Calculate the resistances r_1, r_2, r_3 and r_4 given that the ammeter resistance is negligible and that the voltmeter resistance is 1000 Ω.

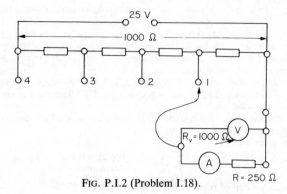

FIG. P.I.2 (Problem I.18).

19. For the circuit represented in Fig. P.I.3, calculate (i) the resistance at the terminals AB, given that the numbers on the diagram represent the conductances in siemens, (ii) the conductance at the terminals AB, given that the numbers represent the resistances in ohms.

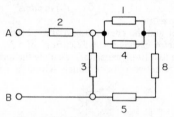

FIG. P.I.3 (Problem I.19).

20. The circuit represented in Fig. P.I.4 is driven by the ramp function $v(t) = 12t$ volts, where t is time in seconds. Given that the current $i_1(t) = at + b$, evaluate the constants a and b and hence determine the voltage across AB and the currents in the inductive and capacitive branches.

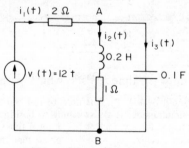

FIG. P.I.4 (Problem I.20).

CHAPTER 2

THE NATURAL AND FORCED RESPONSES OF SIMPLE CIRCUITS

2.1 FIRST-ORDER SYSTEMS

A first-order system is one which gives rise to a first-order differential equation. One such system is the circuit of Problem 1.23, since the relationship between voltage and current is expressed by:

$$Ri(t) + L\frac{di(t)}{dt} = v(t).$$

The equation may be solved for current, given the form of $v(t)$, by classical methods, but a slightly different method will be used which, although applying only to a restricted range of voltage functions, gives deeper insight into the behaviour of the circuit.

After considering the waveforms of Fig. 1.21 it may be wondered whether a waveform of current exists, the time derivative of which has the same waveform. The voltages across R and L would then be of the same form, as also would the combined voltage. As an extension, by Kirchhoff's second Law, the voltage across any combination of resistors and inductors would be, in the steady state, of the same form.

Only one function of time exists which satisfies these requirements—the exponential function—and, in addition, it has the property that its time integral is the same function of time.

Thus, if

$$i(t) = I\,e^{st}$$

43

where s is a real constant, then,

$$\frac{\mathrm{d}i(t)}{\mathrm{d}t} = sI\,\mathrm{e}^{st},$$

i.e. s times the original function, and

$$\int i(t)\,\mathrm{d}t = \frac{1}{s}I\,\mathrm{e}^{st},$$

i.e. $1/s$ times the original function.

Note that I is a constant equal to the current at $t = 0$, or

$$I = i(0).$$

2.1.1 Circuits containing inductance and resistance

PROBLEM 2.1

A current given by

$$i(t) = I\,\mathrm{e}^{st} \tag{2.1}$$

flows through a circuit consisting of resistance R and inductance L connected in series. Determine the voltage across the circuit. The circuit diagram and current waveform are shown in Fig. 2.1.

Solution

Substituting (2.1) into

$$v(t) = Ri(t) + L\frac{\mathrm{d}i(t)}{\mathrm{d}t}, \tag{2.2}$$

$$v(t) = RI\,\mathrm{e}^{st} + sLI\,\mathrm{e}^{st}$$
$$= I(R + sL)\,\mathrm{e}^{st}. \tag{2.3}$$

Equation (2.3) is clearly of the form:

$$v(t) = V\,\mathrm{e}^{st},$$

where

$$V = I(R + sL). \tag{2.4}$$

Hence, the voltage is of exponential form (with the same exponent as the current) having a magnitude at $t = 0$ given by (2.4). It is shown

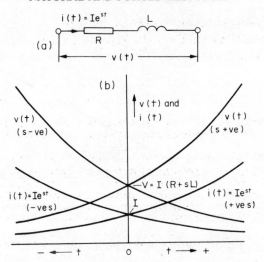

FIG. 2.1. Circuit and current and voltage waveforms for Problem 2.1. (a) Circuit. (b) Graphs of $i(t)$ and $v(t)$.

plotted in Fig. 2.1(b) for the two possible signs of s. Equation (2.4) may be rearranged, for comparison with Ohm's Law of eqn. (1.5), to give

$$\frac{V}{I} = R + sL \qquad (2.5)$$

and so, for exponential waveforms, the impeding effect of resistance and inductance taken together may be combined into a single factor known as the *Impedance Function* and denoted by $Z(s)$. Because the current, I, may be considered to flow as a result of the application of the voltage V to the circuit, V and I are known, respectively, as the *Forcing Function* and the *Response Function*. The current may also be referred to as the *Forced Response*.

Clearly $Z(s)$ is a linear function of s for the simple example chosen (R in series with L) and it may be plotted against s as shown in Fig. 2.2. When $s = 0$, $v(t) = V$, a steady voltage, and $Z(s) = R$. This result is consistent with the conclusion reached in Chapter 1, namely that the presence of inductance is not felt when the current is steady.

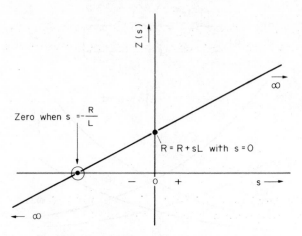

FIG. 2.2. Plot of $Z(s)$ vs. s for R and L in series.

A case of special interest occurs when the graph of $Z(s)$ crosses the axis of s. Here, $Z(s) = 0$, or $(R + sL) = 0$ giving

$$s = -\frac{R}{L}. \tag{2.6}$$

This is called a ZERO of the impedance function. When $Z(s) = \pm\infty$ (in this case when $s = \pm\infty$) this is called a POLE of the impedance function. Thus, the function $Z(s) = R + sL$ has one zero and one pole ($\pm\infty$ are counted as the same point).

The impedance function is one example of a general network function. Another is the admittance function which is defined as the reciprocal of $Z(s)$, and is denoted by $Y(s)$. Thus

$$Y(s) = \frac{1}{Z(s)} = \frac{1}{R + sL}$$

in this case.

This function, also, may be plotted against s and such a plot is shown in Fig. 2.3. $Y(s)$ has a pole at $s = -R/L$ and a zero at $\pm\infty$. The steady current case ($s = 0$) gives $Y(s) = 1/R = G$.

Since $I = V . Y(s)$, the graph of $Y(s)$ gives (to a different scale) the response of the circuit to an exponential applied voltage.

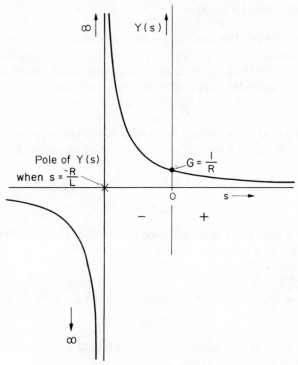

FIG. 2.3. Plot of $Y(s)$ for R and L in series.

It is important to distinguish between the quantities expressed in the graphs of Figs. 2.1 and 2.2. In Fig. 2.1, $v(t)$ and $i(t)$ are plotted against time and are therefore said to be in the *time domain*. The equation

$$v(t) = V e^{st}$$

is a time-domain equation.

The graphs of Figs. 2.2 and 2.3 are plotted against s and are referred to as being in the *s-domain* or *frequency domain*. Equation (2.4) is a frequency-domain equation. Strictly speaking, s is the neper frequency when it is a real (+ve or −ve) quantity and the radian frequency when it is an imaginary quantity.

2.1.1.1 The natural response

Since $I = VY(s)$, the value of s which makes $Y(s) = \infty$ (or $Z(s) = 0$) gives the condition for which the circuit responds with no applied voltage. The pole of $Y(s)$ or the zero of $Z(s)$ yields this condition, given by eqn. (2.6). Substituting this value of s into eqn. (2.1) gives:

$$i(t) = I e^{-(R/L)t} \tag{2.7}$$

and this is called the NATURAL RESPONSE. When the current through the circuit of Fig. 2.1(a) varies in this manner the terminal voltage is zero. When

$$t = 0, I = i(0)$$

$$\therefore \quad \underline{i(t) = i(0) e^{-(R/L)t}}. \tag{2.8}$$

If $i(0) = 0$ then $i(t) = 0$ always, so it is necessary that an initial current flow for $i(t)$ to be finite.

PROBLEM 2.2

A voltage forcing function given by:

$$v(t) = 100 e^{-12t} \text{ volts} \tag{2.9}$$

is applied at $t = 0$ to a circuit consisting of $10\,\Omega$ resistance and $0.25\,\text{H}$ inductance connected in series.

Calculate (i) the forced current response and (ii) the natural current response.

Solution

(i) For the circuit, $Z(s) = R + sL$, and from eqn. (2.9) $s = -12$. Hence

$$Z(s) = 10 + (-12)\,0.25$$
$$= \underline{7\,\Omega}.$$

This is the impedance of the circuit at a neper frequency of -12 neper/second.

The frequency domain expression for the forced current response is:

$$I_F = \frac{V}{Z(s)} = \frac{100}{7} = \underline{14.286 \text{ A}}.$$

Transformation to the time domain is achieved simply by inserting the exponential term.

Thus,

$$i_F(t) = 14.286 \, e^{-12t} \qquad (2.10)$$

since the method used depends on the forcing function and the forced response having the same time function.

(ii) The natural response occurs when $Z(s) = 0$, i.e. when

$$10 + s \, 0.25 = 0 \quad \text{or} \quad s = -40.$$

Thus,

$$i_N(t) = I \, e^{-40t}. \qquad (2.11)$$

The value of the constant I in eqn. (2.11) cannot be determined without additional data.

2.1.1.2 Properties of the exponential decay

Referring to eqn. (2.7), we see that when $(R/L)t = 1$, or $t = L/R$ sec,

$$i(t) = I \, e^{-1} = 0.368 \, I.$$

The time interval, (L/R) sec, is called the *time constant*, τ, of the circuit. Thus, when $t = \tau = L/R$ the current response has dropped to 36.8% of its initial value. (Note that the time constant is dependent only on the ratio L/R and not on the magnitude of the current response.) For any increment of time equal to τ sec the current at the end of the increment is 36.8% of the current at the beginning. In theory, then, the current will never decay to zero, but in practice soon drops to a value which is negligible.

The diagram of Fig. 2.4 shows an exponential decay with a value at $t = 0$ equal to I.

From eqn. (2.7):

$$\frac{di(t)}{dt}\bigg]_{t=0} = -\frac{R}{L}I = -\frac{I}{\tau}$$

so that the curve is tangential to the straight line drawn from I on the current axis to τ on the time axis.

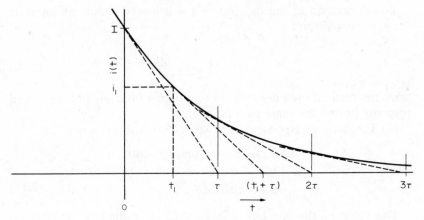

FIG. 2.4. An exponential current decay.

Also:

$$\frac{di(t)}{dt}\bigg]_{t=\tau} = -\frac{R}{L}I\,e^{-1} = -0.368\frac{I}{\tau}$$

so that the exponential graph of $i(t)$ has the property that, at any time, t_1, at which $i(t_1) = i_1$, the graph is tangential to a straight line drawn from $i(t) = i_1$ to $t = (t_1 + \tau)$, as shown in Fig. 2.4.

PROBLEM 2.3

For the circuit of Problem 2.2 calculate the magnitude of the natural current response for $I = 5$ A after (i) τ sec, (ii) 5τ sec. (iii) Determine the time taken for the current to decay to 1 nA.

Solution

For the case cited,

$$\tau = L/R = 0.025 \text{ sec}$$
$$= \underline{25 \text{ msec}}.$$

(i) $i(t)$ at $t = \tau$,

$$i(t) = e^{-1} \times 5 = 0.368 \times 5 = \underline{1.84 \text{ A}}.$$

(ii) $i(t)$ at $t = 5\tau$ (or 0.125 sec),

$$i(t) = (e^{-1})^5 \times 5 = 5 \times e^{-5} = 5 \times 0.00674$$
$$= \underline{0.0337 \text{ A}}.$$

(iii) If $i(t_1) = 10^{-9}$ A at $t = t_1$, then

$$10^{-9} = 5\, e^{-40t_1}$$

or

$$2 \times 10^{-10} = e^{-40t_1}.$$

Taking logs to base e

$$\ln 2 - 10 \ln 10 = -40t_1,$$
$$0.693 - 23.026 = -40t_1$$

giving

$$\underline{t_1 = 0.558 \text{ sec}.}$$

2.1.1.3 *Responses considered as solutions of the differential equation*

It will be recalled that the classical method of solving a differential equation such as (2.2) yields a solution in two parts. One is any particular solution of (2.2) and is called the particular integral; the other is the general solution of (2.2) modified by replacing $v(t)$ by zero. This part is the complementary function. The complete solution of (2.2) is the sum of the two parts.

We are now able to identify these two parts of the solution with the forced and natural responses already discussed. Just as the purpose of the complementary function is to provide arbitrary constants for accommodating different initial conditions, so the natural response accommodates the initial circuit conditions, bridging the gap between the actual response at some specific instant (usually $t = 0$) and the response dictated by the forcing function. Since the natural response is transient in nature (save for the special unreal case of a circuit having no dissipation) it is frequently called the transient response, and the forced response is referred to as the steady-state response. In some ways this is an unfortunate term, implying, as it does, that the response is time-independent—which is clearly not the case when the forcing function is a function of time.

PROBLEM 2.4

For the data of Problem 2.2 determine the total current response for $t > 0$ if, when the forcing function

$$v(t) = 100 \, e^{-12t}$$

is applied, the current in the circuit is already equal to $+8$ A.

In essence, this problem is concerned with the evaluation of I in eqn. (2.11).

Solution

The total or complete response is found by adding the natural and forced responses.

Thus,

$$i_T(t) = i_F(t) + I_N(t)$$
$$= 14.286 \, e^{-12t} + I \, e^{-40t}. \qquad (2.12)$$

But $i_T(t)$ an infinitesimal time before the application of $v(t)$ is $+8$ A or

$$i_T(0^-) = 8.$$

We have seen that the current in an inductive circuit must be a continuous function of time (section 1.2.3) so that

also. $$i_T(0^+) = 8,$$

Hence eqn. (2.12) may be equated to 8 at $t = 0^+$, or

$$8 = 14.286 + I,$$

therefore,

$$\underline{I = -6.286 \, A}$$

and so

$$\underline{i_T(t) = 14.286 \, e^{-12t} - 6.286 \, e^{-40t}}. \qquad (2.13)$$

Figure 2.5 shows graphs of the forcing function $v(t)$ as well as the forced and natural responses and their sum. It is clear from these that the natural response is called into existence only because the value of the forced response at $t = 0$ is not equal to 8A, which is the given current at $t = 0$. The implication is that if the initial current at $t = 0$ had been 14.286 A instead of 8 A there would have been no need for the natural response, and none would have been excited into existence.

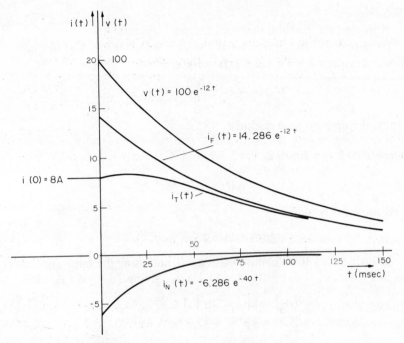

FIG. 2.5. Voltage and current waveforms for Problem 2.4.

PROBLEM 2.5

An exponential voltage given by

$$v(t) = 100 \, e^{st} \tag{2.14}$$

is applied at $t = 0$ to a circuit consisting of resistance $5 \, \Omega$ and inductance $0.2 \, H$ connected in series.

Given that the current for $t < 0$ is $+5 \, A$, determine the total current response for:

(i) $s = +20$,
(ii) $s = -10$,
(iii) $s = -25$,
(iv) $s = -30$.

Solution

Applying the method developed above, evidently:

(i) When $s = 20$, $Z(s) = 5 + 0.2 \times 20 = 9\ \Omega$. Hence, the frequency-domain expression for the forced response is:

$$I_F = \frac{V}{Z(s)} = \frac{100}{9} = \underline{11.1\ \text{A}}.$$

Thus, the time-domain response $= \underline{11.1\ e^{20t}}$.

Since $R = 5$ and $L = 0.2$, $\tau = \frac{1}{25}$ sec and

$$i_N(t) = I_N\,e^{-25t},$$

and the total response

$$i_T(t) = 11.1\ e^{20t} + I_N\,e^{-25t}.$$

Inserting the known conditions at $t = 0$, and using the same arguments as in Problem 2.4 at $t = 0^+$, $5 = 11.1 + I_N$, giving $I_N = -6.1$ A. And

$$i_T(t) = 11.1\ e^{20t} - 6.1\ e^{-25t} \qquad (2.15)$$

$$= 5\,e^{-25t} + 11.1\,(e^{20t} - e^{-25t}). \qquad (2.15a)$$

(ii) When $s = -10$, an identical procedure gives

$$i_T(t) = 33.3\ e^{-10t} - 28.3\ e^{-25t} \qquad (2.16)$$

$$= 5\,e^{-25t} + 33.3\,(e^{-10t} - e^{-25t}). \qquad (2.16a)$$

Equations (2.15) and (2.16) are of identical form to that of eqn. (2.13), viz. each contains two terms corresponding to the forced and natural responses. The alternative forms, (2.15a) and (2.16a), show that the natural response may be considered to be made up of two components: (i) that due simply to the decay of the initial current (the source-free response) with a time constant τ and (ii) that generated by the sudden application of the forcing function; it will always exist and have a magnitude, at $t = 0$, equal to that of the forced response at $t = 0$, but be of opposite sign since its sum with the forced response must equal zero (the initial current is taken care of by the first component).

However, it is customary to lump the two components together and refer to them as the natural response.

Clearly, both the forced response and the second component of the natural response become large as $Z(s)$ becomes small, i.e. as s approaches $(-\tau^{-1})$. In the limit, the graph of Fig. 2.3 shows that the forced response will increase without limit when $s = -\tau^{-1}$ and so also will the second component of the natural response. This case may be dealt with as follows.

(iii) When $s = -25$, the total response results as follows:

$$i_T(t) = 5\,e^{-25t} + \frac{100}{Z(s)}\left[e^{st} - e^{-25t}\right]. \qquad (2.17)$$

The first term again appears, corresponding to the decay of the initial current, and the second term clearly has the limit $\infty \times 0$ when $s = -25$, i.e.

$$\underset{s \to -25}{\text{Limit}}\, f(s)\,\Phi(s) = \infty \times 0, \qquad \text{i.e. indeterminate}$$

or, letting

$$\phi(s) = \frac{1}{f(s)},$$

then

$$\underset{s \to -25}{\text{Limit}}\,\frac{\Phi(s)}{\phi(s)} = \frac{0}{0}.$$

By l'Hôpital's rule,

$$\underset{s \to -25}{\text{Limit}}\,\frac{\Phi(s)}{\phi(s)} = \underset{s \to -25}{\text{Limit}}\,\frac{\Phi'(s)}{\phi'(s)}.$$

Here,

$$\Phi(s) = (e^{st} - e^{-25t}),$$
$$\therefore\ \Phi'(s) = t\,e^{st}$$

since differentiation is with respect to s. And

$$\phi(s) = R + sL,$$
$$\phi'(s) = L,$$
$$\therefore\ \underset{s \to -25}{\text{Limit}}\,\frac{\Phi'(s)}{\phi'(s)} = \frac{t}{L}\,e^{st} = 5t\,e^{-25t}.$$

Substituting into (2.17)

$$i_T(t) = 5\,e^{-25t} + 500t\,e^{-25t}$$
$$= 5(1 + 100t)\,e^{-25t}. \tag{2.18}$$

Thus, although in this special case ($s = -25$) the first component of the natural response is still clearly identifiable, the second component and the forced response are involved together in the second term of (2.18), still completely cancelling one another at $t = 0$.

(iv) When $s = -30$,

$$Z(s) = 5 + 0.2\,(-30) = \underline{-1\,\Omega},$$

$$\therefore\ \ I_F = -100\ \text{A} \quad \text{and} \quad i_F(t) = -100\,e^{-30t}.$$

Since $i_N(t) = I_N\,e^{-25t}$, application of the initial condition $i_T(0) = +5$ A gives:

$$i_T(t) = -100\,e^{-30t} + 105\,e^{-25t}$$
$$= 5\,e^{-25t} + 100\,(e^{-25t} - e^{-30t}). \tag{2.19}$$

Thus, in the case of $s < -1/\tau$ the signs of the natural and forced response components of the second term of (2.19) are reversed and the form of $i_T(t)$ is similar to that of each of the previous cases, as the graphs of Fig. 2.6 show.

2.1.1.4 *The rules for finding solutions*

To summarise, in order to find the total response of a linear system we proceed as follows: First express the forcing function in exponential form—such as eqn. (2.9). In Problems 2.2 and 2.4 this step was not necessary since the forcing function was already of this form. Next, evaluate the impedance by substituting the value of s obtained from the forcing function into the polynomial in s representing the impedance function—an expression such as the R.H.S. of eqn. (2.5)—and hence determine the forced (or steady-state) response. The natural response is then determined as an exponential function of time—the exponent being found from the zero of the impedance function—and added to the forced response. Finally, the magnitude of the natural response is selected to satisfy the known initial conditions.

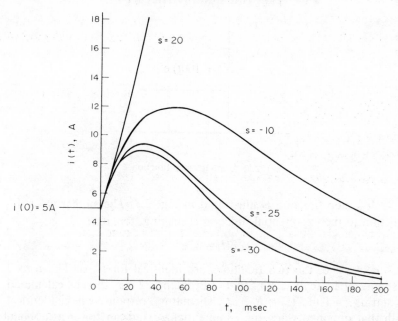

FIG. 2.6. Total responses, for various values of s, of series R, L circuit, Problem 2.5.

2.1.1.5 The step-function response

An alternative forcing function, probably more commonly approximated in practice, is the voltage or current step function. It is an idealisation of the process which takes place when, for example, a switch is closed in a circuit, thus applying an energy source in an extremely short period of time. To simplify discussion of the problem, it is assumed that this short period is actually zero, so that, if the time scale is fixed in the same way as when dealing with exponential applied voltages, $t = 0$ is defined as the instant at which the energy source is applied. Thus, in the circuit to which a step function of voltage, $VU(t)$, is applied

$$v(t) = 0 \quad -\infty < t < 0^-,$$
$$v(t) = V \quad \infty > t > 0^+$$

and $v(t)$ is undefined for $t = 0$.

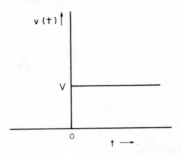

FIG. 2.7. A voltage step function.

Such a step function is illustrated in Fig. 2.7. The similarity of this function to the exponential function is striking, for, if in

$$v(t) = V e^{st}$$

we make $s = 0$, the two functions are identical for $t > 0$. The forced response of a circuit such as that of Problem 2.2 may then be calculated by setting $s = 0$ in $Z(s) = R + sL$. The natural response will be identical with that obtained when the exponential forcing function was applied at $t = 0$.

PROBLEM 2.6
In the circuit of Fig. 2.8(a) determine the total current response after the switch is closed.

Solution
The time scale may be chosen so that the switch is closed at $t = 0$ and if an ideal switch is assumed the forcing function is given by:

$$v(t) = 100U(t),$$

i.e.
$$v(t) = 100 e^{st} \quad \text{with } s = 0, \text{ for } t > 0.$$

$$R = 10 \, \Omega, L = 0.25 \text{ H}, \therefore Z(s) = R = \underline{10 \, \Omega},$$

and the forced response is

$$\frac{100}{10} = 10 \text{ A (constant, since } v(t) \text{ is constant for } t > 0).$$

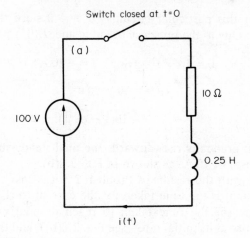

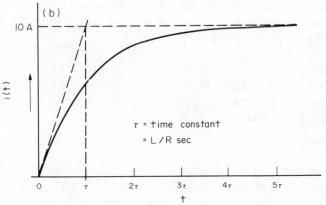

FIG. 2.8. Voltage of 100 V applied at $t = 0$ to R and L in series.

From previous results,

$$i_N(t) = I \, e^{-t/\tau}, \quad \tau = L/R = 0.025 \text{ sec}$$

or

$$i_N(t) = I \, e^{-40t},$$

$$\therefore \quad i_T(t) = 10 + I \, e^{-40t}. \tag{2.20}$$

Clearly, for this particular circuit $i_T(0^-) = 0$ since the switch was initially open. Due to the presence of inductance $i_T(0^+) = 0$ also. Hence

$$0 = 10 + I \quad \text{giving} \quad I = -10\,\text{A},$$

$$\therefore \quad i_T(t) = 10 - 10\,e^{-40t}$$

$$= 10(1 - e^{-40t}). \tag{2.21}$$

The current gradually rises towards the final steady-state value (the forced response) of 10 A, as shown in Fig. 2.8(b).

By analogy with the results of Problem 2.3 it is easy to deduce that the time constant is the time taken for the current to rise to 63.2% of the final value (or the time taken to reach its final value IF it had continued to rise at its initial rate—see Fig. 2.8(b)), and that the current is within 5% of its final value after 3τ sec and within 0.67% after 5τ sec.

It is not necessary for the forcing function always to be a voltage as the following problem illustrates.

PROBLEM 2.7

For the circuit of Fig. 2.9(a) determine the voltage response and the individual currents for $t > 0$, given that the circulating current before $t = 0$ is 3 A, clockwise.

Solution

The instant $t = 0$ is defined as the instant at which the source current jumps to $+10$ A. For $t < 0$, the source current is zero. Hence

$$i(t) = 10U(t)$$

$$= 0 \quad (t < 0)$$

$$= 10 \quad (t > 0).$$

The forcing function is a current and the response function will be a voltage.

Let the response be the sum of a forced and a natural response.

Forced response

$$V = IZ(s).$$

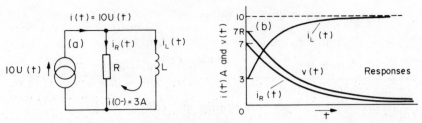

FIG. 2.9.(a, b) Current step function applied to parallel L, R circuit: Problem 2.7.

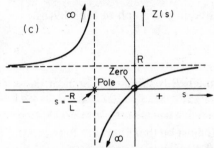

(c) Plot of the response function, $Z(s)$, in the frequency domain.

For this circuit

$$Z(s) = \frac{sLR}{R + sL}. \qquad (2.22)$$

As before, we may represent the step function of current $10U(t)$, for $t > 0$, by an exponential function $10\,e^{st}$ with $s = 0$.

Hence, with $s = 0$, $Z(s) = 0$ and so the forced response does not exist.

Natural response

This is an exponential function having a value of s for which $Z(s) = \infty$, since we wish to find the condition for which voltage exists for no current.

$$Z(s) = \infty \text{ when } s = -\frac{R}{L}, \text{ giving}$$

$$v(t) = V\,e^{-(R/L)t}. \qquad (2.23)$$

V is evaluated by substituting the initial value of $v(0^+)$.

Referring to Fig. 2.9(a),

$$\text{Current through } R, i(0^-) = -3 \text{ A} \quad \text{and} \quad i(0^+) = +7 \text{ A}$$

$$\text{Current through } L, i(0^-) = +3 \text{ A} \quad \text{and} \quad i(0^+) = +3 \text{ A}$$

by the result of section 1.2.3.

Hence $v(0^+) = 7R$ and substituting into eqn. (2.23) gives

$$v(t) = 7R \, e^{-(R/L)t}. \tag{2.24}$$

This is shown plotted in the graph of Fig. 2.9(b).

Currents $t > 0$

The current through R is simply $1/R \cdot v(t)$, or

$$i_R(t) = 7 \, e^{-(R/L)t} \tag{2.25}$$

and that through L must be the difference between this and the constant input current of 10 A. Hence,

$$i_L(t) = 10 - 7 \, e^{-(R/L)t}. \tag{2.26}$$

Both $i_L(t)$ and $i_R(t)$ are included in the graph of Fig. 2.9(b).

Alternatively, $i_L(t)$ may be calculated from eqn. (1.12) as follows:

$$i_L(t) = \frac{1}{L} \int_0^t v(t) \, dt + i_L(0^+)$$

$$= \frac{1}{L} \int_0^t 7R \, e^{-(R/L)t} \, dt + 3$$

$$= \frac{7R}{L} \left(-\frac{L}{R} \right) \left[e^{-(R/L)t} \right]_0^t + 3$$

$$= -7 \left[e^{-(R/L)t} - 1 \right] + 3 = \underline{10 - 7 \, e^{-(R/L)t}},$$

which agrees with eqn. (2.26).

The impedance function

$$Z(s) = \frac{sLR}{R + sL}$$

may be plotted against s and this is shown in Fig. 2.9(c). The plot has one pole (at $s = -(R/L)$) and one zero (at $s = 0$) and, since

$$V = IZ(s),$$

this is also a graph of the voltage response of the circuit in the frequency domain. It clearly shows that when $s = 0$ the circuit has no forced response (a zero of $Z(s)$) and that were s to be equal to $-(R/L)$, the response would be infinite. Again, it is important to remember that the frequency-domain response is not of exponential form, even though both voltage and current may be exponential functions of time.

2.1.2 Circuits containing capacitance and resistance

The ideas concerning similarity of waveforms which, in the case of inductive–resistive circuits, lead to some useful results may be applied also to capacitive circuits. Thus, if we begin by assuming an exponential function of time for the current through a capacitor,

$$i(t) = I\,e^{st},$$

with s real, the voltage, by (1.16), will be

$$v(t) = \frac{1}{C} \int i(t)\,\mathrm{d}t$$

where C is the capacitance

$$= \frac{1}{sC} I\,e^{st}$$

$$= V\,e^{st}$$

where

$$V = \frac{1}{sC} I. \tag{2.27}$$

Thus $v(t)$, also, varies exponentially with time and eqn. (2.27) is the equivalent "Ohm's Law" expression for a capacitor when both the current and the voltage have this form.

PROBLEM 2.8

A current given by

$$i(t) = I e^{st},$$

with s real, flows through a circuit consisting of resistance R and capacitance C connected in series. Determine the voltage required across the circuit for this current and hence, also, the natural response. The circuit diagram is shown in Fig. 2.10(a).

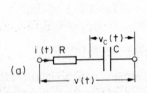

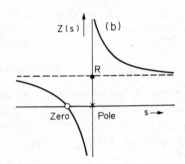

FIG. 2.10. (a) Series R, C circuit; (b) its impedance in the frequency domain: Problem 2.8.

Solution

The basic differential equation of the circuit is:

$$Ri(t) + \frac{1}{C} \int i(t) \, dt = v(t). \tag{2.28}$$

Substituting the given current function of time, this becomes:

$$RI e^{st} + \frac{1}{sC} I e^{st} = v(t)$$

or

$$I e^{st} \left(R + \frac{1}{sC} \right) = v(t)$$

which is clearly of the form

$$v(t) = V e^{st},$$

where

$$V = I \left(R + \frac{1}{sC} \right)$$

$$= IZ(s). \tag{2.29}$$

As expected, the voltage is an exponential function of time and has a magnitude at $t = 0$ given by eqn. (2.29).

Natural response

The impedance function, $Z(s)$, is shown plotted as a function of s in Fig. 2.10(b): it exhibits a pole at $s = 0$ and a zero at the value of s given by

$$Z(s) = \left(R + \frac{1}{sC}\right) = 0$$

or

$$s = -\frac{1}{CR}.$$

Hence, for this value of s the circuit has no impedance and would show a finite response for no forcing function. This, then, is the natural response and is an exponential function of time, the value of s for which is provided by setting $Z(s) = 0$.

Thus,

$$i_N(t) = I\,e^{-(t/\tau)},$$

where $\tau = CR$ is defined as the *time constant* of the circuit.

I is the initial current, which will be zero if the capacitor be uncharged initially.

However, if an initial charge $q(0)$ gives the capacitor an initial voltage $v(0)$, then

$$I = \frac{v(0)}{R}$$

and

$$i_N(t) = \frac{v(0)}{R}\,e^{-(t/\tau)}$$

or

$$v_c(t) = v(0)\,e^{-(t/\tau)}$$

since $v_c(t) = v_R(t)$, i.e. an exponential decay of voltage starting from $v(0)$ at $t = 0$, and having the same properties as the decay of current in the resistive/inductive circuit discussed in section 2.3. Hence, the voltage across the capacitor falls to 36.8% of its initial value after $\tau = CR$ sec, to 5% after 3τ and to 0.67% after 5τ sec.

PROBLEM 2.9

A voltage forcing function given by:

$$v(t) = 100\,e^{-10t} \tag{2.30}$$

is applied, at $t = 0$, to a circuit consisting of 1000-Ω resistance in series with 300-μF capacitance.

Determine the voltage across the capacitor, given that it has a voltage at $t = 0$ of $+30$ V.

Solution

The problem may be solved by first determining the current and then applying eqn. (1.16) to determine $v_c(t)$. However, reference to Fig. 2.10(a) shows that the voltage $v_c(t)$ may be determined as a fraction of $v(t)$ by means of a transfer function $T(s)$ given by:

$$T(s) = \frac{1/sC}{R + (1/sC)} = \frac{1}{1 + sCR} \tag{2.31}$$

since the series-connected resistor and capacitor may be considered as a potential divider of total impedance $(R + (1/sC))$.

Hence,

$$V_c = T(s)\,V$$

$$= \left[\frac{1}{1 + (-10 \times 1000 \times 300 \times 10^{-6})} \right] 100$$

or

$$V_c = -50\,\text{V},$$

$$\therefore \quad \underline{v_c(t) = -50\,e^{-10t}}. \tag{2.32}$$

Natural response

This occurs when $T(s) = \infty$, i.e. when $1 + sCR = 0$ or $s = (1/CR) = -3.33$ neper/sec.

Thus,
$$v_{c_N}(t) = A\,e^{-3.33t} \tag{2.33}$$

where A is a constant, to be determined.

And the total voltage response is given by the sum of eqns. (2.32) and (2.33):
$$v_c(t) = A\,e^{-3.33t} - 50\,e^{-10t}.$$

A is found by substituting $v_c(0) = +\,30$ at $t = 0$.
$30 = A - 50$, giving $A = 80$. So
$$\underline{v_c(t) = 80\,e^{-3.33t} - 50\,e^{-10t}}. \tag{2.34}$$

The initial voltage of 30 V on the capacitor is subject to the exponential decay $e^{-3.33t}$ and is, of course, included in the first term of eqn. (2.34).

The solution may be readily adapted to the case in which a step forcing function is applied to the circuit, by setting $s = 0$.

Thus
$$T(s) = \frac{1}{1 + sCR} = 1 \quad \text{with } s = 0,$$

and so
$$V_c = V$$
$$= 100 \text{ (in frequency domain)}$$

or
$$v_c(t) = V$$
$$= 100 \text{ (in the time domain also)}.$$

The natural response is independent of the forcing function, and so is:
$$v_{c_N}(t) = A\,e^{-3.33t},$$

and the total response is therefore:
$$v_c(t) = A\,e^{-3.33t} + 100.$$

If, as before, $v_c(0) = 30$
$$30 = A + 100, \qquad \therefore \quad \underline{A = -70\,\text{V}},$$

giving
$$\underline{v_c(t) = 100 - 70\,e^{-3.33t}}.$$

If the capacitor had been uncharged, initially, i.e. $v_c(0) = 0$, then:

$$v_c(t) = 100(1 - e^{-3.33t}),$$

i.e. an exponential rise of voltage, exactly equivalent to the rise of current in a resistive–inductive circuit to which a step function of voltage is applied.

When

$$t = \tau = CR = 0.3 \text{ sec},$$

$$v_c(t) = 100(1 - 0.368),$$

or 63.2% of the final voltage.

When $t = 0.9$ sec, v_c is within 5% of the final voltage, and after $t = 1.5$ sec it is within two-thirds of 1% of the final voltage.

The form of the frequency-domain response—obtained by plotting

$$T(s) = \left(\frac{1}{1 + sCR}\right)$$

against s—is evidently exactly the same as that of Fig. 2.3, the pole occurring at $s = (1/CR)$ and the zero at $\pm\infty$. In this case, however, $T(0) = 1$.

An alternative transfer function, $T'(s)$, may be derived by expressing the resistance voltage in terms of the total voltage across the circuit. Thus,

$$T'(s) = \frac{R}{R + (1/sC)} = \frac{sCR}{1 + sCR}. \tag{2.35}$$

Again, we may obtain the form of the plot of this function against s by comparison with eqn. (2.22) and Fig. 2.9(c) of Problem 2.7. The value of $T'(s)$ at $s = 0$ is zero—the circuit has no zero-frequency response—and it is this characteristic which renders the circuit so useful for one application, in particular. It is frequently used as a coupling circuit between the active stages of amplifiers, oscillators, etc., where it is necessary to preserve differences of zero-frequency potential whilst transferring the changes of potential which constitute the signals being handled.

PROBLEM 2.10

As an example of this application, consider the circuit of Fig. 2.11(a). A negative pulse is applied to the base of transistor T_1 which results in a negative pulse of current in the collector load R_1. The positive voltage pulse thereby produced is passed to the base of transistor T_2 via the C–R coupling circuit, and it is desired to find the voltage, as a function of time, at the base of T_2.

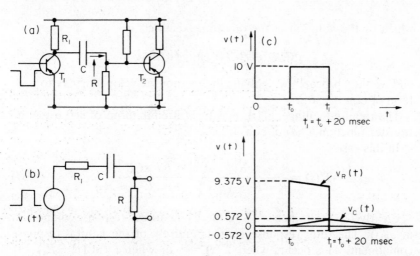

FIG. 2.11. (a) Circuit for Problem 2.10. (b) Equivalent circuit of (a) and voltage waveforms. (c) Waveform of applied pulse.

Let $R_1 = 2000\,\Omega$, $R = 30\,\mathrm{k}\Omega$, $C = 10\,\mu\mathrm{F}$ and the pulse duration be taken as 20×10^{-3} sec. The pulse is applied at time t_0 and is of maximum height 10 V, as shown in Fig. 2.11(c).

Solution

The problem may best be solved by reducing the circuit to its equivalent circuit, shown in Fig. 2.11(b). The voltage pulse is now represented by the voltage source in series with R_1, the total input resistance at the base of T_2 (including the bias chain) by a single resistance R, across which base input voltage appears, and the zero-frequency bias potentials, necessary for the correct functioning of T_1 and T_2, are disregarded.

The voltage pulse is then expressed as follows:

$$v(t) = 0, \qquad t < t_0$$

$$= 10, \quad t_0 < t < t_1$$

$$= 0, \qquad t > t_1$$

which by the notation of the preceding sections, is:

$$v(t) = 10\,[U(t - t_0) - U(t - t_1)], \tag{2.36}$$

and we then proceed by applying the methods developed above to each term of eqn. (2.36).

The required voltage, $v_R(t)$, may be written in terms of $v(t)$ using the transfer function $T'(s)$ of eqn. (2.35).

In this case:

$$T'(s) = \frac{R}{R + R_1 + (1/sC)} = \frac{sCR}{1 + sC(R + R_1)}. \tag{2.37}$$

Clearly $T'(s) = 0$ when $s = 0$, so there is no forced response component in $v_R(t)$. The total response consists entirely of the natural response component. This occurs when $T'(s) = \infty$ or when $1 + sC(R + R_1) = 0$ or $s = -(1/\tau)$, where $\tau = C(R + R_1)$.

Thus

$$v_R(t) = A\,e^{-[(t - t_0)/\tau]}, \quad t_0 < t < t_1 \tag{2.38}$$

where A is a constant.

At $t = t_0^-$, $v_c(t_0^-) = 0$ and $v_R(t_0^-) = 0$. After the application of the 10-V step, i.e. at $t = t_0^+$,

$$v_c(t_0^+) = 0, \quad \therefore v_R(t_0^+) = 10\left(\frac{R}{R + R_1}\right) = 10\left(\frac{30}{32}\right)$$

$$= \underline{9.375\ \text{V}}$$

since R and R_1 are in series across the voltage source, and $v_c(t_0^+) = 0$.

Substituting into (2.38) to find A

$$+ 9.375 = A\, e^{-[(t_0 - t_0)/\tau]} \text{ or } \underline{A = 9.375}.$$

And

$$\underline{v_R(t) = 9.375\, e^{-[(t - t_0)/\tau]}} \quad t_0 < t < t_1.$$

At $t = t_1$ where $(t - t_0) = 20$ msec, $v_R(t)$ has decayed to:

$$v_R(t_1) = 9.375\, e^{-(20/320)} = \underline{8.803 \text{ V}},$$

hence

$$v_c(t_1) = 9.375 - 8.803 = \underline{0.572 \text{ V}}.$$

At this instant the input voltage changes by $-9.375U(t - t_1)$. Again there is no forced response and the natural response, for $t > t_1$, is

$$A_1\, e^{-[(t - t_1)/\tau]}.$$

To find A_1 the conditions at the beginning of the period for which this expression is valid, i.e. t_1, must be substituted.

At $t = t_1^-$ $v_R(t_1^-) = 8.803$ V and $v_c(t_1^-) = 0.572$ V.

And so,

$$v_c(t_1^+) = 0.572 \quad \text{and} \quad v_R(t_1^+) = 8.803 - 9.375$$

$$= \underline{-0.572 \text{ V}}.$$

Hence,

$$-0.572 = A_1\, e^{-[(t_1 - t_1)/\tau]} = A_1,$$

giving

$$\underline{v_R(t) = -0.572\, e^{-[(t - t_1)/\tau]}} \text{ for } t > t_1. \tag{2.39}$$

Graphs of both $v_R(t)$ and $v_c(t)$ are shown in Fig. 2.11(b) from which it will be seen that at no time during or after the pulse does the capacitor become charged to more than 0.572 V. This is because the charge/discharge time constant is very long compared with the pulse duration. If the capacitance had been less, for example 1 μF, there would have been time during the pulse duration of 20 msec for it to charge to 4.36 V, with a corresponding reduction (to 5.016 V) of $v_R(t_1)$.

Hence, in this application, the rectangular shape of the pulse is lost, to some extent, during transfer from one active device to the next, the degree of "droop" of the top and bottom of the pulse being less as the ratio

$$\frac{\text{CR time constant}}{\text{pulse duration}}$$

becomes greater.

2.2 SECOND-ORDER SYSTEMS

A second-order system is one which gives rise to a second-order differential equation. With the usual stipulation as to linearity (no terms involving the dependent variable, or its derivatives, beyond the first degree) and with constant coefficients, this equation may be solved by the methods used in Problems 2.1–2.10 for first-order systems, although the solutions are generally more complicated.

2.2.1 A circuit containing L, C and R

Consider the circuit represented by Fig. 2.12. When current is taken

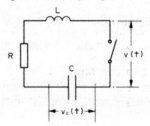

Fig. 2.12. A second-order circuit.

as the response variable and applied voltage as the forcing variable, the differential equation relating them is:

$$Ri(t) + L\frac{\mathrm{d}i(t)}{\mathrm{d}t} + \frac{1}{C}\int i(t)\,\mathrm{d}t = v(t) \tag{2.40}$$

which reduces to an equation of the second order. The natural and forced responses are determined separately, as before, by expressing $v(t)$ in terms of exponentials.

PROBLEM 2.11

A circuit consists of inductance 0.5 H, capacitance 0.0556 F and resistance R all in series. Determine the natural response for $R =$ (i) 10 Ω, (ii) 6 Ω, (iii) 1 Ω and (iv) 0, when the circuit is closed with an initial voltage of 35 V on the capacitor.

Solution

The natural response occurs when $Z(s) = 0$, i.e. when

$$Z(s) = R + \frac{s}{2} + \frac{18}{s} = 0 \qquad (2.41)$$

or

$$s^2 + 2sR + 36 = 0.$$

CASE (i) $R = 10$ Ω

$$s^2 + 20s + 36 = 0$$

or

$$(s + 18)(s + 2) = 0$$

giving

$$s = -18 \text{ or } s = -2.$$

Hence, the natural response is:

$$i_N(t) = A\,e^{-18t} + B\,e^{-2t}, \qquad (2.42)$$

a solution which has two constants, A and B, to be determined from initial conditions, since it arises from a second-order equation.

If $i(t)$ at $t = 0^-$ is 0, then $i(0^+) = 0$ also,

$$\therefore \quad 0 = A + B. \qquad (2.43)$$

Another equation containing A and B can be obtained by evaluating $di_N(t)/dt$. At $t = 0^+$, $i(0^+) = 0$ so that $i_N(0^+)\,R = 0$ and the initial voltage across the capacitor is all applied across the inductor. Hence,

$$35 = L\frac{di_N(t)}{dt} \quad \text{or} \quad \frac{di_N(t)}{dt} = \frac{35}{0.5} = 70 \text{ A/sec.}$$

ELECTRIC CIRCUIT THEORY

From eqn. (2.42),

$$\frac{di_N(t)}{dt} = -18A\,e^{-18t} - 2B\,e^{-2t}$$

$$= -18A - 2B \text{ at } t = (0^+)$$

or

$$70 = -18A - 2B. \tag{2.44}$$

Combining eqns. (2.43) and (2.44),

$$A = -4.375 \quad \text{and} \quad B = 4.375$$

so that

$$i_N(t) = 4.375\,(e^{-2t} - e^{-18t}). \tag{2.45}$$

This response is shown plotted in Fig. 2.13 (curve (a)), and a plot of eqn. (2.41), with $R = 10\,\Omega$, shown in Fig. 2.14, exhibits zeros at the two critical frequencies ($s = -18$ and -2) which appear in the time response of eqn. (2.45). The response of the circuit in the frequency domain could be obtained by plotting $Y(s)$ ($= 1/Z(s)$) and this would exhibit poles at $s = -18$ and -2 and zeros at $s = 0$ and $\pm\infty$.

CASE (ii) $R = 6\,\Omega$,

$$\therefore \quad 6 + \frac{s}{2} + \frac{18}{s} = 0 \tag{2.46}$$

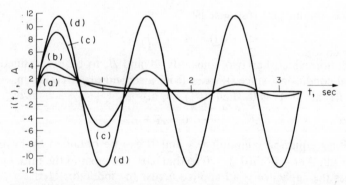

FIG. 2.13. Natural responses of a series R, L, C circuit with different degrees of damping: (a) overdamped, (b) critically damped, (c) under-damped, (d) undamped (see Problem 2.11).

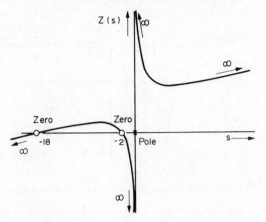

FIG. 2.14. Plot of $Z(s)$ for the circuit of Problem 2.11.

or
$$s^2 + 12s + 36 = 0$$

giving $(s + 6)^2 = 0$ or $s = -6$ twice. In this case, the natural response is:

$$i_N(t) = (At + B)\, e^{-6t}. \tag{2.47}$$

Again A and B may be evaluated by putting

$$\text{(i) } i_N(0^+) = 0 \quad \text{and} \quad \text{(ii) } \frac{di_N(t)}{dt}\bigg]_{0^+} = 70.$$

From condition (i) $B = 0$ so that

$$\frac{di_N(t)}{dt}\bigg]_{0^+} = -6At\, e^{-6t} + A\, e^{-6t} \quad \text{with} \quad t = 0$$
$$= A = 70$$

giving
$$i_N(t) = 70t\, e^{-6t}. \tag{2.48}$$

Curve (b) of Fig. 2.13 shows this response to be greater in magnitude at its peak but to fall more quickly to negligible proportions. The circuit is said to be critically damped in this condition (i.e. when the two roots

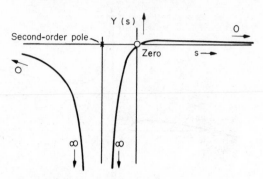

FIG. 2.15. Plot of $Y(s)$ for Case (ii) of Problem 2.11.

of (2.46) are equal) whereas in Case (i) it is overdamped. The pole–zero plot of $Y(s)$, Fig. 2.15, shows that the two poles have now combined to a single point—called a second-order pole.

CASE (iii) $R = 1\,\Omega$,

$$\therefore\ 1 + \frac{s}{2} + \frac{18}{s} = 0 \tag{2.49}$$

or

$$s^2 + 2s + 36 = 0$$

so that

$$s = \frac{-2 \pm \sqrt{4 - 144}}{2} = \underline{-1 \pm j\sqrt{35}}\ \ \text{where } j = \sqrt{-1}.$$

Hence the natural current response in this case is:

$$i_N(t) = A\,e^{(-1 + j\sqrt{35})t} + B\,e^{(-1 - j\sqrt{35})t}. \tag{2.50}$$

Again there are two critical frequencies, this time represented by two complex values of s, s_1 and s_2.

The real and imaginary components of complex s are customarily designated σ and ω, respectively.

Hence $s = \sigma \pm j\omega$ in general, and for particular values, $s = \alpha \pm j\omega_n$.

Equation (2.50) may be simplified to:

$$i_N(t) = e^{-t}(A e^{j\sqrt{35}t} + B e^{-j\sqrt{35}t})$$ (2.51)

where A and B are constants which may be determined by inserting the initial conditions. Thus, when $t = 0^+$, $i_N(t) = 0$.

Hence, $0 = A + B$ or $\underline{A = -B}$. And

$$\frac{di_N(t)}{dt} = e^{-t}(j\sqrt{35} A e^{j\sqrt{35}t} - j\sqrt{35} B e^{-j\sqrt{35}t}) - e^{-t}(A e^{j\sqrt{35}t} + B e^{-j\sqrt{35}t})$$

which at $t = 0^+$,

$$= j\sqrt{35} A - j\sqrt{35} B - (A + B)$$

$$= j2\sqrt{35} A$$

$$= 70 \quad \text{giving } A = j\sqrt{35},$$
$$B = j\sqrt{35},$$

and

$$\therefore \quad i_N(t) = e^{-t}(-j\sqrt{35} e^{j\sqrt{35}t} + j\sqrt{35} e^{-j\sqrt{35}t})$$

$$= j\sqrt{35} e^{-t}(e^{-j\sqrt{35}t} - e^{j\sqrt{35}t}).$$

This may be reduced to a more immediately recognisable and useful form by using Euler's Theorem, viz.

$$e^{\pm j\omega t} = \cos \omega t \pm j \sin \omega t$$

so that

$$i_N(t) = 2\sqrt{35} e^{-t} \sin \sqrt{35}t$$

$$= 11.832 e^{-t} \sin 5.9161t.$$ (2.52)

The simple act of reducing the resistance in the circuit from $6\,\Omega$ to $1\,\Omega$ has completely changed the form of the natural response. Equation (2.52) now represents a sinusoidal oscillation of radian frequency 5.9161 rad/sec and neper frequency -1 neper/sec, i.e. a sinusoid whose amplitude diminishes as t increases (a damped sinusoid). The waveform is shown plotted at (c) in Fig. 2.13, and we can now identify an alternative interpretation of the critical damping condition of Case (ii). For the values of L and C used in this problem, $6\,\Omega$ is the smallest resistance which does not result in the oscillatory condition of Case (iii).

The pole–zero plot of

$$Y(s) = \frac{2s}{s^2 + 2s + 36} \tag{2.53}$$

cannot now be plotted as simply as for Cases (i) and (ii) since the values of s at the poles are complex numbers having two components. The problem can, however, be simplified to some extent by plotting only $|Y(s)|$, the magnitude of $Y(s)$, but there still remain three quantities ($|Y(s)|$, σ and ω) and the result must be a surface in three dimensions. The x- and y-axes are used for σ and ω, respectively, so the x-y plane is the s-plane, and the z-axis is used for $|Y(s)|$. The plot of eqn. (2.53) will therefore appear as shown in Fig. 2.16, and in addition to representing $|Y(s)|$, the height of the surface above the s-plane represents

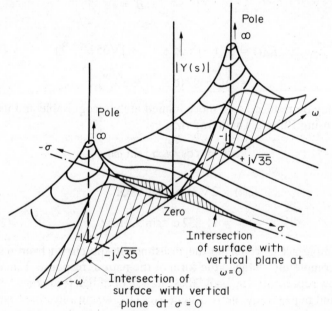

FIG. 2.16. Plot of $|Y(s)|$ as a function of ω and σ for $Y(s) = \dfrac{2s}{s^2 + 2s + 36}$ (see Problem 2.11).

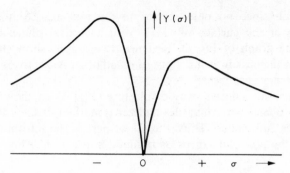

FIG. 2.17. Plot of $Y(s)$ as a function only of σ, with $\omega = 0$, for Case (iii) of Problem 2.11.

the magnitude of the response to a constant applied voltage—i.e. the forced response. This plot, therefore, has revealed the possibility of exponential forcing functions having complex exponents. It has two poles (at $s_{1,2} = -1 \pm j\sqrt{35}$) and zeros at $s = 0$ and $s = \pm\infty$. The intersection of this surface with the vertical plane at $\omega = 0$ would evidently produce a graph such as that of Fig. 2.17. Only zeros appear

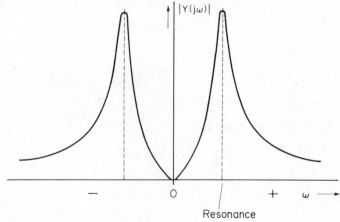

FIG. 2.18. Plot $Y(s)$ as a function only of ω, with $\sigma = 0$, for Case (iii) of Problem 2.11. Vertical scale = one-fifth of that of Fig. 2.17.

on the graph since no poles occur on the real axis. Similarly, the intersection of the surface of $|Y(s)|$ with a vertical plane at $\sigma = 0$ produces the graph of Fig. 2.18. These two graphs show the forced responses of the circuit as functions of σ and of ω, respectively, and are called frequency responses.

An alternative, simpler, way of plotting $|Y(s)|$ is to show only the s-plane (x-y plane) with the poles and zeros marked, respectively, with small crosses and circles. Thus, the major part of the information (the location of the poles and zeros) is retained in the plot of Fig. 2.19.

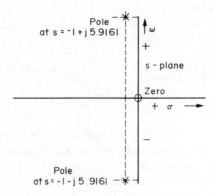

FIG. 2.19. Plot of poles and zeros in the s-plane, from Fig. 2.16.

CASE (iv) $R = 0$,

$$s^2 + 36 = 0 \quad \text{giving} \quad s = \pm j6.$$

Hence, the natural response is:

$$i_N(t) = A\, e^{j6t} + B\, e^{-j6t}.$$

Since

$$i_N(t) = 0 \quad \text{at} \quad t = 0^+, \qquad A + B = 0.$$

And

$$\frac{di_N(t)}{dt} = j6A\, e^{j6t} - j6B\, e^{-j6t} = 70 \quad \text{at} \quad t = 0^+$$

or

$$70 = j6(A - B) = j12A,$$

$$\therefore \quad A = -j5.83 \quad \text{and} \quad B = j5.83,$$

$$\therefore \quad i_N(t) = j5.83 \, (e^{-j6t} - e^{j6t}),$$

$$i_N(t) = 11.66 \sin 6t \text{ by Euler's Theorem.}$$

The response is now a sinusoidal oscillation having an undiminishing peak amplitude of 11.66A and a radian frequency of 6 rad/sec. The time-domain response is shown at (d) in Fig. 2.13 whilst the pole–zero plot of $|Y(s)|$ now appears (plotting only the s-plane) as shown in Fig. 2.20. The two poles now appear on the imaginary axis, which is the

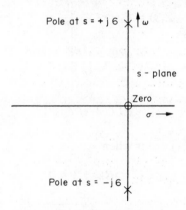

FIG. 2.20. Pole–zero plot for Case (iv) of Problem 2.11.

limit of their movement unless R is allowed to go negative. The oscillation of constant peak amplitude is said to be undamped and occurs in this case because the resistance is zero. The energy in the circuit—originating in the stored charge on the capacitor—is stored alternately in the capacitor and in the inductor. During the exchange, no energy is lost if the circuit is without resistance and so the peak amplitude of oscillation never decreases. However, for a circuit having a finite, but small, resistance, each energy exchange results in some energy dissipation (in the resistance), so causing a steady decrease in peak amplitude. This process occurs in Case (iii) above. For a larger resistance, oscillation ceases altogether and the decay of current is in the form of simple exponentials, as in Cases (ii) and (i) above. The ratio between the degree of damping in a circuit and the critical damping, Case (ii), is termed the damping ratio, and is usually denoted by ζ.

PROBLEM 2.12

A circuit consists of R, L and C in series.

Derive general expressions for the critical frequencies, the undamped natural frequency and the damping ratio. Show that the locus of the poles of $|Y(s)|$ in the s-plane as R is varied is a circle.

$$Z(s) = R + sL + \frac{1}{sC}$$

$$= \frac{sRC + s^2LC + 1}{sc},$$

$$\therefore \quad Y(s) = \frac{sC}{s^2LC + sRC + 1};$$

hence the poles of $Y(s)$ occur when

$$s^2LC + sRC + 1 = 0, \tag{2.54}$$

$$\therefore \quad s_{1,2} = \frac{-RC \pm \sqrt{R^2C^2 - 4LC}}{2LC}$$

$$= -\frac{R}{2L} \pm \sqrt{\frac{R^2}{4L^2} - \frac{1}{LC}}$$

$$= -\alpha \pm \sqrt{\alpha^2 - \omega_0^2}. \tag{2.55}$$

Clearly the two critical frequencies, s_1 and s_2, are real when $\alpha > \omega_0$, giving an exponential natural response, equal and real when $\alpha = \omega_0$, giving a faster exponential response, and complex when $\alpha < \omega_0$ giving a damped oscillatory response. When $\alpha = 0$, corresponding to $R = 0$

(i.e. no damping), $s_{1,2} = \pm j\omega_0$ which is Case (iv) of Problem 2.11. The undamped natural frequency is given, therefore, by

$$\omega_0 = \frac{1}{\sqrt{LC}}. \tag{2.56}$$

The critical damping resistance, R_c, is given by

$$\alpha^2 = \omega_0^2$$

or

$$\frac{R_c^2}{4L^2} = \frac{1}{LC}$$

or

$$R_c = 2\sqrt{\frac{L}{C}} \tag{2.57}$$

and the damping ratio,

$$\zeta = \frac{R}{R_c} = \frac{R}{2}\sqrt{\frac{C}{L}}. \tag{2.58}$$

Then,

$$\zeta\omega_0 = \frac{R}{2}\sqrt{\frac{C}{L}} \cdot \frac{1}{\sqrt{LC}} = \sqrt{\frac{R^2}{4L^2}} = \alpha,$$

$$\therefore \quad s_{1,2} = -\zeta\omega_0 \pm \omega_0\sqrt{\zeta^2 - 1}$$

and when $\zeta^2 < 1$,

$$s_{1,2} = -\alpha \pm j\omega_0\sqrt{1 - \zeta^2}$$

$$= -\alpha \pm j\omega$$

where $\omega = \omega_0\sqrt{1 - \zeta^2}$, the actual frequency of oscillation when damping is present.

Referring to Fig. 2.21 the distance from the origin ($s = 0$) to the poles s_1 and s_2 is equal to $\sqrt{\alpha^2 + \omega^2}$

$$= \sqrt{\alpha^2 + \omega_0^2 (1 - \zeta^2)} = \sqrt{\omega_0^2 + \alpha^2 - \omega_0^2 \zeta^2}$$

$$= \omega_0 \text{ , i.e. constant.}$$

Hence, the poles follow a circular locus. When $\zeta = 0$, the poles lie on the $j\omega$ axis, when $\zeta = 1$ they combine to a second-order pole on the real—σ—axis and, for values of $\zeta > 1$, they separate, one moving along the real axis towards the origin and the other towards infinity.

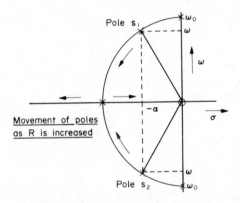

FIG. 2.21. Pole movement for changes in R: Problem 2.12.

The locus is known as the root locus since the poles are obtained from the roots of eqn. (2.54).

The graphical procedure of plotting the poles and zeros of system functions in the s-plane is of great value in the study of linear systems, of which the electric circuit is one example. It not only provides greater insight into the behaviour of such systems but can also act as a valuable design aid. It is, for example, possible to design circuits to meet given specifications by manipulating the pole and zero positions in the s-plane.

2.3 THE SINUSOIDAL FORCING FUNCTION

Probably the most important forcing function of all is that which varies with time according to a sine or cosine function, viz.

$$v(t) = V \cos \omega t. \tag{2.59}$$

Since the limits of cos ωt are ± 1, the voltage $v(t)$ of eqn. (2.59) reverses every half-cycle and therefore represents an alternating voltage. Many practically occurring voltages and currents in power and communication systems approximate closely to this ideal, and so it is necessary to be able to calculate forced responses to such forcing functions.

The methods used so far in this chapter may be adapted to this purpose by expressing the sinusoid in terms of exponentials. This is done using Euler's Theorem:

$$e^{\pm j\omega t} = \cos \omega t \pm j \sin \omega t \tag{2.60}$$

so that

$$\cos \omega t = \Re e\, e^{j\omega t} \tag{2.61}$$

and

$$\sin \omega t = \Im m\, e^{j\omega t} \tag{2.62}$$

where $\Re e$ and $\Im m$ stand, respectively, for "real part of" and "imaginary part of". To apply a forcing function such as that represented by eqn. (2.59), we begin by applying an exponential forcing function having an imaginary exponent. The required response is then the real part of the response to the exponential. Similarly, the response of a system to a forcing function such as

$$v(t) = V \sin \omega t \tag{2.63}$$

is the imaginary part of the response of the system to the forcing function:

$$v(t) = V e^{j\omega t}. \tag{2.64}$$

The method is based on that most important characteristic of linear systems, namely the ability to keep separate the responses to different forcing functions simultaneously applied.

PROBLEM 2.13

For the series L, R circuit of Problem 2.2, in which $R = 10\ \Omega$ and

$L = 0.25$ H, calculate the forced current response to an applied voltage given by:

$$v(t) = 150 \cos 100t. \tag{2.65}$$

Solution
$v(t)$ is first expressed in exponential form.
Evidently, by comparing eqns. (2.65) and (2.61)

$$v(t) = \Re e \, 150 \, e^{j100t}. \tag{2.66}$$

Here,

$$s = j100 \text{ and } Z(s) = \mathbf{Z}(j\omega) = R + j\omega L$$

$$= 10 + j100 \times 0.25$$

$$= (10 + j25) \, \Omega.$$

Since

$$\mathbf{I} = \frac{\mathbf{V}}{Z(s)} = \frac{\mathbf{V}}{\mathbf{Z}(j\omega)},$$

then

$$\mathbf{I} = \frac{150}{10 + j25},$$

a frequency-domain expression.

This may be reduced to a single complex number by multiplying the numerator and the denominator by the conjugate of the denominator:

$$\mathbf{I} = \frac{150 \, (10 - j25)}{(10 + j25)(10 - j25)} = \frac{150 \, (10 - j25)}{10^2 + 25^2}$$

$$= (2.07 - j5.175) \, \text{A}.$$

So that,

$$i(t) = \Re e \, (2.07 - j5.175) \, e^{j100t}, \tag{2.67}$$

the time-domain expression for the current. The complex number within the bracket of eqn. (2.67) may, by again using Euler's Theorem, be written in exponential form.

Thus

$$(2.07 - j5.175) = |\mathbf{I}| \, e^{j\phi} = |\mathbf{I}| \, (\cos \phi + j \sin \phi)$$

where
$$|\mathbf{I}| \cos \phi = 2.07$$
and
$$|\mathbf{I}| \sin \phi = -5.175.$$

Hence,

$$|\mathbf{I}| = \sqrt{2.07^2 + 5.175^2} = 5.574 \text{ A}$$

and

$$\phi = \tan^{-1}\frac{-5.175}{2.07} = -68° 12' \quad \text{or} \quad -1.19 \text{ rad.}$$

So that eqn. (2.67) may be written:

$$i(t) = \Re e\, 5.574\, e^{-j1.19}\, e^{j100t}$$
$$= \Re e\, 5.574\, e^{j(100t - 1.19)}$$

or

$$i(t) = 5.574 \cos (100t - 1.19). \tag{2.68}$$

Equation (2.68) is easily recognised as being identical in form with eqn. (2.65), the time-domain expression for the applied voltage. It represents a current varying as a cosine function of time, whose maximum (or peak) value is 5.574 A, whose frequency is 100 rad/sec but which is retarded by 1.19 rad ($= 68° 12'$) on the voltage of eqn. (2.65). It should be noted that no account has been taken of initial conditions in the circuit since we have calculated only the forced response.

A similar calculation would have produced a similar result had the forcing function been of the form:

$$v(t) = V \sin \omega t.$$

The imaginary part of the exponential would have been used for the forcing function and the desired sinusoidal response would be the imaginary part of the time-domain expression for the current.

2.3.1 The phasor method

It will be clear that, once having performed the calculation in the manner shown in Problem 2.13 there is no need, in further problems, to include $\Re e$ (= real part of) or $\mathscr{I}m$ (= imaginary part of) or even $e^{j\omega t}$, since we know that, for a linear system, the forced response will always be of the same form and frequency as the forcing function. All the information required to calculate $\mathbf{I}$ and ϕ is contained in the complex number, $\mathbf{Z}(j\omega)$, representing the impedance. Thus, in this case:

$$\mathbf{Z}(j\omega) = 10 + j25 \quad \text{in Cartesian coordinates}$$

$$= \sqrt{10^2 + 25^2} \, \angle\tan^{-1} 2.5$$

$$= 26.93 \, \angle 68° \, 12' \text{ in polar coordinates.}$$

Thus:

$$\mathbf{I} = \frac{150}{26.93 \, \angle 68° \, 12'} = 5.574 \, \angle -68° \, 12'.$$

This is called a PHASOR expression and simply indicates that the current response is of peak magnitude 5.574 A and lags in phase on the voltage phasor $150 \, \angle 0°$ by $68° \, 12'$. The phasor may, alternatively, be expressed in Cartesian form as $(2.07 - j5.175)$ A. The use of a phasor expression always implies sinusoidal variations with time. To distinguish a phasor quantity from a pure number it is sometimes written with a bar or a dot below, or, in print, by using **bold-face type**. This last method is adopted here and is used also for complex numbers such as $\mathbf{Z}(j\omega)$.

PROBLEM 2.14

A voltage given by

$$v(t) = 100 \cos 10t$$

is applied to a circuit consisting of 1000 Ω resistance in series with 300 μF capacitance. Calculate, using the phasor method, the forced component of current response.

Solution

$$\mathbf{Z}(j\omega) = R + \frac{1}{sC} \quad \text{with } s = j\omega_F$$

$$= 1000 + \frac{10^6}{j10 \times 300}$$

$$= (1000 - \text{j}333)\Omega \quad \text{since } \frac{1}{\text{j}} = -\text{j}$$

$$= 1054 \angle -18°25' \ \Omega.$$

Hence,

$$\mathbf{I} = \frac{100}{1054 \angle -18°25'} = \underline{0.095 \angle 18°25' \ \text{A}.}$$

And, returning to the time domain,

$$i(t) = 0.095 \cos{(10t + 18°25')}$$

or the current has a maximum value of 0.095 A and leads the voltage in phase by $18°25'$.

The solutions calculated for Problems 2.13 and 2.14 are still referred to as the steady-state solutions since they refer to conditions which obtain so long after the application of the forcing voltage that all natural components of response have died away. The complete response would, of course, include the natural response components and would be valid for any $t > 0$.

PROBLEM 2.15

For the series L, C, R circuit of Problem 2.11, Case (iii), calculate the complete current response when a voltage given by

$$v(t) = 10 \cos 9t \tag{2.69}$$

is applied at the instant when $v(t) = 8 \ \text{V}$ and increasing. Assume that there is no stored energy in the circuit at $t = 0$.

Solution

At $t = 0$, $v(0) = 8$, conditions which are incompatible with eqn. (2.69) as it stands. Referring to Fig. 2.22 we see that in order to make $v(0) = 8$, and increasing, the cosine wave must be retarded by an angle θ, where θ satisfies:

$$v(0) = 10 \cos \theta = 8$$

or

$$\theta = \cos^{-1} 0.8 = \underline{36°52'},$$

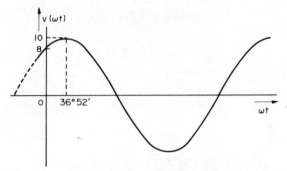

FIG. 2.22. The forcing function for Problem 2.15.

giving

$$v(t) = 10 \cos (9t - 36°\,52') \qquad (2.70)$$

as the necessary form of eqn. (2.69). The complete response is found, as usual, by adding the forced and natural responses.

Forced response

Using the phasor method, the expression for the voltage is:

$$\mathbf{V} = 10\,e^{-j\theta} = 10\,e^{-j36°52'}$$

$$= 10\,e^{-j0.64344}$$

or

$$\mathbf{V} = 10\angle -36°\,52',$$

$$\mathbf{Z}(j\omega) = R + sL + \frac{1}{sC} \quad \text{with } s = j\omega_F = j9$$

$$= 1 + j4.5 + \frac{18}{j9} = \underline{1 + j2.5} \quad \text{in Cartesian form}$$

or

$$\mathbf{Z}(j\omega) = \sqrt{1^2 + 2.5^2}\ \angle\tan^{-1} 2.5$$

$$= 2.693\ \angle 68°\,12' \quad \text{in polar form.}$$

Hence

$$I = \frac{V}{Z(j\omega)} = \frac{10 \angle -36° 52'}{2.693 \angle 68° 12'} = 3.7139 \angle -105° 4'.$$

Reverting to the time domain:

$$i_F(t) = 3.7139 \cos (9t - 105° 4'). \tag{2.71}$$

Natural response

For $R = 1\,\Omega$ this has already been determined in Problem 2.11, Case (iii), and is given by eqn. (2.51).

The complete response is therefore:

$$i(t) = 3.7139 \cos (9t - 105° 4') + e^{-t}(A\, e^{-j\sqrt{35}t} + B\, e^{j\sqrt{35}t}) \tag{2.72}$$

in which the values of A and B must be found by substituting the conditions, (i) when $t = 0^+$, $i(0^+) = 0$, since the circuit contains inductance, and there is no stored energy, and (ii) when

$$t = 0^+, \frac{di(t)}{dt} = \frac{v(0^+)}{L} = \frac{8}{0.5} = 16 \text{ A/sec}$$

since, at $t = 0^+$, there is no charge on the capacitor and no voltage drop across the resistor.

Substituting the first of these conditions:

$$0 = 3.7139 \cos (-105° 4') + A + B$$

or

$$A + B = 0.9654. \tag{2.73}$$

And substituting the second:

$$16 = -9 \times 3.7139 (-0.9656) + (-j\sqrt{35}A + j\sqrt{35}B) - A - B$$

$$= 32.276 - A(j\sqrt{35} + 1) - B(1 - j\sqrt{35})$$

or

$$16.276 = A(j\sqrt{35} + 1) + B(1 - j\sqrt{35}). \tag{2.74}$$

Solving eqns. (2.73) and (2.74) for A and B gives:

$$A = 0.4827 - j1.2940,$$

$$B = 0.4827 + j1.2940.$$

Hence, the natural component of response $i_N(t)$ is:

$$i_N(t) = e^{-t}[(0.4827 - j1.294)\,e^{-j\omega t} + (-0.4827 - j1.294)\,e^{j\omega t}]$$

where

$$\omega = \sqrt{35} = 5.9161 \text{ rad/sec},$$

$$\therefore \quad i_N(t) = e^{-t}[0.4827\,(e^{-j\omega t} + e^{j\omega t}) + j1.294\,(e^{j\omega t} - e^{j\omega t})]$$

$$= -e^{-t}[0.9654\cos\omega t - 2.588\sin\omega t]$$

$$= E\,e^{-t}\cos(\omega t - \phi) \quad \text{where } E \text{ and } \phi \text{ are constants.}$$

$$E = \sqrt{0.9654^2 + 2.588^2} = 2.7622 \quad \text{and} \quad \phi = \tan^{-1}\frac{2.588}{0.9654} = 69°\,32',$$

$$\therefore \quad i_N(t) = 2.7622\,e^{-t}\cos(5.916t + 69°\,32')$$

and

$$i(t) = 3.7139\cos(9t - 105°\,4')$$
$$+ 2.7622\,e^{-t}\cos(5.9161t + 69°\,32'). \quad (2.75)$$

So the total current response consists of two cosine functions of different frequencies, $\omega_F = 9$ rad/sec and $\omega = 5.9161$ rad/sec, the first of constant amplitude and the second of exponentially decaying amplitude. The resulting waveform is therefore far from sinusoidal until the natural response component has decayed to negligible proportions.

For example, the peak value of the natural response component drops to 1% of the forced component when:

$$2.7622e^{-t} = \frac{3.7139}{100}, \quad \text{or when} \quad t = 4.31 \text{ sec.}$$

Now, $\omega_F = 2\pi/T$ where T is the periodic time of the forced component.

$$\therefore \quad T = \frac{2\pi}{\omega_F} = \frac{2\pi}{9} = 0.698 \text{ sec.}$$

Hence, the number of cycles of the forced component before the natural component decays to 1% of the forced component is,

$$\frac{4.31}{0.698} = 6.17 \text{ cycles.}$$

So it can be said that, after a little over 6 cycles, the conditions in the circuit have substantially reached the steady state.

The waveform corresponding to eqn. (2.75) is shown in Fig. 2.23.

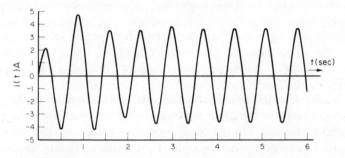

FIG. 2.23. Total current response of series L, C, R circuit to an applied sinusoidal voltage, showing the effect of the summation of the forced and natural responses of different frequencies (Problem 2.15).

Significantly different total response waveforms would be obtained for the remaining three cases of Problem 2.11, since both the forced and natural response components depend on the circuit resistance, in the latter case very critically, as the solutions to Problem 2.11 show. In all cases, however, two constants have to be evaluated using a similar procedure to that adopted for Problem 2.15.

2.4 THE LAPLACE TRANSFORMATION

2.4.1 Summary of the foregoing

The method which has been introduced and developed in this chapter for determining the forced response of linear circuits may be referred to as the exponential transform. The forcing function—or applied signal—was expressed in terms of, i.e. transformed into, an exponential function of time, and, recognising that the forced response must also be an exponential function of time (since all the circuits considered were linear), the result was a transformation of the basic differential equation for the circuit into an algebraic equation in s (referred to as the frequency). The solution of this equation gave the transform of the response, which, by means of an inverse transformation process, yielded the time-function form of the response.

The transient, or natural, component of the response was evaluated separately from the poles of the impedance, admittance, or transfer function (as the case may be), and then added to the forced response to give the total response, the initial conditions being introduced to evaluate constants which appeared as factors in the natural response component.

The method is simple and effective but, unfortunately, is restricted to a limited range of functions which can easily be transformed into an exponential function. On the other hand, it is fortunate that this range includes the sine and cosine functions, the transformation of which gives rise to the complex number transform. This very powerful method enables the whole of steady-state sinusoidal analysis to be carried out with ease—a technique fully explored in Chapter 3.

2.4.2 Using the Laplace transformation

The Laplace transformation is an extension of the exponential transform which not only can be applied to a vastly wider range of functions, but also evaluates both components of the response simultaneously and automatically incorporates the initial conditions in the process.

PROBLEM 2.16
To illustrate the method it will be used to determine the total response of the circuit of Fig. 2.24, i.e. Fig. 2.8 modified to allow an initial current to flow before the switch is closed. Thus, since the switch is shunted by resistance R', the initial current, $i(0^-)$, is given by:

$$i(0^-) = \frac{100}{10 + R'}$$

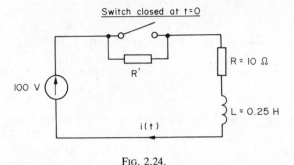

FIG. 2.24.

and, because of the presence of inductance,

$$i(0^+) = \frac{100}{10 + R'}, \text{ also.}$$

It is desired to determine the total response for $t > 0$.

Solution

The differential equation describing conditions in the circuit for $t > 0$ is:

$$Ri(t) + L\frac{di(t)}{dt} = VU(t) \tag{2.76}$$

where $U(t)$ represents the step function as previously defined (section 2.1.1.5).

To derive the Laplace transform of eqn. (2.76) each term is multiplied by e^{-st} (where s is, in general, complex) and the product integrated over the range $0 \rightarrow \infty$. The lower limit of integration (more precisely (0^+)) is chosen so as to include all the initial states in the circuit, i.e. current in inductive branches and stored charge (or initial voltages) on capacitors. The limit would need to be (0^-) if it were desired to include the impulse or the doublet as a forcing function, but neither of these is considered in the present text. Thus,

$$R\int_0^\infty i(t)\,e^{-st}\,dt + L\int_0^\infty \frac{di(t)}{dt}\,e^{-st}\,dt = \int_0^\infty VU(t)\,e^{-st}\,dt. \tag{2.77}$$

ECT - H

Integrating the second term (by parts),

$$L \int_0^\infty \frac{di(t)}{dt} e^{-st} dt = L \left[e^{-st} i(t) \right]_0^\infty + Ls \int_0^\infty e^{-st} i(t) dt$$

$$= -Li(0^+) + sL \int_0^\infty e^{-st} i(t) dt$$

where $i(0^+) = i(t)$ at $t = (0^+)$, so that eqn. (2.77) reduces to:

$$(R + sL) \int_0^\infty i(t) e^{-st} dt = \int_0^\infty VU(t) e^{-st} dt + Li(0^+). \qquad (2.78)$$

An integral of the form $\int_0^\infty f(t) e^{-st} dt$, two examples of which appear in eqn. (2.78), is called the Laplace transform of $f(t)$, and is denoted by $F(s)$, i.e.

$$F(s) = \mathscr{L}f(t) = \int_0^\infty f(t) e^{-st} dt \qquad (2.79)$$

where the symbol $\mathscr{L}$ represents "Laplace transform of". Note that the Laplace transform exists only for $t > 0$.

Note also that for the Laplace transform method to be valid the integral of eqn. (2.79) must converge, at the upper limit, for some value of s. For this to be the case the function $f(t)$ must be of "exponential order", i.e.

$$|f(t)| < M e^{at},$$

a is real and > 0 for +ve t, and M is a constant, and the integral converges for $Re(s) > a$.

The mathematical theory of convergence is beyond the scope of the present text and the interested reader is referred to advanced treatments of the Laplace transformation for further clarification,* or to mathematical texts dealing with convergence of infinite integrals.

We may proceed, however, by observing that all the time functions likely to be encountered in electrical circuit theory are transformable, given certain conditions which are mentioned, where appropriate, in what follows.

---

* See, for example, R. E. Scott, *Linear Circuits*, Addison-Wesley Publishing Co., 1964.

Rearranging (2.78),

$$I(s) = \frac{V(s) + Li(0^+)}{R + sL} \qquad (2.80)$$

where $I(s)$ and $V(s)$ are, respectively, the transforms of the current and of the voltage.

Note that if the initial current, $i(0^+)$, had been equal to zero, then a simple Ohm's Law type of relationship

$$(R + sL) = \frac{V(s)}{I(s)} \qquad (2.81)$$

exists between these transforms. The expression $(R + sL)$ is known, in general, as the system function.

It is usually—though not invariably—desired to express the response, the current in eqn. (2.80), as a time function. To achieve this an inverse transformation must be applied to the equation, but since the direct approach involves complex integration, the simpler approach will be used of invoking the uniqueness property of the Laplace transform, viz. that if a function $f(t)$ has a transform $F(s)$, then $f(t)$ is the *only* inverse transform of $F(s)$.

Quite simply, the problem is solved by reference to tables of Laplace transform pairs, i.e. corresponding pairs of values of $F(s)$ and $f(t)$. In fact such a table can be prepared beforehand and used both for the evaluation of $F(s)$ from the known function $f(t)$, and for the inversion back to the time domain from the problem-generated value of $F(s)$.

Before proceeding to the solution of eqn. (2.80), therefore, we now look at the evaluation of a few transforms, in order to build up a table, and consider a theorem which will extend its usefulness.

2.4.3 Some Laplace transforms evaluated

We make use of eqn. (2.79) by applying it first to two commonly used time functions, the step function and the exponential function.

(a) Let

$$f(t) = VU(t) \qquad (2.82)$$

where V is a constant, and $U(t)$ is the unit step function.

Making use of the fact that the step function is zero for $t < 0$,

$$\mathcal{L}f(t) = \int_0^\infty V e^{-st}\,dt = V \int_0^\infty e^{-st}\,dt$$

$$= V \left[-\frac{1}{s} \cdot e^{-st} \right]_0^\infty = \frac{V}{s} \tag{2.83}$$

converges for $Re(s) > 0$.

(b) Let

$$f(t) = e^{\alpha t}, \quad \text{where } \alpha \text{ is a constant,}$$

$$\mathcal{L}f(t) = \int_0^\infty e^{\alpha t} e^{-st}\,dt = \int_0^\infty e^{(\alpha - s)t}\,dt$$

$$= \left[\frac{-1}{s - \alpha} e^{-(s - \alpha)t} \right]_0^\infty. \tag{2.84}$$

This expression converges at the upper limit (∞) so long as $Re(s) > Re(\alpha)$. Its value then is:

$$\mathcal{L}f(t) = F(s) = \frac{1}{s - \alpha}, \quad Re(s) > Re(\alpha). \tag{2.85}$$

Likewise, with $f(t) = e^{-\alpha t}$,

$$F(s) = \frac{1}{s + \alpha}, \quad Re(s) > -\alpha. \tag{2.86}$$

These results, eqns. (2.85) and (2.86), may be extended by the use of our first theorem relating to Laplace transforms.

THEOREM 1. *The Addition Theorem*
Let $f_1(t)$ and $f_2(t)$ be two functions of time. Then:

$$\mathcal{L}[f_1(t) + f_2(t)] = \int_0^\infty [f_1(t) + f_2(t)]\,e^{-st}\,dt$$

$$= \int_0^\infty f_1(t)\,e^{-st}\,dt + \int_0^\infty f_2(t)\,e^{-st}\,dt$$

$$= \mathcal{L}f_1(t) + \mathcal{L}f_2(t), \tag{2.87}$$

i.e. the transform of the sum of two functions is the sum of their transforms.

Applying this theorem to the results of (a) and (b), above:

(c) Let

$$f(t) = 1 - e^{\pm \alpha t},$$

then,

$$F(s) = \frac{1}{s} - \frac{1}{s \mp \alpha}$$

$$= \frac{\mp \alpha}{s(s \mp \alpha)}. \tag{2.88}$$

(d) Let

$$f(t) = \cosh \omega t$$

$$= \tfrac{1}{2}(e^{\omega t} + e^{-\omega t}),$$

$$\therefore \quad F(s) = \mathscr{L} \cosh \omega t = \tfrac{1}{2}[\mathscr{L} e^{\omega t} + \mathscr{L} e^{-\omega t}] \quad \text{by eqn. (2.87)}$$

$$= \tfrac{1}{2}\left[\frac{1}{s - \omega} + \frac{1}{s + \omega}\right]$$

$$= \frac{s}{s^2 - \omega^2}. \tag{2.89}$$

(e) Similarly,

$$\mathscr{L} \sinh \omega t = \frac{\omega}{s^2 - \omega^2}. \tag{2.90}$$

(f) Let

$$f(t) = \cos \omega t$$

$$= \tfrac{1}{2}[e^{j\omega t} + e^{-j\omega t}],$$

$$\therefore \quad F(s) = \mathscr{L} \cos \omega t = \tfrac{1}{2}[\mathscr{L} e^{j\omega t} + \mathscr{L} e^{-j\omega t}]$$

$$= \tfrac{1}{2}\left[\frac{1}{s - j\omega} + \frac{1}{s + j\omega}\right]$$

$$= \frac{s}{s^2 + \omega^2}. \tag{2.91}$$

(g) Similarly,

$$\mathscr{L}\sin \omega t = \frac{1}{j2}[\mathscr{L}\,e^{j\omega t} - \mathscr{L}\,e^{-j\omega t}]$$

$$= \frac{1}{j2}\left[\frac{1}{s - j\omega} - \frac{1}{s + j\omega}\right]$$

$$= \frac{\omega}{s^2 + \omega^2}. \tag{2.92}$$

(h) Let

$$f(t) = t, \text{ i.e. the so-called ramp function.}$$

$$F(s) = \mathscr{L}f(t) = \int_0^\infty t\,e^{-st}\,dt \quad t > 0$$

$$= \left[-\frac{t}{s}e^{-st}\right]_0^\infty - \int_0^\infty \frac{-1}{s}e^{-st}\,dt$$

$$= 0 + \frac{1}{s}\left[\frac{1}{s}e^{-st}\right]_0^\infty = \frac{1}{s^2}. \tag{2.93}$$

It is easy to show that, for integral values of n,

$$\mathscr{L}\frac{t^n}{\underline{|n - 1}} = \frac{1}{s^n}. \tag{2.94}$$

(i) Let

$$f(t) = t\,e^{\alpha t}, \quad \alpha \text{ is a constant and } t > 0,$$

$$F(s) = \mathscr{L}f(t) = \int_0^\infty t\,e^{\alpha t}\,e^{-st}\,dt$$

$$= \int_0^\infty t\,e^{-(s - \alpha)t}\,dt.$$

Integrating (by parts) gives:

$$F(s) = \frac{1}{(s - \alpha)^2}. \tag{2.95}$$

Also,

$$\mathscr{L}\left[\frac{t^{n-1}}{\underline{|n - 1}}e^{\alpha t}\right] = \frac{1}{(s - \alpha)^n}. \tag{2.96}$$

For ease of reference, we now collect these results together in tabular form, see $(1) \to (12)$ of Table 2.1.

TABLE 2.1 LAPLACE TRANSFORM PAIRS

$f(t)$	$F(s)$	Conditions
(1) 1 or $U(t)$	$\dfrac{1}{s}$	$Re(s) > 0$
(2) t	$\dfrac{1}{s^2}$	
(3) $e^{\alpha t}$	$\dfrac{1}{s - \alpha}$	$Re(s) > \alpha$
(4) $e^{-\alpha t}$	$\dfrac{1}{s + \alpha}$	$Re(s) > -\alpha$
(5) $\dfrac{t^{n-1}}{\underline{\lvert n-1}}$	$\dfrac{1}{s^n}$	+ve integral n
(6) $\dfrac{t^{n-1}}{\underline{\lvert n-1}} e^{\alpha t}$	$\dfrac{1}{(s - \alpha)^n}$	$Re(s) > \alpha$
(7) $t\, e^{\alpha t}$	$\dfrac{1}{(s - \alpha)^2}$	$Re(s) > \alpha$
(8) $1 - e^{\pm \alpha t}$	$\dfrac{\mp \alpha}{s(s \mp \alpha)}$	$Re(s) > \pm \alpha$
(9) $\sin \omega t$	$\dfrac{\omega}{s^2 + \omega^2}$	$s > 0$
(10) $\cos \omega t$	$\dfrac{s}{s^2 + \omega^2}$	$s > 0$
(11) $\sinh \omega t$	$\dfrac{\omega}{s^2 - \omega^2}$	$s > \lvert \omega \rvert$
(12) $\cosh \omega t$	$\dfrac{s}{s^2 - \omega^2}$	$s > \lvert \omega \rvert$
(13) $e^{-\alpha t} f(t)$	$F(s + \alpha)$	
(14) $e^{-\alpha t} \sin \omega t$	$\dfrac{\omega}{(s + \alpha)^2 + \omega^2}$	
(15) $e^{-\alpha t} \cos \omega t$	$\dfrac{s + \alpha}{(s + \alpha)^2 + \omega^2}$	
(16) $e^{-\alpha t} \sinh \omega t$	$\dfrac{\omega}{(s + \alpha)^2 - \omega^2}$	
(17) $e^{-\alpha t} \cosh \omega t$	$\dfrac{s + \alpha}{(s + \alpha)^2 - \omega^2}$	

2.4.4 Solution of Problem 2.16

We return at last to the problem of performing the inverse transformation on eqn. (2.80) in order to derive $i(t)$, the total current response as a time function. More precisely, we search Table 2.1 for a transform pair for which $F(s)$ has the same form as the R.H.S. of eqn. (2.80).

Before doing this, however, we must determine the transform, $V(s)$, of the applied signal and substitute it into eqn. (2.80). When the switch closes at $t = 0$ the signal applied to the circuit is a step function of 100 volts, i.e. $v(t) = 100\,U(t)$, with an initial current $i(0^+) = 100/(R' + 10)$.

Hence, $V(s) = 100/s$, from (1), Table 2.1, and eqn. (2.80) becomes:

$$I(s) = \frac{100}{s(R + sL)} + \frac{Li(0^+)}{R + sL}$$

$$= \frac{100}{Ls\,[s + (R/L)]} + \frac{i(0^+)}{s + (R/L)}$$

$$= \frac{100\,(R/L)}{Rs\,[s + (R/L)]} + \frac{i(0^+)}{s + (R/L)}. \qquad (2.97)$$

We have now modified the first term on the R.H.S. into the form of (8), Table 2.1, and the second term into the form of (4). Hence:

$$i(t) = \frac{100}{R}\,[1 - e^{-(R/L)t}] + i(0^+)\,e^{-(R/L)t}. \qquad (2.98)$$

In this case, $R = 10\,\Omega$, $L = 0.25\,\text{H}$ and $i(0^+) = 100/(R' + 10)$, giving,

$$i(t) = 10\,(1 - e^{-40t}) + \frac{100}{10 + R'}\,e^{-40t} \qquad t > 0, \qquad (2.99)$$

a result identical—except for the initial current component—with eqn. (2.21). Note that the initial current component, as well as the natural component, is subject to the exponential decay having a time constant of $\frac{1}{40}$ sec, or 25 msec.

2.4.5 Three more theorems

We now derive three more theorems which will generalise and extend existing results.

THEOREM 2. *The Differentiation Theorem*

(a) *First derivative*

If $F(s)$ is the transform of $f(t)$, then the transform of $\mathrm{d}f(t)/\mathrm{d}t$ is:

$$sF(s) - f(0^+) \tag{2.100}$$

or

$$\mathscr{L}f'(t) = s\mathscr{L}f(t) - f(0^+) \tag{2.101}$$

(using the prime notation $f'(t)$ to represent the first time-derivative) given that $f(t)$ is a continuous function for $t = 0$ and that $f(0^+)$ is the limit of $f(t)$ as $t \to (0^+)$.

(b) *Second derivative*

Substituting $f'(t)$ for $f(t)$ and $f''(t)$ for $f'(t)$ in eqn. (2.101) gives:

$$\mathscr{L}f''(t) = s\mathscr{L}f'(t) - f'(0^+)$$
$$= s^2F(s) - sf(0^+) - f'(0^+),$$

(c) or, in general,

$$\mathscr{L}f^n(t) = s^nF(s) - s^{n-1}f(0^+) - \ldots - sf^{n-2}(0^+) - f^{n-1}(0^+) \tag{2.102}$$

where $f^n(t)$ represents the nth derivative of $f(t)$, and s^n represents the nth power of s.

THEOREM 3. *The Integral Theorem*
Let the function be $\int f(t)\mathrm{d}t$.

$$\mathscr{L}\left[\int f(t)\,\mathrm{d}t \right] = \int_0^\infty \int f(t)\,\mathrm{d}t\, e^{-st}\,\mathrm{d}t.$$

Integrating by parts, letting $\int f(t)\, dt = u$ and $e^{-st}\, dt = v$,

$$= \left[-\frac{1}{s} \int f(t)\, dt\, e^{-st} \right]_0^\infty + \frac{1}{s} \int_0^\infty f(t)\, e^{-st}\, dt$$

$$= 0 + \frac{1}{s} I_{(0^+)} + \frac{1}{s} \mathscr{L}f(t)$$

where $I_{(0^+)}$ is the value of the integral $\int f(t)\, dt$ at $t = 0^+$. Hence

$$\mathscr{L}\left[\int f(t)\, dt \right] = \frac{1}{s} \mathscr{L}f(t) + \frac{1}{s} I_{(0^+)}. \tag{2.103}$$

For the definite integral $\int_0^t f(t)\, dt$ the transform is simply

$$\frac{1}{s} \mathscr{L}f(t). \tag{2.104}$$

THEOREM 4. *The Attenuation Theorem*
Let the function be $e^{-\alpha t}f(t)$.

$$\mathscr{L}[e^{-\alpha t}f(t)] = \int_0^\infty f(t)\, e^{-\alpha t} e^{-st}\, dt$$

$$= \int_0^\infty f(t)\, e^{-(\alpha+s)t}\, dt$$

$$= F(s + \alpha).$$

Or, in words, given that $\mathscr{L}[f(t)] = F(s)$. Then,

$$\mathscr{L}[e^{-\alpha t} f(t)] = F(s + \alpha). \tag{2.105}$$

Using the attenuation theorem, any of the transforms so far developed may be extended to include an exponential term, thus producing another transform pair.

For example, let, in eqn. (2.105),

$$f(t) = \cos \omega t.$$

Then,

$$\mathscr{L}[e^{-\alpha t} \cos \omega t] = \frac{s + \alpha}{(s + \alpha)^2 + \omega^2} \tag{2.106}$$

by eqn. (2.105) and (10) of Table 2.1.

Table 2.1 has been extended in this way to include the transforms of the circular and hyperbolic functions multiplied by $e^{-\alpha t}$, giving (14), (15), (16) and (17).

Very extensive tables are available in more advanced treatises on the Laplace transform, to which the reader is referred for further study.*

2.4.6 Expansion by partial fractions

In general, the determination of the response transform by the Laplace transformation method—corresponding to eqn. (2.80)—will result in the quotient of two polynomials in s, the degree of the numerator being less than that of the denominator. If this is not so, the quotient must be divided out leaving a polynomial and a "proper" fraction (i.e. one of the desired form). However, the treatment here will be restricted to "proper" fractions since the inverse transforms of the polynomial terms consist of the impulse function and its derivatives—which we have not considered.

Thus, in general

$$F(s) = \frac{P(s)}{Q(s)}. \tag{2.107}$$

It is unlikely that in general $P(s)/Q(s)$ will appear in any table of transform pairs, so the quotient must be split into partial fractions by first determining the roots of $Q(s)$. It is then usually possible, with some algebraic manipulations, to express these fractions in forms appearing in Table 2.1 or in any other table being used.

Thus, let

$$Q(s) = a(s + s_1)(s + s_2) \ldots (s + s_n). \tag{2.108}$$

Because of the nature of the problem (i.e. that it derives from a real, physical system) the roots of $Q(s)$ are either

(i) simple and real,

or (ii) conjugate complex pairs,

or (iii) repeated,

or (iv) combinations of these.

---

* See, for example, B. J. Starkey, *Laplace Transforms for Electrical Engineers*, Iliffe & Sons Ltd., 1958 or P. E. Pfeiffer, *Linear Systems Analysis*, McGraw-Hill Book Co. Ltd., 1961.

If the roots are complex, they occur in conjugate pairs. If $Q(s)$ is an odd-order polynomial at least one root must be real and the remainder must be either real or conjugate complex pairs. If $Q(s)$ is of even order the roots are real or occur in conjugate complex pairs.

Consider these in turn:

(a) *Simple, non-repeated roots*

$$\frac{P(s)}{Q(s)} = \frac{P(s)}{(s + s_1)(s + s_2)\ldots(s + s_n)} \qquad (2.109)$$

$$= \frac{A_1}{s + s_1} + \frac{A_2}{s + s_2} + \ldots + \frac{A_n}{s + s_n}. \qquad (2.110)$$

The partial fraction coefficients A_1, A_2, ..., A_n may be evaluated by first multiplying throughout by $Q(s)$ and equating coefficients of similar powers of s and then solving the n simultaneous equations which result. Alternatively, the so-called "cover-up" rule usually provides a simpler means of solution.* Both methods will be illustrated in an example.

PROBLEM 2.17

Given

$$P(s) = s^2 + 3s + 8$$

and

$$Q(s) = s^3 + 12s^2 + 47s + 60,$$

determine the partial fraction expansion.

Solution

$$\frac{P(s)}{Q(s)} = \frac{s^2 + 3s + 8}{s^3 + 12s^2 + 4s + 60} = \frac{s^2 + 3s + 8}{(s + 3)(s + 4)(s + 5)} \qquad (2.111a)$$

$$= \frac{A_1}{s + 3} + \frac{A_2}{s + 4} + \frac{A_3}{s + 5}. \qquad (2.111b)$$

---

* See advanced algebra texts, e.g. W. L. Ferrer, *Higher Algebra,* Oxford University Press, 1948.

METHOD 1. Multiply (2.111b) by $s^3 + 12s^2 + 47s + 60$.

$$s^2 + 3s + 8 = A_1(s + 4)(s + 5) + A_2(s + 3)(s + 5) + A_3(s + 3)(s + 4)$$
$$= s^2(A_1 + A_2 + A_3) + s(9A_1 + 8A_2 + 7A_3)$$
$$+ 20A_1 + 15A_2 + 12A_3.$$

Equating coefficients of s^2:

$$1 = A_1 + A_2 + A_3. \tag{2.112}$$

Equating coefficients of s:

$$3 = 9A_1 + 8A_2 + 7A_3. \tag{2.113}$$

Equating constant terms:

$$8 = 20A_1 + 15A_2 + 12A_3. \tag{2.114}$$

Solving equations (2.112), (2.113) and (2.114) gives
$$A_1 = 4, A_2 = -12 \text{ and } A_3 = 9.$$

Hence,
$$\frac{P(s)}{Q(s)} = \frac{4}{s+3} - \frac{12}{s+4} + \frac{9}{s+5} \tag{2.115}$$

and the inverse transform of $I(s)$ is, by (4), Table 2.1,

$$i(t) = 4 e^{-3t} - 12 e^{-4t} + 9 e^{-5t} \quad t > 0. \tag{2.116}$$

The values of A_1, A_2 and A_3 may be easily verified by recombining the fractions of eqn. (2.115) to produce the original fraction.

METHOD 2. The "cover-up" rule. The three denominator factors in eqn. (2.111a) are covered up, in turn, and the value of s which makes the cover-up factor equal to zero is substituted into that which remains. This gives the coefficient, A_n, corresponding to the covered-up factor.

Thus, in eqn. (2.111a), putting $s = -3$ and substituting into the remainder gives:

$$A_1 = \frac{(-3)^2 + 3(-3) + 8}{(-3 + 4)(-3 + 5)} = \frac{8}{2} = 4,$$

substituting $s = -4$,

$$A_2 = \frac{(-4)^2 + 3(-4) + 8}{(-4 + 3)(-4 + 5)} = \frac{12}{-1} = -12,$$

substituting $s = -5$,

$$A_3 = \frac{(-5)^2 + 3(-5) + 8}{(-5 + 3)(-5 + 4)} = \frac{18}{(-2)(-1)} = 9.$$

(b) *Conjugate complex roots*

Two methods are available for dealing with this case.
(i) The partial fraction expansion is carried through exactly as in the case of real roots, i.e. by equating coefficients of like powers of s or by the "cover-up" rule, when the coefficients, also, will be found to be conjugate complex pairs, or
(ii) Instead of expanding into partial fractions, we complete the square and make use of the attenuation theorem to obtain the inverse transform.
An example should clarify these alternatives.

PROBLEM 2.18
Expand

$$I(s) = \frac{P(s)}{Q(s)} = \frac{2s + 5}{s^2 + 6s + 34}$$

and invert to obtain the time function $i(t)$.

Solution
METHOD (i)

$$\frac{2s + 5}{s^2 + 6s + 34} = \frac{2s + 5}{(s + 3 - j5)(s + 3 + j5)} \tag{2.117}$$

$$= \frac{A_1}{(s + 3 - j5)} + \frac{A_2}{(s + 3 + j5)}. \tag{2.118}$$

Using the "cover-up" rule:

Let $s = -3 + j5$ and cover up $(s + 3 - j5)$ in (2.117) gives:

$$A_1 = \frac{-6 + j10 + 5}{j10} = \frac{-1 + j10}{j10} = 1 + j0.1.$$

Let $s = -3 - j5$ and cover up $(s + 3 + j5)$ in (2.117) gives:

$$A_2 = \frac{-6 - j10 + 5}{-j10} = \frac{-1 - j10}{-j10} = 1 - j0.1,$$

i.e. A_1 and A_2 are conjugates.

Substituting these values into (2.118):

$$\frac{2s + 5}{s^2 + 6s + 34} = \frac{1 + j0.1}{s + 3 - j5} + \frac{1 - j0.1}{s + 3 + j5},$$

i.e. fractions having the form of (4), Table 2.1. Hence

$$i(t) = (1 + j0.1)\, e^{(-3 + j5)t} + (1 - j0.1)\, e^{(-3 - j5)t}$$

$$= e^{-3t}[e^{j5t} + e^{-j5t} + j0.1\,(e^{j5t} - e^{-j5t})]$$

or

$$i(t) = e^{-3t}(2\cos 5t - 0.2\sin 5t) \quad t > 0. \tag{2.119}$$

METHOD (ii)

$$\frac{2s + 5}{s^2 + 6s + 34} = \frac{2s + 5}{(s^2 + 6s + 9) + 25} = \frac{2s + 5}{(s + 3)^2 + 5^2}$$

$$= \frac{2(s + 3) - 1}{(s + 3)^2 + 5^2} = \frac{2(s + 3)}{(s + 3)^2 + 5^2} - \frac{1}{5} \cdot \frac{5}{(s + 3)^2 + 5^2},$$

i.e. two fractions having the forms of (15) and (14) of Table 2.1. Hence,

$$i(t) = 2\,e^{-3t}\cos 5t - \tfrac{1}{5} \cdot e^{-3t}\sin 5t$$

$$= e^{-3t}(2\cos 5t - 0.2\sin 5t),\, t > 0,$$

a result identical with eqn. (2.119).

The introduction of a linear factor in the numerator of a partial-fraction expansion is particularly useful when the denominator is the product of factors at least one of which is quadratic. By this means, much tedious complex algebra can be avoided when the denominator roots are complex and/or imaginary.

PROBLEM 2.19

Let $F(s) = \dfrac{1}{(s + 1)(s^2 + 4)}$. Determine the partial-fraction expansion and hence the inverse transform.

Solution

The second denominator term could be factorised into $(s + j2)(s - j2)$, giving a denominator with three linear factors which could be dealt with as in Problem 2.17, Method 2. However, it is simpler to expand as follows:

$$\frac{1}{(s + 1)(s^2 + 4)} = \frac{A}{s + 1} + \frac{Bs + C}{s^2 + 4}. \tag{2.120}$$

By the "cover-up" rule, $A = \frac{1}{5}$, and this is as far as the cover-up rule takes us.

Multiplying throughout by $(s + 1)(s^2 + 4)$ and using the result $A = \frac{1}{5}$, gives:

$$1 = \frac{s^2 + 4}{5} + (s + 1)(Bs + C)$$

$$= s^2 (B + \tfrac{1}{5}) + s(B + C) + C + \tfrac{4}{5}.$$

Equating coefficients of s^2: $B = -\frac{1}{5}$.

Equating coefficients of s: $C = \frac{1}{5}$.

$$\therefore \quad F(s) = \frac{1}{5(s + 1)} - \frac{s - 1}{5(s^2 + 4)}$$

or

$$F(s) = \frac{1}{5} \left[\frac{1}{s + 1} - \frac{s}{s^2 + 4} + \frac{1}{s^2 + 4} \right],$$

$$\therefore \quad f(t) = \tfrac{1}{5} e^{-t} - \tfrac{1}{5} \cos 2t + \tfrac{1}{10} \sin 2t \quad t > 0. \tag{2.121}$$

(c) *Repeated roots (or multiple poles)*

If $F(s) = P(s)/Q(s) = P(s)/(s + s_1)^n$, i.e. the function $F(s)$ has an nth order pole at $s = -s_1$, the partial-fraction expansion is

$$F(s) = \frac{A_1}{(s + s_1)^n} + \frac{A_2}{(s + s_1)^{n-1}} + \frac{A_3}{(s + s_1)^{n-2}} + \ldots + \frac{A_n}{(s + s_1)}. \quad (2.122)$$

The evaluation of $A_1, A_2 \ldots, A_n$ is carried out by the method used for simple poles.

If the multiple pole is at the origin, i.e. if

$$F(s) = \frac{P(s)}{s^n},$$

then

$$F(s) = \frac{A_1}{s^n} + \frac{A_2}{s^{n-1}} + \ldots + \frac{A_n}{s} \quad (2.123)$$

when $A_1, A_2, \ldots, A_n$ may be determined as before.

PROBLEM 2.20

Given $F(s) = \dfrac{2s^2 + 3s + 2}{(s + 1)^3}$ determine the partial-fraction expansion.

Solution

$$\frac{2s^2 + 3s + 2}{(s + 1)^3} = \frac{A_1}{(s + 1)^3} + \frac{A_2}{(s + 1)^2} + \frac{A_3}{s + 1}.$$

By the "cover-up" rule, $A_1 = 1$. Then, multiplying both sides by $(s + 1)^3$ and inserting the value for A_1,

$$2s^2 + 3s + 2 = 1 + (s + 1)A_2 + (s + 1)^2 A_3.$$

Equating coefficients of s^2, $A_3 = 2$.
Equating coefficients of s, $3 = A_2 + 2A_3$, or $A_2 = -1$,

$$\therefore \quad F(s) = \frac{1}{(s + 1)^3} - \frac{1}{(s + 1)^2} + \frac{2}{s + 1} \quad (2.124)$$

and inverting by (6), (7) and (4) of Table 2.1 to obtain $f(t)$ gives:

$$f(t) = \frac{t^2}{2}e^{-t} - t\,e^{-t} + 2\,e^{-t} \quad t > 0. \quad (2.125)$$

PROBLEM 2.21

Given

$$F(s) = \frac{2s^3 + 3s^2 + s + 1}{s^2(s + 1)^2},$$

expand in partial fractions and deduce the inverse transform.

Solution

Let

$$F(s) = \frac{A_1}{s^2} + \frac{A_2}{s} + \frac{A_3}{(s + 1)^2} + \frac{A_4}{s + 1}. \qquad (2.126)$$

A_1 and A_3 may be found immediately by the "cover-up" rule. Let

$$s = 0, A_1 = \frac{1}{1} = 1.$$

Let

$$s = -1, A_3 = \frac{-2 + 3 - 1 + 1}{1} = 1.$$

Hence,

$$F(s) = \frac{1}{s^2} + \frac{A_2}{s} + \frac{1}{(s + 1)^2} + \frac{A_4}{s + 1}$$

$$= \frac{2s^3 + 3s^2 + s + 1}{s^2(s + 1)^2}.$$

Multiplying both sides by $s^2(s + 1)^2$ gives:

$$2s^3 + 3s^2 + s + 1 = (s + 1)^2 + A_2 s(s + 1)^2 + s^2 + A_4 s^2(s + 1).$$

Equating coefficients of s^3:

$$2 = A_2 + A_4. \qquad (2.127)$$

Equating coefficients of s^2:

$$3 = 1 + 2A_2 + 1 + A_4$$

or

$$1 = 2A_2 + A_4. \qquad (2.128)$$

Combining eqns. (2.127) and (2.128) gives:

$$A_2 = -1 \quad \text{and} \quad A_4 = 3.$$

Hence,

$$F(s) = \frac{1}{s^2} - \frac{1}{s} + \frac{1}{(s+1)^2} + \frac{3}{s+1} \tag{2.129}$$

and from (2), (1), (7) and (4) of Table 2.1,

$$f(t) = t - 1 + t\,e^{-t} + 3\,e^{-t} \quad t > 0. \tag{2.130}$$

This problem illustrates the fact that it is not always possible to evaluate *all* the partial-fraction coefficients by means of the cover-up rule. However, it is usually possible to determine one or more by the rule before resorting to another method for the remainder.

2.4.7 Complete solutions

PROBLEM 2.22
Solve Problem 2.15 by the Laplace transform method.

Solution
The differential equation for this circuit is:

$$Ri(t) + L\frac{di(t)}{dt} + \frac{1}{C}\int i(t)\,dt = v(t). \tag{2.131}$$

We found that the correct form of $v(t)$ to accord with the given instant of switching was:

$$v(t) = 10\cos(9t - 36°\,52')$$

$$= 8\cos 9t + 6\sin 9t.$$

The transformed version of the eqn. (2.131) is, therefore:

$$RI(s) + sLI(s) + \frac{1}{sC}I(s) = \frac{8s}{s^2 + 81} + \frac{54}{s^2 + 81}$$

$$= \frac{8s + 54}{s^2 + 81}.$$

No initial condition terms are included since $i(0^+) = 0$ and $q(0^+)/C = 0$, also.

Given that $R = 1\,\Omega$, $L = 0.5\,\text{H}$ and $C = \frac{1}{18}\text{F}$,

$$I(s)\left(1 + 0.5s + \frac{18}{s}\right) = \frac{8s + 54}{s^2 + 81}$$

or

$$I(s) = \frac{8s^2 + 54s}{(s^2 + 81)(0.5s^2 + s + 18)}$$

or

$$\frac{I(s)}{4} = \frac{4s^2 + 27s}{(s^2 + 81)(s^2 + 2s + 36)}, \tag{2.132}$$

i.e. a rational function of s having two imaginary and two complex poles. However, as explained in the introduction to Problem 2.19, a linear numerator factor may be introduced to avoid the complex algebra to which expressions such as (2.132) would otherwise lead. The partial fractions are as follows:

$$\frac{4s^2 + 27s}{(s^2 + 81)(s^2 + 2s + 36)} = \frac{As + B}{s^2 + 81} + \frac{Cs + D}{s^2 + 2s + 36}. \tag{2.133}$$

Solving by multiplying both sides by $(s^2 + 81)(s^2 + 2s + 36)$ and equating coefficients of similar powers of s gives:

$$A = -0.2414,$$

$$B = 8.0690,$$

$$C = 0.2414$$

$$\text{and} \quad D = -3.5862,$$

i.e.

$$\frac{I(s)}{4} = \frac{-0.2414s + 8.069}{s^2 + 9^2} + \frac{0.2414s - 3.5862}{s^2 + 2s + 36}. \tag{2.134}$$

The first fraction on the R.H.S. of eqn. (2.134) may be reduced to the forms of (10) and (9) of Table 2.1, as follows:

$$\frac{I_1(s)}{4} = -0.2414 \cdot \frac{s}{s^2 + 9^2} + \frac{8.069}{9} \cdot \frac{9}{s^2 + 9^2}$$

or

$$I_1(s) = -0.9656 \cdot \frac{s}{s^2 + 9^2} + 3.5862 \cdot \frac{9}{s^2 + 9^2},$$

$$\therefore \quad i_1(t) = -0.9656 \cos 9t + 3.5862 \sin 9t \qquad (2.135)$$

by (10) and (9) of Table 2.1.

The second fraction of eqn. (2.134) is converted to the forms of (15) and (14) of Table 2.1:

$$\frac{I_2(s)}{4} = \frac{0.2414s - 3.5862}{s^2 + 2s + 36} = \frac{0.2414s - 3.5862}{(s+1)^2 + 35}$$

$$= \frac{0.2414(s + 1) - 0.2414 - 3.5862}{(s + 1)^2 + 35}$$

$$= 0.2414 \frac{s + 1}{(s + 1)^2 + 35} - \frac{3.8276}{\sqrt{35}} \cdot \frac{\sqrt{35}}{(s + 1)^2 + 35},$$

$$\therefore \quad I_2(s) = 0.9656 \frac{s + 1}{(s + 1)^2 + 35} - 2.5879 \frac{\sqrt{35}}{(s + 1)^2 + 35}$$

and

$$i_2(t) = e^{-t}(0.9656 \cos \sqrt{35}t - 2.5879 \sin \sqrt{35}t) \qquad (2.136)$$

by (15) and (14) of Table 2.1.

The total current response is the sum of $i_1(t)$ and $i_2(t)$, and expressing them in the form $A \cos(\omega t \pm \phi)$, we have

$$i(t) = I_1 \cos (9t - \phi_1) + I_2 e^{-t} \sin (\sqrt{35}t + \phi_2) \qquad (2.137)$$

where

$$\tan \phi_1 = -\frac{3.5862}{0.9656} = -3.7139, \cos \phi_1 \text{ is } -\text{ve and } \sin \phi_1 \text{ is } +\text{ve}$$

or

$$\phi_1 = -105°\, 4', \text{ and } I_1 = \sqrt{3.5862^2 + 0.9656^2}$$

$$= 3.7139$$

and

$$\tan \phi_2 = \frac{2.5879}{0.9656} = 2.6801, \cos \phi_2 \text{ and } \sin \phi_2 \text{ both } +ve$$

or

$$\phi_2 = 69°\, 32' \text{ and } I_2 = \sqrt{2.5879^2 + 0.9656^2} = 2.7622.$$

Hence,

$$i(t) = 3.7139 \cos (9t - 105°\, 4')$$
$$+ 2.7622\, e^{-t} \cos (5.9161t + 69°\, 32') \quad t > 0, \quad (2.138)$$

i.e. the same result as eqn. (2.75).

It should be pointed out that the first step in the solution of a problem like 2.22—that of writing down the time-domain differential equation —may be dispensed with. The starting point can be the frequency-domain equation(s) relating the transforms of the currents and voltages. The next problem illustrates this point.

PROBLEM 2.23

For the circuit represented by Fig. 2.25, determine the current $i_1(t)$ given that the capacitor is initially charged to 9 volts, the top plate positive. The voltage source has a generated e.m.f. $e(t) = 12t$, i.e. a ramp function.

Solution

The currents I_1, I_2 and $(I_1 - I_2)$ are shown in Fig. 2.25 and these are frequency-domain values, i.e. I_1 and I_2 are functions of s.

Applying Kirchhoff's second Law to the first mesh:

$$2I_1 + (I_1 - I_2)(1 + 0.2s) = \frac{12}{s^2} \qquad (2.139)$$

or

$$I_1(3 + 0.2s) - I_2(1 + 0.2s) = \frac{12}{s^2}. \qquad (2.140)$$

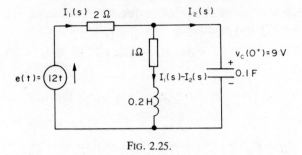

FIG. 2.25.

Applying the second Law to the second mesh:

$$I_2 \cdot \frac{10}{s} + \frac{9}{s} - (I_1 - I_2)(1 + 0.2s). \qquad (2.141)$$

The term $9/s$ represents $q(0^+)/sC$, following the integral theorem, Theorem 3, or

$$I_2 \left(\frac{10}{s} + 1 + \frac{s}{5} \right) = I_1 \left(1 + \frac{s}{5} \right) - \frac{9}{s}. \qquad (2.142)$$

From eqn. (2.142):

$$I_2 = \frac{(s^2 + 5s)I_1 - 45}{s^2 + 5s + 50} \qquad (2.143)$$

and substituting (2.143) into (2.140) gives, eventually:

$$I_1 = \frac{-4.5s^3 - 16.5s^2 + 30s + 300}{s^2(s^2 + 10s + 75)}. \qquad (2.144)$$

Expressing as partial fractions:

$$I_1 = \frac{A}{s^2} + \frac{B}{s} + \frac{Cs + D}{s^2 + 10s + 75}. \qquad (2.145)$$

By the "cover-up" rule (covering s^2 and putting $s = 0$ into 2.144) gives:

$$A = \frac{300}{75} = 4.$$

Multiplying the R.H.S. of eqns. (2.144) and (2.145) by $s^2(s^2 + 10s + 75)$ and equating:

$$-4.5s^3 - 16.5s^2 + 30s + 300 = 4(s^2 + 10s + 75) + Bs(s^2 + 10s + 75)$$
$$+ s^2(Cs + D)$$
$$= s^3(B + C) + s^2(4 + 10B + D)$$
$$+ s(40 + 75B) + 300,$$

$$\therefore \quad B + C = -4.5, 4 + 10B + D = -16.5, 30 = 40 + 75B$$

from which

$$B = -\frac{2}{15}, C = -4.367 \text{ and } D = -19.167,$$

$$\therefore \quad I_1 = \frac{4}{s^2} - \frac{2}{15s} - \frac{4.367s + 19.167}{s^2 + 10s + 75}$$

$$= \frac{4}{s^2} - \frac{2}{15s} - \frac{4.367(s + 5) - 21.835 + 19.167}{(s + 5)^2 + 50}$$

$$= \frac{4}{s^2} - \frac{2}{15s} - 4.367\frac{s + 5}{(s + 5)^2 + 7.071^2} + \frac{2.668}{(s + 5)^2 + 7.071^2}$$

$$= \frac{4}{s^2} - \frac{2}{15s} - 4.367\frac{s + 5}{(s + 5)^2 + 7.071^2} + 0.3773\frac{7.071}{(s + 5)^2 + 7.071^2}.$$

Finally, transforming back to the time domain, using (2), (1), (15) and (14) of Table 2.1,

$$i_1(t) = 4t - \frac{2}{15} - e^{-5t}(4.367 \cos 7.071t$$
$$- 0.3773 \sin 7.071t) \quad t > 0. \quad (2.146)$$

2.4.8 Other functions

The impedance function $Z(s)$ is just one example of the general system function. Other examples are the admittance function, $Y(s)$, and the transfer function, $T(s)$, which have been encountered, respectively, in section 2.1.1 and in Problem 2.9. All are ratios between the transforms of the appropriate variables and are susceptible to all the techniques associated with the Laplace transformation.

Thus,

$$I(s) = V(s)\,Y(s) \qquad (2.147)$$

may be used to replace

$$I(s) = \frac{V(s)}{Z(s)} \qquad (2.148)$$

and

$$T(s) = \frac{V_0(s)}{V_i(s)} \qquad (2.149)$$

may express the ratio between the transforms of the voltages (or currents) at two different places in a network—for example, between the output and the input variables of an amplifier or of a four-terminal transmission network.

Moreover, it is not always necessary to revert to the time-domain form of the response function after the frequency-domain $F(s)$ has been derived.

The steady-state component of the response as a function of s is as important in the study of electrical networks as is the time response.

This property—the frequency response in the steady state—is dealt with at some length in Chapter 5.

2.5 SUMMARY

To summarise the chapter, the Laplace transformation provides a straightforward tabular method of solving differential equations of the type encountered in the analysis of linear circuits. Provided that the conditions as to convergence are satisfied, which, as far as the standard of this text is concerned, includes all forcing signals, the greatest difficulty is likely to be found in expanding the frequency-domain solution into partial fractions.

However, for the simpler forcing functions—the exponential, the step and the sinusoid—the exponential transform not only gives a simpler solution but provides a clearer insight into the behaviour of circuits. The application of the rules for finding solutions (section 2.1.1.4) more easily identifies the natural and forced response components of the total solution because these have been evaluated by two distinct procedures. The influence of the initial conditions on the form of the final response is also more readily appreciated.

PROBLEMS II

1. A current $i(t) = 30\,e^{-10t}\,\text{A}$, $t > 0$ (sec) flows in a circuit.
   Calculate (a) the current flowing at $t = 0.7\,\text{sec}$, (b) the time taken for the current to fall to $1\,\mu\text{A}$.

2. A 250-Ω resistor and a charged 10-μF capacitor are connected in parallel. Given that $i(t) = 0.4\,\text{A}$ at $t = 0$, calculate the voltage across the resistor at (a) $t = 0$, (b) $t = 2.5\,\text{msec}$, (c) $t = 10\,\text{msec}$. Determine the time required for the capacitor voltage to fall to $1\,\text{V}$.

3. In the circuit of Fig. P.II.1, the switch has been open for a long time and is closed at $t = 0$.
   Derive an expression for $v_c(t)$ for (a) $t < 0$, (b) $t > 0$.

4. In the circuit of Fig. P.II.2, the switch has been open for a long time and is closed at $t = 0$.
   Derive an expression for $i(t)$ for (a) $t < 0$, (b) $t > 0$.

5. In the circuit of Fig. P.II.3, the switch has been open for a long time and is closed at $t = 0$.
   Determine the current through the switch for $t > 0$.

6. For the circuits of Fig. P.II.4 (a) and (b) the switches have been open for a long time and are closed at $t = 0$.
   Determine, in (a) $i(t)$ for $t < 0$ and $t > 0$, and in (b) $v_c(t)$ for $t < 0$ and for $t > 0$.

7. A voltage $v(t) = 20\,e^{-3t}$, $t > 0$ (sec), is applied to a circuit consisting of resistance of $10\,\Omega$ in series with inductance of $8\,\text{H}$.
   Determine (a) the forced current response, (b) the natural current response, (c) the total current response, given that the current in the circuit at $t = (0^-)$ is $-3\,\text{A}$, (d) the total current at $t = 1\,\text{sec}$.

8. A voltage source, generating a step voltage $100U(t)$, in series with a 1000-Ω resistor, supplies a 10-μF capacitor in parallel with a 250-Ω resistor.
   By evaluating the forced and natural responses, determine the voltage across the capacitor as a function of time, given that its initial voltage, at $t = 0$, is zero.

9. A 4-μF capacitor and a 5000-Ω resistor are connected, at $t = 0$, in series to a voltage source for which $E = 250\,\text{V}$.
   Calculate (a) the current at $t = (0^+)$,
   　　　　　 (b) the current at $t = \infty$,
   　　　　　 (c) the capacitor voltage as a function of time, $t > 0$,
   　　　　　 (d) the energy stored in the capacitor at $t = 10\,\text{msec}$,
   　　　　　 (e) the total energy dissipated in the resistor at $t = \infty$.
   The capacitor is uncharged at $t = (0^-)$.

10. In the circuit of Fig. P.II.5 the switch, S, has been open for a long time and is closed at $t = 0$.
    Determine an expression for the current $i(t)$ for $t > 0$.

11. A voltage $v(t) = 200\,e^{-500t}$ is applied at $t = 0$ to a coil of resistance $5\,\Omega$ and of time constant $4\,\text{msec}$. The current $i(0)$ at $t = 0$ was $+10\,\text{A}$.
    By evaluating the natural and forced responses, determine the current $i(t)$ for $t > 0$.

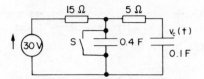

FIG. P.II.1 (Problem II.3).

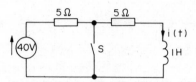

FIG. P.II.2 (Problem II.4).

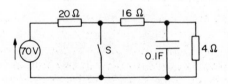

FIG. P.II.3 (Problem II.5).

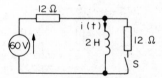

FIG. P.II.4(a) (Problem II.6).

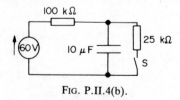

FIG. P.II.4(b).

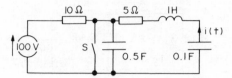

FIG. P.II.5 (Problem II.10).

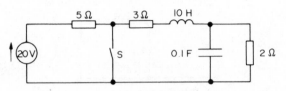

FIG. P.II.6 (Problem II.13).

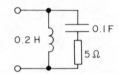

FIG. P.II.7 (Problem II.14).

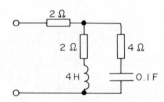

FIG. P.II.8 (Problem II.15).

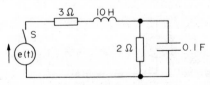

FIG. P.II.9 (Problem II.19).

NATURAL AND FORCED RESPONSES 123

12. A current source having a generated current $10U(t)$ mA supplies a parallel circuit consisting of a coil, of inductance 100 µH and resistance 2000 Ω, shunted by 500 pF capacitance.
  Given that there is no stored energy in the circuit at $t = 0$, derive the voltage across the coil for $t > 0$.

13. In the circuit of Fig. P.II.6, the switch has been open for a long time and is closed at $t = 0$.
  Derive an expression for the current through the inductor for $t > 0$.

14. For the circuit of Fig. P.II.7, derive an expression for $Z(s)$ and sketch the pole–zero plot. Evaluate $Z(s)$ when s is (a) -3, (b) j3.

15. For the circuit of Fig. P.II.8, determine the number and positions of the poles and zeros of $Y(s)$. Determine $Y(s)$ at $s = 0$.

16. A circuit has an impedance $Z(s) = 10 + 0.25s$, where $s = \sigma + j\omega$. Sketch the form of the frequency-domain response to an applied voltage of the form:

$$v(t) = VU(t)\, e^{-at}$$

where a is real, and hence determine the natural response.
  A voltage $v(t) = 100U(t)\, e^{\sigma t} \cos \omega t$ is applied to the circuit at $t = 0$.
  Calculate the forced response $i(t)$, $t > 0$, when s is (a) -10, (b) j6, (c) $-10 + j10$.

17. Explain what is meant by the *critical frequencies* of a circuit.
  A voltage $v(t) = 3\, e^{\sigma t}$ is applied at $t = 0$ to a circuit consisting of $R = 5\,\Omega$, $L = 0.5\,H$ and $C = \frac{1}{12}\,F$, all in series.
  Sketch the form of the frequency-domain forced response for real values of σ and evaluate the forced response at $\sigma = -5$.
  Determine the critical frequencies of the circuit and hence the natural response in the time domain.
  Given that the capacitor is uncharged and that there is no current in the circuit when $t = 0$, evaluate the complete response.

18. A voltage $v(t) = 200 \cos 5000t$ is applied to a circuit consisting of inductance, $L = 4$ mH and resistance $R = 15\,\Omega$ in series and steady-state conditions are established.
  Calculate (a) the impedance $Z(j\omega)$ of the circuit expressed in polar and Cartesian forms, (b) the steady-state current in Cartesian, polar and time-domain forms.

19. In the circuit of Fig. P.II.9, the voltage-source e.m.f. is $e(t) = 20 \cos \frac{1}{2}t$ and the switch S is closed at $t = 0$ when $e(t) = 10$ V and decreasing.
  Derive the current $i(t)$ for $t > 0$, given that there is no stored energy in the circuit at $t = 0$.

20. Expand into partial fractions:

(a) $\dfrac{s+1}{s(s-1)}$ (b) $\dfrac{s+1}{s^2(s-1)^2}$ (c) $\dfrac{s^2}{(s+3)(s-4)^2}$

(d) $\dfrac{3}{(s-3)(s-4)(s-5)}$ (e) $\dfrac{s^3+1}{(s-2)(2s-3)(s^2+1)}$ (f) $\dfrac{s}{(s+1)^2(s+2)^2}$.

21. For each of the following $F(s)$, invert to derive the corresponding $f(t)$:

(a) $\dfrac{1}{s^2+4s+10}$ (b) $\dfrac{s+5}{(s+4)(s+7)(s+1)}$ (c) $\dfrac{s^3+1}{(s-2)(2s-3)(s^2+1)}$.

(d) $\dfrac{1+s}{s^2+2s+26}$ (e) $\dfrac{s}{(s^2+16)(s^2+25)}$ (f) $\dfrac{s}{(s+1)^2(s+2)^2}$.

22. Solve the following differential equations for $i(t)$, subject to the given initial conditions, using the Laplace transformation:

(a) $3\dfrac{di}{dt} - 2i = e^{-t}\cos 2t$, given $i = 0$ at $t = 0$.

(b) $2\dfrac{d^2i}{dt^2} + 3\dfrac{di}{dt} - 4i = 4t$, given $\dfrac{di}{dt} = -1$ and $i = 2$ at $t = 0$.

(c) $\dfrac{d^2i}{dt^2} - 2\dfrac{di}{dt} - 3i - 1 - 2t = 0$, given $\dfrac{di}{dt} = -\dfrac{4}{9}$ and $i = \dfrac{1}{3}$ at $t = 0$.

23. For the circuit of Fig. P.II.10, determine the current $i_1(t)$ for $t > 0$, given that the voltage source generates the ramp function $e(t) = 12t$ volts and that the capacitor is charged, as shown, to 9 V at $t = 0$.

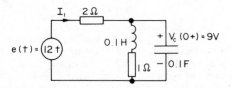

FIG. P.II.10 (Problem II.23).

24. For the circuit of Fig. P.II.11, evaluate the transfer function $T(s)$ between output and input voltages, and determine, using the Laplace transformation, the output voltage $v_0(t)$, for $t > 0$, when a 10-V step function is applied at $t = 0$ to the input terminals.

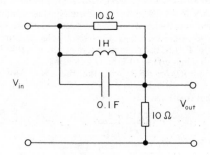

FIG. P.II.11 (Problem II.24).

CHAPTER 3

THE SINUSOIDAL STEADY STATE

3.0 INTRODUCTION

In this chapter we consider only the steady-state (forced) response component of linear circuits to one particular forcing function—the sinusoidal variation with time. As the solution to Problem 2.13 shows, the (forced) response to this forcing function is also sinusoidal, and (since the sinusoid may be regarded as the sum of exponentials) a little thought will reveal that the same is true of all voltages and currents in the circuit.

This property of identity of waveform has led to its universal use in power systems and to its adoption as the prototype waveform in many electronic and communication systems.

A powerful extension of linear theory, due to Fourier, allows the response of a linear system to any repetitive waveform to be considered as the superposition of the separate responses to a series of sine (and/or cosine) functions.

Hence the importance of this waveform, already referred to in section 2.3.

3.1 POWER DUE TO A SINUSOIDALLY VARYING CURRENT: R.M.S. VALUE

Our prototype waveform is, then,

$$v(t) = V \cos \omega t. \qquad (3.1)$$

Clearly, the maximum value of $v(t)$ is $\pm V$ and this quantity is referred to as the PEAK or MAXIMUM value. Also,

$$v(t) = v\left(t + \frac{2\pi}{\omega}\right) = v(t + T)$$

where T is the PERIODIC TIME (sec). Hence

$$f = \frac{1}{T} = \frac{\omega}{2\pi}$$

or

$$\omega = 2\pi f. \tag{3.2}$$

f is the FREQUENCY of the voltage defined by eqn. (3.1) and is measured in HERTZ (preferred) or cycles per second and their decimal multiples and submultiples. ω is the RADIAN FREQUENCY in radians/second.

If this voltage be applied to resistance R, the current which flows, since at any instant

$$i(t) = \frac{1}{R} v(t),$$

will be

$$i(t) = I \cos \omega t \tag{3.3}$$

where

$$I = \frac{V}{R}.$$

From eqn. (1.8) the power, $p(t)$, will be given by:

$$p(t) = i^2(t) R$$
$$= I^2 R \cos^2 \omega t. \tag{3.4}$$

Graphs of $i(t)$ and $p(t)$ are shown plotted in Fig. 3.1. Since (3.4) may be written as:

$$p(t) = I^2 R(\tfrac{1}{2} + \tfrac{1}{2} \cos 2\omega t) \tag{3.5}$$

we see that $p(t)$ is the sum of a constant term $I^2 R/2$, and a cosine term of radian frequency 2ω and of amplitude $I^2 R/2$.

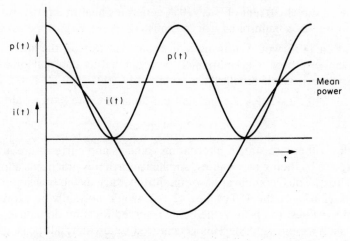

FIG. 3.1. Variations of current and power in resistive circuit.

In the majority of cases, however, we are interested in calculating the mean or average power over at least one cycle of the current. The component which varies as cos $2\omega t$ has a mean value of zero, so the total mean power is given by:

$$P = \tfrac{1}{2}I^2R \qquad (3.6)$$

$$= \left(\frac{I^2}{2}\right)R$$

$$= (I_{\text{r.m.s.}})^2 R \qquad (3.7)$$

where $I_{\text{r.m.s.}} = I/\sqrt{2}$ is the ROOT MEAN SQUARE value (also known as the effective or virtual value) of the current. It is defined as that value of direct current which has the same capacity for developing power in a resistor as the alternating current has. An identical argument could, of course, be used for voltage, since

$$p(t) = \frac{1}{R}v^2(t), \qquad (3.8)$$

giving

$$V_{\text{r.m.s.}} = \frac{V}{\sqrt{2}}. \qquad (3.9)$$

Thus, a direct current of, say, 10 A generates heat in a resistor at the same rate as a sinusoidal (or cosinusoidal) current of peak value $10\sqrt{2} = 14.14$ A would, flowing in the same resistor. In the latter case, the average power is accompanied by a fluctuating component whose mean value is zero. Similarly, a voltage of 240 V (r.m.s.) has a peak value of $240\sqrt{2} = 339.4$ V, and its time-domain expression would be:

$$v(t) = 339.4 \cos \omega t.$$

Unless otherwise stated, alternating voltages and currents are always referred to by their r.m.s. values, and henceforth this practice is adopted in this text. Thus, complex phasor quantities, such as the bracketed part of eqn. (2.67), or the 150 of eqn. (2.66), would normally be expressed as r.m.s. values, the peak value being reserved for time-domain expressions such as eqn. (2.68). This is achieved by dividing all peak values by $\sqrt{2}$ to obtain the r.m.s. phasor values. Thus, the transition from eqn. (2.65) to eqn. (2.66) would, on this basis, be:

$$v(t) = 150 \cos 100t \tag{2.65a}$$

$$= \mathfrak{Re}\, 106\, e^{j100t} \tag{2.66a}$$

which appears wrong until it is realised that the transition includes the change from peak to r.m.s. value.

Using eqn. (2.66a), eqn. (2.67) would appear as:

$$i(t) = \mathfrak{Re}\, (1.464 - j3.66)\, e^{j100t} \tag{2.67a}$$
$$= \mathfrak{Re}\, 3.94\, e^{j(100t - 1.19)} \tag{2.67b}$$

and eqn. (2.68) would remain unchanged.

More generally, the r.m.s. value of any other waveform may be found by integrating, analytically or graphically, the square of the given curve over one complete cycle, determining the average, and finally, taking the square root of this.

PROBLEM 3.1

A voltage given by

$$v(t) = 100 \cos 200t$$

is applied to a circuit which has a resistance of 10 Ω when $v(t)$ is positive and $20\,\Omega$ when $v(t)$ is negative. Determine the r.m.s. value of the current.

Solution

The positive half-cycle of current will be a half cosine wave of peak value $100/10 = 10$ A, the negative half-cycle having a peak value of $100/20 = 5$ A, as shown in Fig. 3.2. The corresponding $i^2(t)$ curves are

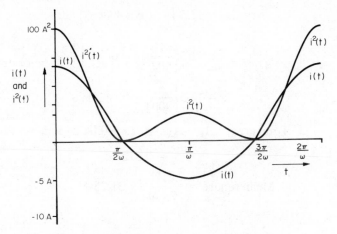

FIG. 3.2. Variation of $i(t)$ and $i^2(t)$ in Problem 3.1.

also shown in the diagram and it is necessary to determine the total area before dividing by the base length, $2\pi/\omega$, to obtain the mean. For period $0 < t < \pi/\omega$,

$$i(t) = 10 \cos 200t,$$

$$\therefore \quad i^2(t) = 100 \cos^2 200t$$

$$= \frac{100}{2} (\cos 400t + 1),$$

$$\therefore \quad \text{Area } A_1 = 50 \int_0^{\pi/\omega} (\cos 400t + 1)\, dt = 50\left[\frac{1}{400} \sin 400t + t\right]_0^{\pi/\omega}$$

$$= 50\left[\frac{\pi}{200}\right] = \frac{\pi}{4}.$$

For period $\dfrac{\pi}{\omega} < t < \dfrac{2\pi}{\omega}$,

$$i(t) = 5 \cos 200t,$$

$$i^2(t) = 25 \cos^2 200t$$

$$= 25 . \tfrac{1}{2}(\cos 400t + 1),$$

$$\therefore \quad \text{Area } A_2 = 12.5 \int_{\pi/\omega}^{2\pi/\omega} (\cos 400t + 1) \, dt$$

$$= 12.5 \left[\frac{1}{400} \sin 400t + t \right]_{\pi/\omega}^{2\pi/\omega}$$

$$= 12.5 \left[\frac{\pi}{200} \right] = 0.0625\pi.$$

$$\text{Total area} = A_1 + A_2 = (0.25 + 0.0625)\pi$$

$$= 0.3125\pi.$$

$$\text{Mean square} = \frac{0.3125\pi}{2\pi/\omega} = 31.25 \text{ A}^2,$$

$$\therefore \quad \text{Root mean square} = \sqrt{31.25} = 5.59 \text{ A}.$$

3.2 PHASOR DIAGRAMS

Phasor quantities, being complex numbers, may be plotted on an Argand diagram. In this diagram, a point in a plane is defined by reference to a pair of perpendicular axes—the real part of the complex number being plotted along the x-axis and the imaginary part along the y-axis. If, for example, the point $1.464 + j3.66$ be joined to the origin, the line, of length $\sqrt{1.464^2 + 3.66^2} = 3.94$ making an angle $\tan^{-1} 3.66/1.464 = 68° \, 12'$ with the real axis, may be said to represent the complex number. Lines drawn in this way are usually drawn with arrow-heads at one end to indicate the positive direction, as shown in Fig. 3.3.

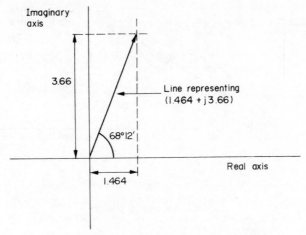

FIG. 3.3. Phasor representing a complex number.

The line also represents the current:

$$i(t) = \Re e(1.464 + j3.66)\, e^{j100t}$$

because it is understood to be rotating anticlockwise at constant angular velocity ω (100 rad/sec in this case) and that we require only the real part, i.e. the projection of the line upon the real axis. By removing the e^{j100t} term the rotating line is "frozen" in one position and by removing $\Re e$ (= "real part of") we remove also the necessity of continually thinking of the projection of the line upon the real axis.

All the voltages and currents in a circuit may be plotted in this way (since they are all sinusoidal and of the same frequency) and the diagram formed is called a PHASOR DIAGRAM. The technique is a very useful one when dealing with circuits in the steady state.

3.2.1 Addition and subtraction of phasors

Consider the phasors $\mathbf{P}_1 = (a + jb)$ and $\mathbf{P}_2 = (c + jd)$ as shown in Fig. 3.4. By the rules for the addition of complex numbers:

$$\mathbf{P} = \mathbf{P}_1 + \mathbf{P}_2 = (a + c) + j(b + d).$$

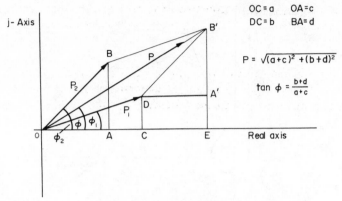

FIG. 3.4. Addition of phasors.

The new phasor, **P**, will therefore have a real part equal to $(a + c)$ and an imaginary part equal to $(b + d)$, and, in Fig. 3.4, can be drawn by sliding the triangle OAB along the phasor P_1 to a new position DA′B′. Thus, OB′ is the sum **P**, since

$$OE = OC + OA = (a + c)$$

and

$$EB' = CD + AB = (b + d).$$

Hence

$$|\mathbf{P}| = \sqrt{(a + c)^2 + (b + d)^2}$$

and

$$\phi = \tan^{-1}\frac{(b + d)}{(a + c)}.$$

Clearly, it is not necessary always to draw the complete triangles OAB, OCD and DA′B′ when adding two phasors such as P_1 and P_2: it is necessary only to draw P_1 and then P_2 ($=$DB′) from the end of P_1. Then **P** is the remaining side of the triangle ODB′. By an extension, any number of phasors may be added by repeated application of this rule. A succession of phasors may be added by drawing each one from the end of the previous one, when the closing side of the resulting polygon is their sum, as shown in Fig. 3.5(a).

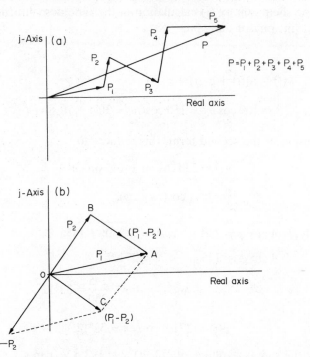

Fig. 3.5. Addition and subtraction of phasors.

A phasor P_2 may be subtracted from P_1 by first reversing P_2 (i.e. multiplying it by -1) and then adding it to P_1. In Fig. 3.5(b) OA and OB are the phasors P_1 and P_2, and OC is, clearly, $(OA + AC)$ which is $P_1 + (-P_2) = P_1 - P_2$. Obviously, $P_1 - P_2$ is also equal to BA since OCAB is a parallelogram, so the difference between two phasors may be found, graphically, by joining their ends.

It is not, of course, necessary to draw the axes each time a phasor diagram is constructed. One phasor is usually taken as the reference and all others drawn in the correct relation to it.

PROBLEM 3.2

Three voltages represented by $v_1(t) = 100 \cos \omega t$, $v_2(t) = 150 \cos (\omega t - 30°)$ and $v_3(t) = 70 \sin \omega t$ act together in the same circuit. Determine their sum by (i) calculation in the time domain; (ii) phasor methods; (iii) phasor diagram.

Solution

(i) $v(t) = v_1(t) + v_2(t) + v_3(t)$

           $= 100 \cos \omega t + 150 \cos(\omega t - 30°) + 70 \sin \omega t.$

By expansion of the second term, this reduces to:

$$v(t) = 230 \cos \omega t + 145 \sin \omega t$$

$$= A \cos(\omega t - \phi).$$

Obviously, $\left. \begin{array}{l} A \cos \phi = 230 \\ A \sin \phi = 145 \end{array} \right\}$ $\begin{array}{l} \therefore A = \sqrt{230^2 + 145^2} \\ = 271.9 \end{array}$

and

$$\text{and } \phi = \tan^{-1} \frac{145}{230} = 32°12',$$

$$\therefore \quad v(t) = 271.9 \cos(\omega t - 32°12').$$

Hence the sum is a voltage of $271.9/\sqrt{2} = 192.5$ V (r.m.s.), at a phase angle of $32°12'$ behind V_1. V is said to be lagging on V_1 by $32°12'$, and, in this case, V_1 is the reference phasor.

(ii) The voltages V_1, V_2 and V_3 are first expressed as phasors; thus,

$$\left. \begin{array}{l} V_1 = \dfrac{100}{\sqrt{2}} \angle 0°, \\[4mm] V_2 = \dfrac{150}{\sqrt{2}} \angle -30°, \\[4mm] V_3 = \dfrac{70}{\sqrt{2}} \angle -90° \end{array} \right\} \quad \text{in polar form.}$$

Or:

$$V_1 = \frac{100}{\sqrt{2}}\,e^{j0} \quad = 70.71,$$

$$V_2 = \frac{150}{\sqrt{2}}\,e^{-j30} = 106\cos 30° - j106\sin 30°,$$

$$V_3 = \frac{70}{\sqrt{2}}\,e^{-j90} = \underline{49.5\cos 90° - j49.5\sin 90°.}$$

Adding

$$\text{sum} = (162.6 - j102.5)\ \text{volts}$$

or

$$|V| = \sqrt{162.6^2 + 102.5^2} = 192.5\ \text{volts}$$

and

$$\phi = -\tan^{-1}\frac{102.5}{162.6} = -32°12',$$

$$V = 192.5\ \angle -32°12'\ \text{volts (r.m.s.)}$$

$$= 192.5\ e^{-j32°12'}\ \text{volts (r.m.s.)}.$$

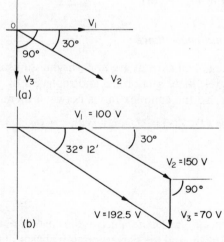

Fig. 3.6. Addition of three phasors: Problem 3.2.

(iii) The original phasors are drawn to scale in their appropriate phase relationships with each other as in Fig. 3.6(a). Adding can be achieved by drawing them end to end or by adding them in pairs, the former method being used in Fig. 3.6(b). The result is (within drawing accuracy) the same as in (i) and (ii).

In Fig. 3.6(a) V_1 is said to lead V_2 by $30°$ and V_3 by $90°$. Conversely, V_3 lags V_2 by $60°$ and V_1 by $90°$. V_1 and V_3 are said to be in quadrature.

3.2.2 Phase relationships between voltage and current in the three circuit elements

(i) *Resistance*

Since the ratio between the instantaneous voltage and the instantaneous current for the resistance parameter is constant (see eqn. (1.5)) we can apply it also to complex phasors. Thus

$$V = IR \tag{3.10}$$

and hence V and I are in phase because R is real. Graphs of voltage and current, for cosinusoidal variations, and the corresponding phasor diagram are shown in Fig. 3.7(a).

(ii) *Inductance and capacitance*

Since the voltage and current are now varying sinusoidally with time, we may use the results of section 2.3 and replace s by $j\omega$ in eqns. (2.5) and (2.27) to derive the complex ratios between them, as follows:

(a) Inductance (L) $Z(s) = sL$, and, with $s = j\omega$,

$$Z(j\omega) = j\omega L.$$

Thus

$$V = j\omega L I \tag{3.11}$$

or the voltage phasor is $\pi/2$ *in advance* of the current phasor. The graphs of voltage and current and the corresponding phasor diagram are shown in Fig. 3.7(b).

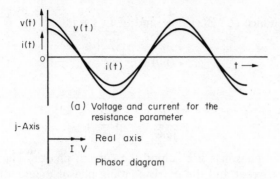

(a) Voltage and current for the resistance parameter

Phasor diagram

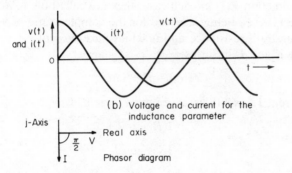

(b) Voltage and current for the inductance parameter

Phasor diagram

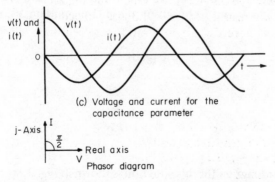

(c) Voltage and current for the capacitance parameter

Phasor diagram

FIG. 3.7. Voltage and current relationships for L, C and R.

(b) Capacitance (C) $Z(s) = \dfrac{1}{sC}$ and, with $s = j\omega$,

$$\mathbf{Z}(j\omega) = \frac{1}{j\omega C}.$$

Thus

$$\mathbf{V} = \frac{I}{j\omega C} = -j\left(\frac{I}{\omega C}\right) \qquad (3.12)$$

or the voltage phasor is $\pi/2$ behind the current phasor. The graphs of voltage and current and the corresponding phasor diagram are shown in Fig. 3.7(c). Although the ratios $j\omega L$ and $-j/\omega C$ are derived from the impedance function $Z(s)$ in each case, they are called the REACTANCES, the term IMPEDANCE being reserved for the complex ratio of voltage to current when both resistance and reactance are present.

Thus, for R and L in series:

$$\mathbf{Z}(j\omega) = R + j\omega L \qquad (3.13)$$

and if a current $\mathbf{I}$ flows through them,

$$\mathbf{V} = \mathbf{I}(R + j\omega L)$$

$$= \mathbf{I}R + j\omega L\mathbf{I} \qquad (3.14)$$

$$= \mathbf{V}_R + j\mathbf{V}_L,$$

so the voltage $\mathbf{V}$ is made up of two voltages, $\mathbf{V}_R$ and $\mathbf{V}_L$, added in quadrature, and $\mathbf{V}$ and $\mathbf{I}$ are out of phase ($\mathbf{I}$ lagging on $\mathbf{V}$) by an angle ϕ, where

$$\phi = \tan^{-1}\frac{\mathbf{V}_L}{\mathbf{V}_R}$$

$$= \tan^{-1}\frac{X_L}{R} \qquad (3.15)$$

$$= \tan^{-1}\frac{\omega L}{R}.$$

The phasor diagram for this situation is shown in Fig. 3.8(a). Equation (3.15) shows that for R and L in series the phase angle between $\mathbf{I}$ and

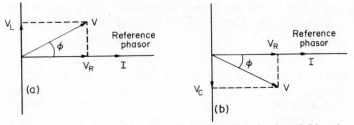

FIG. 3.8. Phasor diagrams for (a) resistive–inductive circuit and (b) resistive–capacitive circuit.

V always lies in the range $0 \to \pi/2$, approaching $\pi/2$ when $X_L \gg R$ and approaching 0 when $X_L \ll R$. When $X_L = R$, $\phi = 45°$.

For R and C connected in series,

$$\mathbf{Z}(j\omega) = R + \frac{1}{j\omega C}$$

$$= R - \frac{j}{\omega C} \tag{3.16}$$

and if a current I flows through them,

$$\mathbf{V} = \mathbf{I}\left(R - \frac{j}{\omega C}\right)$$

$$= \mathbf{I}R - j\frac{\mathbf{I}}{\omega C} \tag{3.17}$$

$$= \mathbf{V}_R - j\mathbf{V}_C.$$

Again, the voltage $\mathbf{V}$ is made up of two voltages in quadrature, $\mathbf{V}_R$ and $\mathbf{V}_C$, so that $\mathbf{V}$ and $\mathbf{I}$ are out of phase ($\mathbf{I}$ leading on $\mathbf{V}$) by an angle ϕ, where

$$\phi = \tan^{-1}\frac{V_C}{V_R}$$

$$= \tan^{-1}\frac{X_C}{R}$$

$$= \tan^{-1}\frac{1}{\omega CR}. \tag{3.18}$$

Figure 3.8(b) shows the phasor diagram for this situation and again it is clear that ϕ approaches $\pi/2$ if $1/\omega C \gg R$, and 0 if $1/\omega C \ll R$. $\phi = 45°$ when $\omega CR = 1$.

3.3 POWER AS A FUNCTION OF VOLTAGE AND CURRENT

Taking the general case of a resistive–reactive circuit in which $\mathbf{V}$ and $\mathbf{I}$ are out of phase by ϕ.

Let

$$v(t) = \sqrt{2}V \cos \omega t,$$

then

$$i(t) = \sqrt{2}I \cos(\omega t - \phi) \quad \text{for } R \text{ and } L.$$

Hence

$$p(t) = v(t)\, i(t)$$

$$= 2VI \cos \omega t \cos(\omega t - \phi)$$

$$= 2\frac{VI}{2}[\cos(2\omega t - \phi) + \cos \phi]. \tag{3.19}$$

The mean power is therefore:

$$P = \frac{2}{\pi}\int_0^\pi \frac{VI}{2}[\cos(2\omega t - \phi) + \cos \phi]\, d\omega t$$

$$= \frac{VI}{\pi}[\tfrac{1}{2} \sin(2\omega t - \phi) + \omega t \cos \phi]_0^\pi$$

$$= \frac{VI}{\pi}[\tfrac{1}{2} \sin(2\pi - \phi) + \pi \cos \phi - \tfrac{1}{2}\sin(-\phi)]$$

$$= VI \cos \phi.$$

When the circuit is purely resistive, i.e. when $\phi = 0$, $\cos \phi = 1$ and

$$P = VI,$$

the same expression as that used for determining the power in d.c. circuits.

3.3.1 Power factor

The product VI in general is called the volt-amperes (VA) and the ratio:

$$\frac{\text{Power}}{\text{Volt-amperes}}$$

is defined as the POWER FACTOR. Evidently, since $P = VI \cos \phi$, for sinusoidal waveforms,

$$\text{Power Factor} = \cos \phi. \tag{3.20}$$

It should be noted that eqn. (3.20) is not a definition of power factor, though it is true for sinusoidal waveforms. For any other waveform ϕ has no meaning and

$$\text{P.F.} = \frac{\text{Watts}}{\text{Volt-amperes}}. \tag{3.21}$$

3.3.2 Complex power

The total VA taken by a load is sometimes expressed by a complex number, S, where

$$S = P \pm jQ,$$

$$P = \text{Power},$$

$$Q = \text{Reactive Volt-amperes}.$$

This usage leads one to suppose that the complex power is the product of the complex phasor expressions for voltage and current, but this is not so. It is, in fact, necessary to take the product of one phasor and the conjugate of the other. Thus, denoting the conjugate of $\mathbf{I}$ by $\mathbf{I}^*$,

$$S = \mathbf{V}\mathbf{I}^*.$$

Referring to Fig. 3.9,

$$\left.\begin{array}{l} \mathbf{V} = V_1 + jV_2 \\[2mm] \mathbf{I} = I_1 + jI_2. \end{array}\right\} \tag{3.22}$$

and

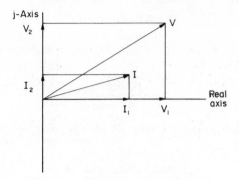

FIG. 3.9. To illustrate complex power.

The power is obviously $V_1I_1 + V_2I_2$ since V_1 and I_1 are in phase and so are V_2 and I_2. V_1 and I_2 are in quadrature and so produce only negative VAr (reactive volt-amperes), whereas V_2 and I_1 produce positive VAr.

Hence

$$S = (V_1I_1 + V_2I_2) + j(V_2I_1 - V_1I_2). \qquad (3.23)$$

Taking the product of eqns. (3.22) gives

$$S = (V_1I_1 - V_2I_2) + j(V_2I_1 + V_1I_2)$$

which does not agree with eqn. (3.23). But

$$\mathbf{VI}^* = (V_1I_1 + V_2I_2) + j(V_2I_1 - V_1I_2)$$

is correct.

This apparent anomaly in the use of complex numbers arises from the fact that the phasor expression for a voltage or current is only part of the complete expression.

PROBLEM 3.3

A voltage $\mathbf{V} = (200 + j100)$ volts is applied to a circuit having an impedance $\mathbf{Z} = (10 + j10)\ \Omega$. Determine the current as a frequency-domain phasor and the power absorbed, by (i) phasor product, (ii) time-domain product, (iii) power factor.

Solution

$$\mathbf{V} = 200 + j100 = 100\sqrt{5} \angle\tan^{-1}\tfrac{1}{2} = 223.6 \angle 26°34' \text{ V},$$

$$\mathbf{Z} = 10 + j10 = 14.14 \angle 45° \,\Omega,$$

$$\therefore \quad \mathbf{I} = \frac{223.6}{14.14} \angle (26°34' - 45°) = 15.81 \angle -18°26' \text{ A}.$$

Power (i) $S = \mathbf{VI}^* = 223.6 \times 15.81 \angle (26°34' + 18°26') \text{ A}$

$$= 3450 \angle 45°$$

$$= 2500 + j2500$$

$$= P + jQ.$$

Hence

Power $(P) = 2500 \text{ W}.$

(ii) Converting the frequency-domain voltage and current phasors to the time domain:

$$v(t) = \mathfrak{Re}[\sqrt{2}\,(200 + j100)\,e^{j\omega t}]$$

$$= \mathfrak{Re}[\sqrt{2} \times 223.6\,e^{j(\omega t + 26°34')}]$$

$$= \sqrt{2} \times 223.6\cos(\omega t + 26°34'),$$

$$i(t) = \mathfrak{Re}[\sqrt{2} \times 15.81\,e^{j(\omega t - 18°26')}]$$

$$= \sqrt{2} \times 15.81\cos(\omega t - 18°26').$$

And

Power $p(t) = v(t)\,i(t)$

$$= \frac{7071}{2}[\cos(2\omega t + 8°8') + \cos 45°],$$

the mean value of which is the time-independent term:

$$P = \frac{7071}{2}\cos 45° = 2500 \text{ W}.$$

(iii) $\mathbf{V} = 223.6$ volts, leading the reference phasor by $26°34'$,

$\quad \mathbf{I} = 15.81$ A, lagging the reference phasor by $18°26'$.

$$\therefore \quad \text{Power factor} = \cos(26°34' + 18°26') = 0.7071,$$

$$\therefore \quad P = 223.6 \times 15.81 \times 0.7071$$

$$= 2500 \text{ W}.$$

3.4 SERIES CIRCUITS

A circuit may be said to be fully solved if the voltage, current, power, power factor and impedance for each part of the circuit are known.

When only some are known it is usually possible to determine the others by methods based on Kirchhoff's voltage law. The law applies to instantaneous voltages or currents or to effective (r.m.s.) values provided phase is taken into account—hence phasors must be used.

PROBLEM 3.4

A coil, possessing inductance and resistance, is connected in series with a non-reactive resistor across a voltage source $100 \angle 0°$ volt, $\omega = 300$ rad/sec, and the resulting current $\mathbf{I} = 2$ A. The voltage across the coil, $\mathbf{V}_1 = 80$ V, and that across the resistor, $\mathbf{V}_2 = 50$ V. Determine the inductance and resistance of the coil, the resistance of the series resistor, the power dissipated in the coil, the total power absorbed and the overall power factor.

Solution

The problem is best solved by first sketching the phasor diagram, see Fig. 3.10. The current (2 A) is drawn first and taken as the reference

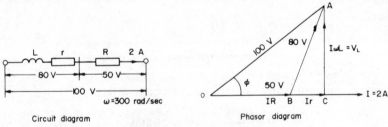

Circuit diagram   Phasor diagram

FIG. 3.10. Diagrams for Problem 3.4.

phasor. OB (=50 V) is drawn in phase with **I**, since it is the voltage across pure resistance, and the triangle OAB is completed by striking an arc, centre O, radius 100 V, and another arc, centre B, radius 80 V, to find the intersection at A. This is the voltage triangle for the circuit, the phasor addition of OB and BA producing OA.

Applying the cosine rule to $\triangle$OAB,

$$80^2 = 100^2 + 50^2 - 2.100.50 \cos \phi, \quad \text{giving} \cos \phi = 0.61.$$

Hence,

$$\text{Power factor} = 0.61.$$

Clearly, $R = \dfrac{50}{2} = 25 \,\Omega$, by Ohm's Law.

In the triangle BCA, BA, the voltage across the coil, is made up from the phasor addition of BC and CA, where AC is the perpendicular from A on to OB produced. Hence, BC is the voltage across the resistive part of the coil, or:

$$BC = \mathbf{I}r.$$

And CA is the voltage across the reactive part, or:

$$CA = \mathbf{I}\omega L.$$

$$\frac{OC}{100} = \cos \phi = 0.61,$$

$$\therefore \quad OC = 61 \,\text{V},$$

giving

$$BC = 61 - 50 = 11 \,\text{V},$$

$$\therefore \quad r = \frac{11}{2} = 5.5 \,\Omega$$

and

$$\frac{CA}{100} = \sin (\cos^{-1} 0.61) = 0.7923,$$

$$\therefore \quad CA = 79.23 \,\text{V}$$

and

$$L = \frac{79.23}{2 \times 300} = 132 \,\text{mH}.$$

Total power $= VI \cos \phi = 100 \times 2 \times 0.61 = 122$ W, of which $I^2r = 4 \times 5.5 = 22$ W is dissipated in the coil. As a check, the difference $122 - 22 = 100$ W should agree with the power dissipated in the series resistor:

$$I^2R = 4 \times 25 = 100 \text{ W,}$$

since no mean power is lost in the inductance of the coil.

PROBLEM 3.5

A voltage $v(t) = 400 \cos 1000t$ is applied to a circuit, resulting in a current of $i(t) = 8 \cos(1000t + (\pi/6))$. Determine the resistance and reactance of the circuit, the power dissipated and the power factor.

Solution

This problem is most easily solved by first converting the time-domain expressions for voltage and current into phasors.

Thus,

$$\mathbf{V} = \frac{400}{\sqrt{2}} \angle 0° \text{ V,}$$

used as the reference phasor, and

$$\mathbf{I} = \frac{8}{\sqrt{2}} \angle 30° \text{ A.}$$

Hence,

$$\mathbf{Z} = \frac{\mathbf{V}}{\mathbf{I}} = \frac{400 \angle 0°}{8 \angle 30°} = 50 \angle -30°$$

$$= 50(\cos 30 - \text{j} \sin 30) \, \Omega$$

$$= (43.3 - \text{j}25) \, \Omega.$$

So the circuit impedance of 50 Ω is made up of 43.3 Ω resistance and 25 Ω reactance—in this case capacitive, since the current leads the voltage.

Power factor, $\cos \phi = \cos 30°$

$$= 0.866 \text{ (leading)}$$

$$= \frac{400}{\sqrt{2}} \cdot \frac{8}{\sqrt{2}} \cdot 0.866$$

$$= 1.385 \text{ kW.}$$

PROBLEM 3.6

A resistor, a coil and a capacitor form a series circuit to which a 0.4-A current source is connected, as shown in Fig. 3.11(a). The voltages measured across the components are, respectively, 30 V, 50 V and 70 V, whilst that across the coil and resistor together is 60 V.

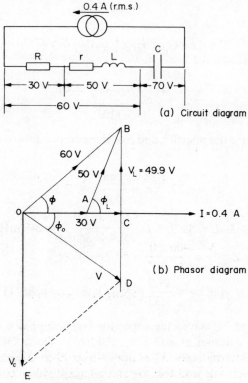

Fig. 3.11. Circuit and phasor diagrams for Problem 3.6.

Determine the values of all the components, the power and power factor, the phase angle of the coil and the source voltage ($f = 80\,\text{Hz}$).

Solution

All voltages and the current are r.m.s. values and their phase relationships may be determined from a phasor diagram. Triangle OAB (Fig. 3.11(b)) is drawn as for Problem 3.4 and the perpendicular BC dropped on to the current phasor (the phasor of reference). Applying the cosine rule to triangle OAB:

$$50^2 = 60^2 + 30^2 - 2.30.60 \cos \phi,$$

giving

$$\phi = 56° 15'.$$

Now,

$$V_L = 60 \sin \phi = 49.9\,\text{V}$$

and

$$AC = 60 \cos \phi - 30$$
$$= 3.33\,\text{V}.$$

AC and BC are the resistive and reactive components of the coil voltage.

Thus,

$$\mathbf{I}r = 3.33, \therefore r = \frac{3.33}{0.4} = 8.33\,\Omega,$$

$$\mathbf{I}\omega L = 49.9, \therefore L = \frac{49.9}{0.4 \times 2\pi.80} = 248\,\text{mH}.$$

Hence

$$\tan \phi_L = \frac{49.9}{3.33} = 15, \quad \text{giving } \phi_L = 86° 11'.$$

The voltage $\mathbf{V}_C$ across the capacitor lags the phasor of reference by $\pi/2$; hence is drawn at BD (Fig. 3.11(b)). Thus, OD is the source voltage, $\mathbf{V}$. Alternatively, $\mathbf{V}_C$ is drawn from O at OE and the parallelogram, of which OB and OE are the adjacent sides, completed, giving the diagonal OD.

Thus,

$$V = \sqrt{OC^2 + CD^2} \quad \text{and} \quad CD = BD - CB = 70 - 49.9 = 20.1$$

$$= \sqrt{33.33^2 + 20.1^2}$$

$$= 38.92 \text{ V}$$

and

$$\phi_0 = \tan^{-1}\frac{-20.1}{33.3} = -31°\,6',$$

$$\therefore \quad \cos\phi_0 = 0.856.$$

Hence,

$$\mathbf{V} = 38.92 \angle -31°\,6',$$

$$R = \frac{\mathbf{V}_R}{\mathbf{I}} = \frac{30}{0.4} = 75\,\Omega$$

and

$$C = \frac{\mathbf{I}}{\mathbf{V}\omega} = \frac{0.4 \times 10^6}{70 \times 2\pi.80} = 11.43\,\mu\text{F},$$

$$\text{Power} = VI\cos\phi_0 = 38.92 \times 0.4 \times 0.856$$

$$= 13.32 \text{ W}.$$

$$[\text{OR: Power} = I^2(r + R) = 0.4^2(75 + 8.33)$$

$$= 0.16 \times 83.33$$

$$= 13.32 \text{ W.}]$$

3.4.1 Series resonance

It should be noted that, had the capacitor voltage been 49.9 V instead of 70 V (Problem 3.6), the points C and D would coincide and **V** would have been equal to 33.33 V and in phase with **I**. Thus, ϕ_0 would have been zero and, under these conditions, the circuit is said to be in resonance. Resonance is defined as the condition, in a circuit having both kinds of reactance, which makes the overall power factor equal to unity, i.e. when the reactances cancel making the total reactance equal to zero.

In phasor notation:

$$\text{Voltage across } R = \mathbf{I}R,$$

$$\text{Voltage across } L = j\omega L\mathbf{I},$$

$$\text{Voltage across } C = -\frac{j}{\omega C}\mathbf{I}$$

and the total voltage is the sum of the three,

$$\therefore \quad \mathbf{V} = \mathbf{I}\left[R + j\left(\omega L - \frac{1}{\omega C}\right)\right] \tag{3.24}$$

$$= \mathbf{IZ}$$

or

$$\mathbf{Z} = R + j\left(\omega L - \frac{1}{\omega C}\right) \tag{3.25}$$

and

$$\phi = \tan^{-1}\left(\frac{\omega L - (1/\omega C)}{R}\right).$$

Resonance occurs when:

$$\left(\omega_0 L - \frac{1}{\omega_0 C}\right) = 0,$$

giving

$$\omega_0^2 = \frac{1}{LC} \tag{3.26}$$

and

$$f_0 = \frac{1}{2\pi}\sqrt{\frac{1}{LC^2}}. \tag{3.27}$$

Obviously, from eqn. (3.25) the impedance is a minimum when the circuit is in resonance and is equal to R. For the circuit of Problem 3.6 the resonant condition would be reached for a value of C given by:

$$\omega C V_C = 0.4$$

or

$$C = \frac{0.4 \times 10^6}{2\pi.80 \times 49.9} = 15.97 \,\mu F.$$

If the magnitude of C be varied over a wide range, $\mathbf{V}_C$ would be inversely proportional to C and the voltage across R, r and L in series

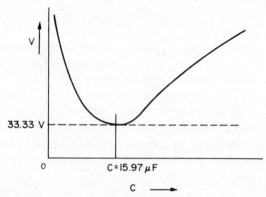

FIG. 3.12. Variation of source voltage as a function of capacitance for the circuit of Fig. 3.11(a).

would remain constant at 60 V (since $\mathbf{I}$ is constant). The source voltage would vary as shown in the graph of Fig. 3.12, increasing on either side of the minimum, resonant, value of 33.33 V as C passed through 15.97 μF. Since $\mathbf{Z} = \mathbf{V}/\mathbf{I}$, and $\mathbf{I}$ is constant, this is also the graph of $|\mathbf{Z}|$.

It is important to note that the voltage across either L or C at resonance is considerably greater than the total voltage across the source, so that the circuit provides voltage magnification. For this reason, series resonance is studiously avoided in power systems since dangerously high voltages could result. On the other hand, the phenomenon finds wide application in communication, control and information transmission circuits. In a radio receiver, for example, a resonant circuit enables a signal of one frequency to be selected in preference to others having different frequencies.

3.4.2 The Q-factor

In a circuit having L, C and R in series:

$$V_L = V \frac{\omega_0 L}{R}$$

and

$$V_C = V \frac{1}{\omega_0 CR},$$

where ω_0 = resonant frequency, since $I = V/R$ at resonance.

The ratio V_L/V (or V_C/V) is the circuit magnification factor. The quality factor, or Q-factor, of the circuit may be defined* as the ratio (at resonance) of the reactance, of either kind, to the resistance, so that the circuit magnification factor and the Q-factor are equal.

In practice, most of the circuit resistance is associated with the inductor (the resistance of the wire, principally) only a little being due to dielectric losses in the capacitor. If r is the inductor resistance, then the Q-factor of the coil is given by:

$$Q_L = \frac{\omega_0 L}{r} \tag{3.28}$$

and that of the capacitor by:

$$Q_C = \frac{1}{\omega_0 Cr'} \tag{3.29}$$

where

$$r' = R - r.$$

When advantage is to be taken of the resonance phenomenon, considerable care is taken to reduce the losses in the reactive components.

---

* Other definitions are possible; see, for example, J. R. Barker, *Mechanical and Electrical Vibrations,* Methuen & Co. Ltd., London, 1964, p. 11.

Practical coils may have Q-factors lying within the range 1 (at low frequencies) to 500 (at high frequencies) whilst good-quality capacitors may have Q-factors 10 times higher.

The losses in a capacitor are more usually expressed in terms of power factor. Thus, for a capacitor having capacitance C and equivalent loss-resistance r',

$$\text{Power factor} = \frac{r'}{\sqrt{(r')^2 + (1/\omega_0 C)^2}}$$

$$= \frac{1}{\sqrt{1 + (1/\omega_0 C r')^2}}$$

$$= \frac{1}{\sqrt{1 + Q_C^2}}. \tag{3.30}$$

Hence,

$$\text{p.f.} \simeq \frac{1}{Q_C}.$$

3.4.3 Tuning

A series L, C, R circuit may be brought to the resonant condition in any one of three different ways. When the frequency is fixed, as, for example, in a radio receiver, the aerial circuit may be adjusted by varying either L or C. In other applications where L and C are both fixed, resonance may be achieved by frequency adjustment. The process in all cases is called tuning.

PROBLEM 3.7

For a series L, C, R circuit compare the three methods of tuning, and, for a Q-factor of 4, determine the conditions which give (i) resonance, (ii) maximum reactance voltages, when fed from a voltage source.

Solution
  (i) *Frequency variation*
At a frequency much below that of resonance the capacitive reactance

is high and the inductive reactance is low. Hence, the circuit is predominantly capacitive and the power factor is leading. As the frequency is increased, $1/\omega C$ decreases and ωL increases (see Fig. 3.13(a)) so that a frequency, ω_0, must be reached when they are equal and so cancel.

As the frequency is still further increased, ωL exceeds $1/\omega C$ and the circuit becomes inductive, giving a lagging power factor. Hence, Z first falls to a minimum value, equal to R, and then rises again. The magnitude and phase of I vary with frequency as shown in the graphs of Fig. 3.13 (b) and (c).

The voltage across R will clearly vary with frequency in the same manner as I (Fig. 3.13(b)) but with the stipulation that, for any particular value of R, the peak of the graph, at resonance, must be equal to V, the applied voltage.

Dealing next with the inductance voltage:

$$V_L = I\omega L = \frac{V\omega L}{\sqrt{R^2 + [\omega L - (1/\omega C)]^2}}$$

or

$$\left(\frac{V_L}{V}\right)^2 = \frac{1}{(R^2/\omega^2 L^2) + [1 - (1/\omega^2 LC)]^2}.$$

Letting $(\omega/\omega_0) = \alpha$, $Q = \omega_0 L/R$ and $\omega_0^2 LC = 1$, where ω_0 = resonant frequency,

$$\left(\frac{V_L}{V}\right)^2 = \frac{1}{(1/\alpha^2 Q^2) + [1 - (1/\alpha^2)]^2}. \tag{3.31}$$

Thus, when $\alpha = 1$, i.e. at resonance, $(V_L/V) = Q$. Letting this value of V_L be V'_L,

$$\left(\frac{V_L}{V'_L}\right)^2 = \frac{1}{(1/\alpha^2) + Q^2[1 - (1/\alpha^2)]^2}. \tag{3.32}$$

The maximum value of this ratio occurs when the denominator is a minimum

$$\frac{d}{d\alpha}(\text{denom.}) = -\frac{2}{\alpha^3} + 2Q^2\left(1 - \frac{1}{\alpha^2}\right)\left(\frac{2}{\alpha^3}\right) = 0,$$

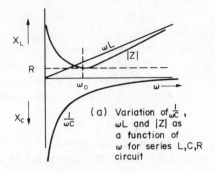

(a) Variation of $\frac{1}{\omega C}$, ωL and $|Z|$ as a function of ω for series L,C,R circuit

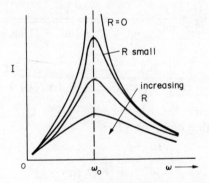

(b) Magnitude of current as a function of ω

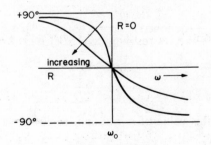

(c) Phase of current as a function of ω

FIG. 3.13.

giving

$$\alpha = \frac{1}{\sqrt{1 - 1/2Q^2}}. \qquad (3.33)$$

Substituting this value of α into eqn. (3.32) gives

$$\frac{V_L}{V'_L} = \frac{1}{\sqrt{1 - 1/4Q^2}}. \qquad (3.34)$$

Thus, for a Q of 4, the maximum value of the inductance voltage occurs at $\omega = 1.016\omega_0$ and is 1.0079 times its value at resonance. Finally, the capacitance voltage,

$$V_C = \frac{I}{\omega C} = \frac{V}{\omega C \sqrt{R^2 + [\omega L - (1/\omega C)]^2}}$$

or

$$\left(\frac{V_C}{V}\right)^2 = \frac{1}{\omega^2 C^2 R^2 + (\omega^2 LC - 1)^2} = \frac{1}{(\alpha^2/Q^2) + (\alpha^2 - 1)^2}. \qquad (3.35)$$

Again, at resonance, i.e. when $\alpha = 1$, $V_C/V = Q$.

Letting this value of V_C be V'_C,

$$\left|\frac{V_C}{V'_C}\right|^2 = \frac{1}{\alpha^2 + Q^2(\alpha^2 - 1)^2}. \qquad (3.36)$$

The maximum value of V_C/V'_C occurs when the denominator is a minimum:

$$\frac{d}{d\alpha}(\text{denom.}) = 2\alpha + 2Q^2(\alpha^2 - 1)2\alpha,$$

giving

$$\alpha = \sqrt{1 - \frac{1}{2Q^2}}. \qquad (3.37)$$

And substituting this value of α into eqn. (3.36) gives

$$\frac{V_C}{V'_C} = \frac{1}{\sqrt{1 - 1/4Q^2}} \qquad (3.38)$$

or the same ratio as the inductance voltage given by eqn. (3.34).

For a Q-factor of 4, the maximum value of the capacitance voltage occurs at $\omega = 0.984\omega_0$ and is 1.0079 times its value at resonance. Graphs of the current, and the three voltages, V_R, V_L and V_C, against ω are shown in Fig. 3.14(a).

(ii) *Inductance variation*

For fixed values of ω, R and C the value of L for resonance is L_0, where

$$L_0 = \frac{1}{\omega^2 C}.$$

The current, V_R and V_C are all maximum at this value of L and are given by:

$$\left.\begin{array}{c} I = \dfrac{V}{R}, \\[2mm] V_R = V \\[2mm] V_C = QV \end{array}\right\} \text{at resonance.}$$

and

But,

$$V_L = \frac{V\omega L}{\sqrt{R^2 + [\omega L - (1/\omega C)]^2}}$$

or

$$\left(\frac{V_L}{V}\right)^2 = \frac{1}{(R^2/\omega^2 L^2) + [1 - (1/\omega^2 LC)]^2}.$$

Defining $Q = \omega L_0/R = 1/\omega CR$ and $\beta = L/L_0$

$$\left(\frac{V_L}{V}\right)^2 = \frac{1}{(1/\beta^2 Q^2) + [1 - (1/\beta)]^2} \tag{3.39}$$

since $\omega^2 L_0 C = 1$.

When $\beta = 1$, $V_L/V = Q$. Let this value of V_L be V'_L,

$$\therefore \left(\frac{V_L}{V'_L}\right)^2 = \frac{1}{(1/\beta^2) + Q^2[1 - (1/\beta)]^2}. \tag{3.40}$$

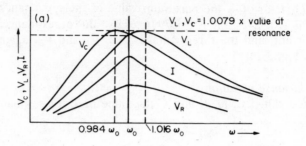

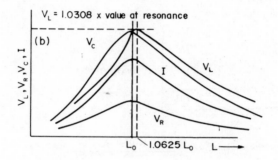

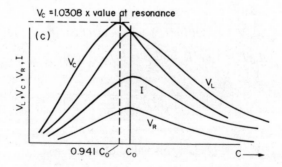

FIG. 3.14. Graphs of V_L, V_C, V_R and I for a series resonant circuit with $Q = 4$: (a) plotted against ω, (b) plotted against L, (c) plotted against C.

The maximum value of this expression occurs when the denominator is a minimum. Or when

$$\frac{d}{d\beta}(\text{denom.}) = -\frac{2}{\beta^3} + 2Q^2\left(1 - \frac{1}{\beta}\right)\frac{1}{\beta^2} = 0,$$

giving

$$\beta = 1 + \frac{1}{Q^2}. \tag{3.41}$$

Substituting this value of β into eqn. (3.40) gives:

$$\frac{V_L}{V_L'} = \sqrt{1 + \frac{1}{Q^2}}. \tag{3.42}$$

Thus, for a Q of 4, the maximum value of the inductance voltage occurs at $L = 1.0625L_0$ and is 1.0308 times its value at resonance.

Graphs of I, V_R, V_C and V_L plotted against L are shown in Fig. 3.14(b).

(iii) *Capacitance variation*

For fixed values of ω, R and L the value of C which produces resonance is:

$$C_0 = \frac{1}{\omega^2 L}.$$

The current, V_R and V_L all reach their maximum values at this value of C and are given by:

$$\left.\begin{array}{c} I = \dfrac{V}{R}, \\[2mm] V_R = V, \\[2mm] V_L = QV \end{array}\right\} \text{ at resonance.}$$

However, from eqn. (3.35)

$$\left|\frac{V_C}{V}\right|^2 = \frac{1}{\omega^2 C^2 R^2 + (\omega^2 LC - 1)^2}.$$

Defining $Q = 1/\omega C_0 R$, $\omega^2 L C_0 = 1$ and $C/C_0 = \delta$

$$\left|\frac{V_C}{V}\right|^2 = \frac{1}{(\delta^2/Q^2) + (\delta - 1)^2} = \frac{Q^2}{\delta^2 + Q^2(\delta - 1)^2}. \quad (3.43)$$

When $\delta = 1$, $V_C/V = Q$.
Letting this value of V_C be V'_C,

$$\left|\frac{V_C}{V'_C}\right|^2 = \frac{1}{\delta^2 + Q^2(\delta - 1)^2}. \quad (3.44)$$

The maximum value of this expression occurs when the denominator is a minimum; or when

$$\frac{d}{d\delta}(\text{denom.}) = 2\delta + 2Q^2(\delta - 1) = 0,$$

giving

$$\delta = \frac{1}{1 + 1/Q^2}. \quad (3.45)$$

Substituting this value of δ into eqn. (3.44) gives:

$$\frac{V_C}{V'_C} = \sqrt{1 + \frac{1}{Q^2}}. \quad (3.46)$$

For a Q of 4, maximum V_C occurs at $\delta = 0.941$ or $C = 0.941 C_0$, and is $\sqrt{1.0625} = 1.0308$ times its value at resonance.

Graphs of I, V_L, V_R and V_C are shown, plotted against C, in Fig. 3.14(c).

It is clear from the expressions developed in this solution that for Q values of, say, 10 or more, negligible errors are introduced by assuming that maximum voltages across all elements occur at the same value of the variable.

3.4.4 Bandwidth

Although a resonant circuit has its maximum response at (or very near to) resonance, the response at neighbouring frequencies is generally still appreciable. The bandwidth is defined as the range of frequencies over which the response is equal to or greater than a given fraction (usually $1/\sqrt{2}$) of that at resonance. The two frequencies which define the upper and lower limits of this range occur one above and one below resonance, and since the power in the circuit at either of these frequencies is one-half of the resonant value, they are known as the half-power-point frequencies—or simply, the half-power points.

PROBLEM 3.8

For a series circuit having $L = 100\,\mu\text{H}$, $C = 2500\,\text{pF}$ and $Q = 70$, determine the resonant frequency, the half-power points and the bandwidth.

Solution

(a) Resonant frequency,

$$f_0 = \frac{1}{2\pi} \sqrt{\frac{1}{LC}}$$

$$= \frac{1}{2\pi} \sqrt{\frac{10^{18}}{100 \times 2500}} = \frac{10^6}{\pi} = \underline{318.3\ \text{kHz.}}$$

(b) Working generally,

$$\mathbf{I}_0 = \frac{\mathbf{V}}{R},$$

at resonance.

And

$$\mathbf{I} = \frac{\mathbf{V}}{R + j[\omega L - (1/\omega C)]}$$

at any frequency, ω.

$$\therefore \frac{\mathbf{I}}{\mathbf{I}_0} = \frac{R}{R + j[\omega L - (1/\omega C)]} = \frac{1}{1 + j\,(1/R)\,[\omega L - (1/\omega C)]} \qquad (3.47)$$

$$= \frac{1}{1 + jyQ} \qquad (3.48)$$

where

$$y = \left(\frac{\omega}{\omega_0} - \frac{\omega_0}{\omega}\right) \quad \text{and} \quad Q = \frac{\omega_0 L}{R}.$$

When $yQ = \pm a$, say,

$$\left|\frac{I}{I_0}\right| = \frac{1}{\sqrt{1 + a^2}}. \tag{3.49}$$

Two values of ω satisfy this equation. Let them be $\omega_2 > \omega_0$ and $\omega_1 < \omega_0$.

Thus,

$$\frac{\omega_2}{\omega_0} - \frac{\omega_0}{\omega_2} = \frac{a}{Q} \tag{3.50}$$

and

$$\frac{\omega_1}{\omega_0} - \frac{\omega_0}{\omega_1} = -\frac{a}{Q}. \tag{3.51}$$

Adding and rearranging gives:

$$\omega_0^2 = \omega_1 \omega_2. \tag{3.52}$$

Note that this relationship is independent of a so that ω_0 is always the geometric mean of the two frequencies defined by the intersections of the resonance curve with any line parallel to the ω-axis, as shown in Fig. 3.15.

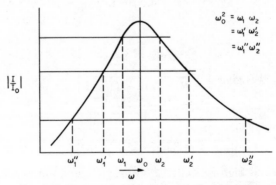

FIG. 3.15. Resonance curve for series L, C, R circuit.

Subtracting (3.51) from (3.50) gives:

$$\frac{\omega_2}{\omega_0} - \frac{\omega_0}{\omega_2} - \frac{\omega_1}{\omega_0} + \frac{\omega_0}{\omega_1} = \frac{2a}{Q}$$

from which

$$\frac{\omega_2 - \omega_1}{\omega_0} = \frac{a}{Q}. \tag{3.53}$$

The half-power points occur when $a = 1$, since then,

$$\frac{\mathbf{I}}{\mathbf{I}_0} = \frac{1}{1 \pm j}, \quad \text{from (3.48)}$$

$$= \frac{1}{\sqrt{2}} \angle \pm \frac{\pi}{4}.$$

Also, when $a = 1$

$$\omega_2 - \omega_1 = \Delta\omega = \frac{\omega_0}{Q}$$

or

$$f_2 - f_1 = \Delta f = \frac{f_0}{Q}.$$

Thus, in this case, the bandwidth, $\Delta f, = \dfrac{318.3}{70}$, or

$$f_2 - f_1 = 4.55 \text{ kHz}$$

and

$$f_2 f_1 = f_0^2 = 318.3^2.$$

Solving for f_1 and f_2 gives:

$$f_1 = 316.04 \text{ kHz}$$

and

$$f_2 = 320.59 \text{ kHz}.$$

For a Q-factor as high as 70 there is negligible error in assuming that the half-power points are equidistant from the resonant frequency.

3.4.5 Solutions using complex algebra

PROBLEM 3.9

Three impedances $\mathbf{Z}_1 = 8 \angle 30°\ \Omega$, $\mathbf{Z}_2 = 10 \angle -40°\ \Omega$ and $\mathbf{Z}_3 = 12 \angle 50°\ \Omega$ are connected in series across a voltage source for which $\mathbf{V} = 100 \angle 0$. Calculate the voltage developed across each impedance and the total power supplied.

Solution

Note that (a) the frequency is not given, being implicit in the impedance values, and (b) the voltage is given as the reference phasor.

The total impedance $\mathbf{Z}$ is first calculated. Thus,

$$\mathbf{Z} = 8 \angle 30° + 10 \angle -40° + 12 \angle 50°$$

$$= 8(\cos 30° + j \sin 30°) + 10(\cos 40° - j \sin 40°)$$

$$+ 12(\cos 50° + j \sin 50°)$$

$$= (6.928 + 7.66 + 7.714) + j(4 - 6.428 + 9.912)$$

$$= 22.30 \angle 16° 53'\ \Omega.$$

Hence

$$\mathbf{I} = \frac{100 \angle 0°}{22.30 \angle 16° 53'} = 4.29 \angle -16° 53'\ \text{A},$$

$$\therefore \quad \mathbf{V}_1, \text{the voltage across } \mathbf{Z}_1 = (4.29 \angle -16° 53') (8 \angle 30°)$$

$$= 34.32 \angle 13° 7'\ \text{V},$$

$$\mathbf{V}_2 = (4.29 \angle -16° 53') (10 \angle -40°) = 42.9 \angle -56° 53'\ \text{V}$$

and

$$\mathbf{V}_3 = (4.29 \angle -16° 53') (12 \angle 50°) = 51.48 \angle 33° 7'\ \text{V}.$$

$$\text{Power} = VI \cos \phi$$

$$= 100.4.29 \cos 16° 53'$$

$$= 411\ \text{W}.$$

Save for the need to determine the power, there was no necessity to calculate the current. Each voltage can be related to the total voltage by the ratio of the impedance across which it is developed to the total impedance.

Thus,

$$\mathbf{V}_1 = \left(\frac{\mathbf{Z}_1}{\mathbf{Z}_1 + \mathbf{Z}_2 + \mathbf{Z}_3}\right) 100 \angle 0°$$

$$= \frac{8 \angle 30°}{22.3 \angle 16°53'} 100 \angle 0° = 34.32 \angle 13°7' \text{ V.}$$

PROBLEM 3.10

A coil, of resistance 3 Ω and inductance L, is connected in series with a load of impedance 15 Ω across a 240-V, 50-Hz mains supply. The total power absorbed is 375 W of which 300 W is dissipated in the load.

Calculate (a) the magnitude of the current supplied by the mains, (b) the two possible values of L and (c) the load power factor.

Solution

(a) The power dissipated in the coil (due only to its resistance) = $375 - 300 = 75$ W.

If $|\mathbf{I}|$ is the (r.m.s.) magnitude of the current,

$$75 = |\mathbf{I}|^2 . 3,$$

giving

$$|\mathbf{I}| = 5 \text{ A.}$$

(b) If $|\mathbf{Z}_L|$ is the impedance of the load,

$$|\mathbf{Z}_L| = \sqrt{R_L^2 + X_L^2} = 15 \ \Omega.$$

The power is dissipated entirely in R_L.

$$\therefore \quad 5^2 . R_L = 300,$$

giving

$$R_L = 12 \ \Omega$$

and

$$X_L = j\sqrt{15^2 - 12^2} = \pm j9 \ \Omega.$$

For the circuit as a whole

$$|\mathbf{Z}| = \frac{240}{5} = 48\,\Omega$$

$$= \sqrt{(3 + 12)^2 + X_T^2}$$

where X_T is the total reactance.

$$\therefore \quad X_T = \pm j45.6\,\Omega.$$

(i) If the load is capacitive, $X_L = -j9\,\Omega$,

$$\therefore \quad j\omega L - j9 = \pm j45.6$$

or

$$\omega L = 54.6\,\Omega$$

ignoring the negative solution, or

$$L = \frac{54.6}{2\pi \times 50} = 174\,\text{mH}.$$

(ii) If the load is inductive, $X_L = +j9\,\Omega$,

$$\therefore \quad j\omega L + j9 = \pm j45.6$$

or

$$\omega L = 36.6\,\Omega$$

ignoring the negative solution, or

$$L = \frac{36.6}{2\pi \times 50} = 117\,\text{mH}.$$

(c) Power factor of the load

$$= \cos\phi_L = \frac{R_L}{Z_L} = \frac{12}{15} = 0.8\ (\text{lead or lag}).$$

3.5 PARALLEL CIRCUITS

A circuit in which several impedances are connected in parallel across

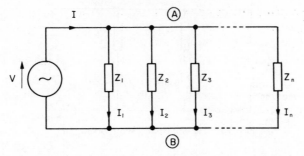

FIG. 3.16. A simple parallel circuit.

a common source is shown in Fig. 3.16. The application of Kirchhoff's current law at either node A or node B enables one to write:

$$I = I_1 + I_2 + I_3 + \ldots + I_n. \qquad (3.54)$$

Each current may be calculated separately since

$$I_1 = \frac{V}{Z_1}, I_2 = \frac{V}{Z_2}, \text{etc.},$$

so that:

$$I = \frac{V}{Z_1} + \frac{V}{Z_2} + \frac{V}{Z_3} + \ldots + \frac{V}{Z_n} \qquad (3.54a)$$

$$= V\left[\frac{1}{Z_1} + \frac{1}{Z_2} + \frac{1}{Z_3} + \ldots + \frac{1}{Z_n}\right] = \frac{V}{Z}$$

where Z is the equivalent impedance of the given n impedances. Hence:

$$\frac{1}{Z} = \frac{1}{Z_1} + \frac{1}{Z_2} + \frac{1}{Z_3} + \ldots + \frac{1}{Z_n}. \qquad (3.55)$$

Complex numbers must be used throughout.

PROBLEM 3.11

For the circuit of Fig. 3.17, calculate each branch current, the total current and the power absorbed from the supply.

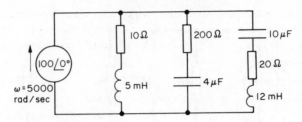

FIG. 3.17. Parallel circuit, see Problem 3.11.

Solution

Each current is calculated in phasor notation.

$$\mathbf{I}_1 = \frac{100 \angle 0°}{10 + j5000 \times 5 \times 10^{-3}} = \frac{100}{10 + j25}$$

$$= \frac{100(10 - j25)}{725} = (1.38 - j3.45)\,\text{A}$$

$$= 3.72 \angle -68° 11'\,\text{A},$$

$$\mathbf{I}_2 = \frac{100}{200 - (j10^6/5000 \times 4)} = \frac{100}{200 - j50}$$

$$= (0.471 + j0.1178)\,\text{A}$$

$$= 0.4855 \angle 14° 2'\,\text{A}$$

and

$$\mathbf{I}_3 = \frac{100}{20 + j[5000 \times 12 \times 10^{-3} - (10^6/5000 \times 10)]}$$

$$= \frac{100}{20 + j(60 - 20)}$$

$$= (1 - j2)\,\text{A} = 2.236 \angle -63° 26'\,\text{A},$$

$$\mathbf{I} = \mathbf{I}_1 + \mathbf{I}_2 + \mathbf{I}_3 = (1.38 + 0.471 + 1) + j(0.1178 - 3.45 - 2)$$

$$= (2.851 - j5.332)\,\text{A}$$

$$= 6.046 \angle -61° 52'\,\text{A}.$$

The power absorbed is equal to the product of the voltage and the in-phase component of the current.

$$P = 100 \times 2.851 = 285.1 \text{ W}$$

or

$$P = 100 \times 6.046 \cos 61° 52'$$

$$= 285.1 \text{ W}.$$

3.5.1 The admittance concept

The admittance of a circuit or circuit element is the ratio of current to voltage (phasor values). Thus,

$$\mathbf{Y} = \frac{\mathbf{I}}{\mathbf{V}} = \frac{1}{\mathbf{Z}} \qquad (3.56)$$

or

$$\mathbf{I} = \mathbf{VY}. \qquad (3.57)$$

The concept is particularly useful when dealing with parallel circuits since, for example, eqn. (3.54a) may be written:

$$\mathbf{I} = \mathbf{VY}_1 + \mathbf{VY}_2 + \mathbf{VY}_3 + \ldots + \mathbf{VY}_n$$

$$= \mathbf{V}(\mathbf{Y}_1 + \mathbf{Y}_2 + \mathbf{Y}_3 + \ldots + \mathbf{Y}_n), \qquad (3.58)$$

$$\therefore \quad \mathbf{Y} = \mathbf{Y}_1 + \mathbf{Y}_2 + \mathbf{Y}_3 + \ldots + \mathbf{Y}_n. \qquad (3.59)$$

The admittance of each branch can be calculated from its two components, G, the conductance, and B, the susceptance.
Thus

$$Y = G \pm jB. \qquad (3.60)$$

The units of $\mathbf{Y}$ and B are, like those of G, reciprocal ohms or siemens (S), and can be related to R and X as follows:
Let

$$\mathbf{Z} = R + jX$$

then,

$$\mathbf{Y} = \frac{1}{\mathbf{Z}} = \frac{R - jX}{R^2 + X^2} = \frac{R}{|\mathbf{Z}|^2} - j\frac{X}{|\mathbf{Z}|^2}.$$

Hence,

$$G = \frac{R}{|\mathbf{Z}|^2} \quad \text{and} \quad B = \frac{-X}{|\mathbf{Z}|^2}. \tag{3.61}$$

Conversely, if

$$\mathbf{Y} = G + jB = \frac{1}{\mathbf{Z}}$$

then,

$$\mathbf{Z} = \frac{1}{G + jB} = \frac{G}{|\mathbf{Y}|^2} - j\frac{B}{|\mathbf{Y}|^2} \tag{3.62}$$

$$= R + jX$$

where

$$R = \frac{G}{|\mathbf{Y}|^2} \quad \text{and} \quad X = \frac{-B}{|\mathbf{Y}|^2}. \tag{3.63}$$

PROBLEM 3.12

A circuit having two parallel branches, one having a conductance of 0.1 S and a susceptance of -0.3 S and the other a conductance of 0.5 S and a susceptance of $+0.2$ S, is connected to a voltage source for which $\mathbf{V} = 10 \angle 0°$.

Determine the total current and power taken from the supply and the equivalent series circuit.

Solution

For branch 1,

$$\mathbf{Y}_1 = (0.1 - j0.3) \text{ S}$$

and for branch 2,

$$\mathbf{Y}_2 = (0.5 + j0.2) \text{ S}.$$

And total

$$\mathbf{Y} = \mathbf{Y}_1 + \mathbf{Y}_2$$
$$= (0.1 + 0.5) + j(0.2 - 0.3)$$
$$= (0.6 - j0.1) \text{ S.}$$

Current

$$\mathbf{I} = \mathbf{VY}$$
$$= 10 \angle 0° (0.6 - j0.1)$$

or

$$\underline{\mathbf{I} = (6 - j1) \text{ A.}}$$

Power

$$V^2G = V^2(G_1 + G_2)$$
$$= 100(0.1 + 0.5) = 60 \text{ W.}$$

[Alternatively: Power = V (In-phase component of current)
$$= 10 \times 6$$
$$= 60 \text{ W.}]$$

Let R and X be the components of the equivalent series circuit. Then:

$$R = \frac{G}{|\mathbf{Y}|^2} = \frac{G_1 + G_2}{(G_1 + G_2)^2 + (B_1 + B_2)^2}$$
$$= \frac{0.1 + 0.5}{(0.1 + 0.5)^2 + (-0.3 + 0.2)^2} = \underline{1.62 \ \Omega}$$

and

$$X = \frac{-(B_1 + B_2)}{(G_1 + G_2)^2 + (B_1 + B_2)^2} = \frac{+0.1}{0.37}$$
$$= \underline{+0.27 \ \Omega.}$$

Hence,

$$\mathbf{Z} = (1.62 + j0.27) \ \Omega.$$

Thus, a resistance of $1.62\,\Omega$ and an inductive reactance of $0.27\,\Omega$ connected in series would be indistinguishable, by any electrical test, from the given circuit.

Even when the data are in impedance form it is often advantageous, when dealing with parallel circuits, to convert to admittance form to simplify solution.

PROBLEM 3.13

Three impedances $Z_1 = (3 + j8)\,\Omega$, $Z_2 = (7 - j6)\,\Omega$ and $Z_3 = (5 + j9)\,\Omega$ are connected in parallel and together carry a current of $5\,\angle 40°$ A.

Determine the current carried by each branch.

Solution

For each branch calculate G and B.

$$G_n = \frac{R_n}{|Z_n|^2} \quad \text{and} \quad B_n = \frac{X_n}{|Z_n|^2},$$

$$G_1 = \frac{3}{73}\,S, G_2 = \frac{7}{85}\,S \quad \text{and} \quad G_3 = \frac{5}{106}\,S,$$

$$B_1 = -j\frac{8}{73}\,S, B_2 = +j\frac{6}{85}\,S \quad \text{and} \quad B_3 = -j\frac{9}{106}\,S.$$

Thus,

$$G = G_1 + G_2 + G_3 = 0.0411 + 0.0824 + 0.0472$$

$$= \underline{0.1707\,S}$$

and

$$B = B_1 + B_2 + B_3$$

$$= j(-0.1096 + 0.0706 - 0.0849)$$

$$= \underline{-j0.1239\,S},$$

$$\therefore \quad \underline{\mathbf{Y} = (0.1707 - j0.1239)\,S.}$$

Now each current is calculated from $\mathbf{I}_n = \mathbf{I}(\mathbf{Y}_n/\mathbf{Y})$.

Thus,

$$I_1 = \frac{5 \angle 40°(0.0411 - j0.1096)}{0.1707 - j0.1239} = \underline{2.77 \angle 6° 34' \text{ A}},$$

$$I_2 = \frac{5 \angle 40°(0.0824 + j0.0706)}{0.1707 - j0.1239} = \underline{2.57 \angle 116° 38' \text{ A}},$$

$$I_3 = \frac{5 \angle 40°(0.0472 - j0.0849)}{0.1707 - j0.1239} = \underline{2.305 \angle 15° 3' \text{ A}}.$$

3.5.2 Parallel resonance; half-power points; bandwidth

When two circuits having reactances of opposite kinds are connected in parallel, the possibility of resonance exists. The condition is defined in the same way as for series circuits—namely, that which makes the combined impedance resistive, though in other respects the phenomenon of parallel resonance is more complicated.

Taking first the simplest case of pure inductance in parallel with pure capacitance, as shown in Fig. 3.18(a), fed from a current source.

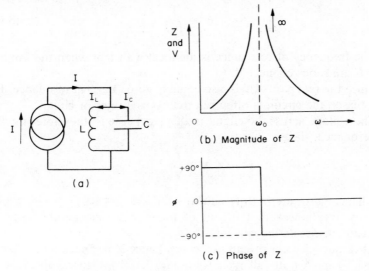

(b) Magnitude of Z

(c) Phase of Z

FIG. 3.18. A loss-less parallel rejector circuit.

Total admittance,

$$\mathbf{Y} = G_1 + jB_1 + G_2 + jB_2$$

$$= \frac{R_1}{Z_1^2} + j\frac{(-\omega L)}{Z_1^2} + \frac{R_2}{Z_2^2} + j\frac{(1/\omega C)}{Z_2^2}.$$

Since

$$R_1 = R_2 = 0, Z_1^2 = \omega^2 L^2 \quad \text{and} \quad Z_2^2 = \frac{1}{\omega^2 C^2},$$

$$\therefore \mathbf{Y} = \frac{-j}{\omega L} + j\omega C.$$

For resonance, the imaginary component of $\mathbf{Y} = 0$.
Hence,

$$\frac{1}{\omega L} = \omega C$$

or

$$\omega^2 = \frac{1}{LC}. \tag{3.64}$$

The frequency of resonance is identical with that when the same L and C are series-connected.

Since the real part of $\mathbf{Y}$ is also equal to zero, $\mathbf{Y} = 0$ at resonance. For this reason the circuit is often referred to as a rejector circuit.

The voltage across the circuit in this ideal case is, therefore, infinite at resonance, since

$$\mathbf{V} = \frac{\mathbf{I}}{\mathbf{Y}},$$

and hence, also, are both $\mathbf{I}_L$ and $\mathbf{I}_C$.

They are, however, 180° out of phase with one another and so constitute a circulating current.

At frequencies above and below resonance $\mathbf{Y}$ becomes finite, hence $\mathbf{Z}$ ($= 1/\mathbf{Y}$) and $\mathbf{V}$ both fall as shown in Fig. 3.18(b). Figure 3.18(c) shows the change of the phase angle of $\mathbf{Z}$ as ω changes.

PROBLEM 3.14

For a three-branch parallel circuit in which the branches are G, L and C, as shown in Fig. 3.19, determine the resonant frequency, the impedance and admittance at resonance and the frequencies for half-power when fed by a current source.

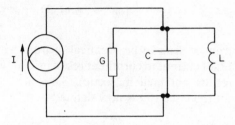

FIG. 3.19. Parallel circuit for Problem 3.14.

Solution

$$\mathbf{Y} = G + j\omega C + \frac{1}{j\omega L}$$

$$= G + j\left(\omega C - \frac{1}{\omega L}\right).$$

Resonance will be given when $\mathbf{Y}$ has no imaginary component; or

$$\omega C - \frac{1}{\omega L} = 0,$$

giving

$$\omega_0^2 = \frac{1}{LC}.$$

At resonance, therefore,

$$\mathbf{Y} = G \quad \text{and} \quad \mathbf{Z} = \frac{1}{G} = R.$$

So that the voltage across the circuit at resonance is:

$$\mathbf{V}_0 = \mathbf{I}R. \qquad (3.65)$$

At any other frequency, ω, the voltage across the circuit is:

$$V = \frac{I}{Y} = \frac{I}{G + j[\omega C - (1/\omega L)]},$$

$$\therefore \quad \frac{V}{V_0} = \frac{1}{1 + j\dfrac{1}{G}[\omega C - (1/\omega L)]}. \tag{3.66}$$

This equation can be seen to be identical in form with eqn. (3.47) expressing the ratio of current to current at resonance for a series circuit. The remaining results obtained in section 3.4.4 are therefore valid providing only that the circuit Q is now defined by:

$$Q = \frac{\omega_0 C}{G} \tag{3.67}$$

or

$$Q = \frac{1}{\omega_0 L G}. \tag{3.68}$$

The half-power points occur when $yQ = \pm 1$, so that if, as before, ω_2 is the greater and ω_1 the lesser of these, then

$$\frac{\omega_2}{\omega_0} - \frac{\omega_0}{\omega_2} = \frac{1}{Q} \tag{3.69}$$

and

$$\frac{\omega_0}{\omega_1} - \frac{\omega_1}{\omega_0} = \frac{1}{Q}. \tag{3.70}$$

Solving eqn. (3.69) for ω_2 gives

$$\omega_2 = \omega_0 \left[\frac{1}{2Q} + \sqrt{1 + \frac{1}{4Q^2}} \right]. \tag{3.71}$$

And eqn. (3.70) gives:

$$\omega_1 = \omega_0 \left[-\frac{1}{2Q} + \sqrt{1 + \frac{1}{4Q^2}} \right]. \tag{3.72}$$

Graphs of voltage against frequency for various values of Q-factor would be identical with those of Fig. 3.13(b). Similarly the variations of R and X with frequency would be identical with those of G and B for the series circuit.

Pairs of circuits for which voltage, current, conductance, susceptance and admittance for one stand in the same relationship as do current, voltage, resistance, reactance and impedance, respectively, for the other are termed DUALS. Thus, the circuit of Fig. 3.19 and that of Problem 3.7 are duals, and results developed for one may be used for the other provided that these parameters are interchanged as defined above.

A more realistic form of the parallel resonant circuit of Fig. 3.18 is produced when some resistance is included in the inductive arm. Such a circuit would result, for example, if the coil and capacitor—series connected in Fig. 3.11(a)—were reconnected in parallel.

PROBLEM 3.15

For the circuit of Fig. 3.20(a), determine (a) the resonant frequency (sometimes referred to as the anti-resonant frequency, in parallel circuits) and dynamic impedance of the circuit at resonance, (b) the ratio

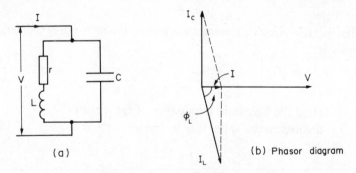

(a)   (b) Phasor diagram

FIG. 3.20. Diagrams for Problem 3.15.

of circulating current to supply current at resonance, (c) the frequency for maximum impedance and (d) the bandwidth, when $L = 1\,\text{mH}$, $C = 1\,\text{nF}$ and $r = 100\,\Omega$, comparing with the bandwidth when r, L and C are series connected.

Solution

(a) $$\mathbf{Y} = (G_1 + G_2) + j(B_1 + B_2) \tag{3.73}$$

$$= \left(\frac{r}{r^2 + \omega^2 L^2} + 0\right) + j\left(\frac{-\omega L}{r^2 + \omega^2 L^2} + \omega C\right).$$

Resonance occurs when $\mathbf{Y}$ is real:

$$\therefore \quad \frac{\omega_r L}{r^2 + \omega_r^2 L^2} = \omega_r C$$

or

$$\omega_r^2 = \frac{1}{LC} - \frac{r^2}{L^2}, \tag{3.74}$$

i.e. a frequency slightly lower than for the corresponding series circuit. For this condition

$$G = \frac{r}{r^2 + \omega_r^2 L^2}$$

$$= \frac{Cr}{L}. \tag{3.75}$$

That is, the circuit at resonance behaves like a pure resistance of magnitude:

$$R_D = \frac{L}{Cr}. \tag{3.76}$$

R_D is called the Dynamic Impedance of the circuit.

If Q is defined in the same way as before, i.e.

$$Q = \frac{\omega_0 L}{r} \tag{3.28}$$

then eqns. (3.74) and (3.76) may be expressed in terms of Q, as follows:

$$\omega_r^2 = \frac{1}{LC}\left(1 - \frac{1}{Q^2}\right) \tag{3.77}$$

and

$$R_D = Q^2 r. \tag{3.78}$$

Thus, for high-Q circuits the parallel resonant frequency is very close to that for series resonance; R_D may reach very high values.

(b) Figure 3.20(b) shows the phasor diagram at resonance.

The resultant current of I_L (lagging V by ϕ_L) and I_C (leading V by $\pi/2$) is I, in phase with V.

Thus, the circulating current$= I_C = jV\omega_r C$, where

$$\omega_r = \omega_0 \sqrt{1 - \frac{1}{Q^2}},$$

from eqn. (3.77).

Supply current $= \dfrac{V}{R_D} = \dfrac{V}{Q^2 r}$, from (3.78).

$$\text{Ratio} = j\omega_r C Q^2 r = j\omega_0 C r Q^2 \sqrt{1 - \frac{1}{Q^2}}$$

$$= j\sqrt{Q^2 - 1} \qquad (3.79)$$

$$\simeq jQ$$

when Q is large.

(c) From eqn. (3.73)

$$Y = \frac{r - j\omega L + j\omega C(r^2 + \omega^2 L^2)}{r^2 + \omega^2 L^2}$$

$$= \frac{r + j\omega(Cr^2 - L + \omega^2 L^2 C)}{r^2 + \omega^2 L^2} \qquad (3.80)$$

or

$$|Y|^2 = \frac{r^2 + \omega^2(Cr^2 - L + \omega^2 L^2 C)^2}{(r^2 + \omega^2 L^2)^2}. \qquad (3.81)$$

The minimum value of this expression will give the maximum impedance, i.e. when

$$\frac{d|Y|^2}{d\omega} = 0.$$

This gives a quadratic equation in ω^2:

$$\omega^4 L^4 C^2 + 2\omega^2 L^2 C^2 r^2 + C^2 r^4 - 2LCr^2 - L^2 = 0$$

the positive solution of which is:

$$\omega_m^2 = \sqrt{\frac{1}{L^2 C^2} + \frac{2r^2}{L^3 C} - \left(\frac{r}{L}\right)^2}. \tag{3.82}$$

Substituting $\omega_0^2 = 1/LC$ and $Q = \omega_0 L/r$ gives:

$$\omega_m = \omega_0 \left(\sqrt{1 + \frac{2}{Q^2} - \frac{1}{Q^2}} \right)^{\frac{1}{4}} \tag{3.83}$$

a frequency only marginally below ω_0 unless Q is very low.

For example, if $Q = 10$, the frequency for maximum impedance is:

$$\omega_m = 0.999\,975\,\omega_0$$

and for $Q^2 = 10$,

$$\omega_m = 0.9977\,\omega_0.$$

The frequency for unity power factor, given by eqn. (3.77), is:

$$\text{for } Q = 10, \omega_r = \omega_0 \sqrt{1 - \frac{1}{100}} = 0.994\,99\,\omega_0$$

$$\text{and for } Q^2 = 10, \omega_r = \omega_0 \sqrt{1 - \frac{1}{10}} = 0.948\,68\,\omega_0.$$

(d) It is necessary to redefine bandwidth in the case of the parallel circuit, since the frequencies for the admittance to be $\sqrt{2} \times$ the minimum admittance do not coincide with those for which the power factor is 0.707. Hence, when the circuit is fed from a current source, the half-power condition is less significant than is the case with a series resonant circuit fed from a voltage source. The circuit is most often used as a load for an active device, such as a valve or transistor, and in this application a useful and significant definition of bandwidth is obtained by disregarding the power factor (and power) and considering only the change of magnitude of admittance. Hence, the bandwidth is the frequency range between the two frequencies at which the admittance is $\sqrt{2} \times$ the minimum admittance.

$$\omega_0 = \frac{1}{\sqrt{LC}} = \frac{1}{\sqrt{10^{-3} \times 10^{-9}}} = 10^6 \text{ rad/sec.}$$

Hence,

$$Q = \frac{\omega_0 L}{r} = 10.$$

The frequency for minimum admittance, ω_m, may be calculated from (3.83) and is:

$$\omega_m = 0.999\,975\,\omega_0.$$

The magnitude of $|\mathbf{Y}|^2_{\min}$ may now be calculated from eqn. (3.81), since writing

$$Q = \frac{\omega_0 L}{r} \quad \text{and} \quad \alpha_m = \frac{\omega_m}{\omega_0}$$

gives

$$|\mathbf{Y}|^2_{\min} = \frac{1 + [(\alpha_m/Q) - \alpha_m Q + \alpha_m^3 Q]^2}{r^2(1 + \alpha_m^2 Q^2)^2} \tag{3.84}$$

which reduces to:

$$|\mathbf{Y}|^2_{\min} \simeq \frac{1}{r^2 Q^2 (Q^2 + 1)} \tag{3.85}$$

when α_m is very close to unity, as is the case here.

Substituting $r = 100\,\Omega$ and $Q = 10$,

$$|\mathbf{Y}|^2_{\min} = 9.901 \times 10^{-9} \,(\text{S})^2.$$

The frequencies for which $|\mathbf{Y}|^2 = 2|\mathbf{Y}|^2_{\min}$ can now be found by solving

$$\frac{1 + [(\alpha/10) - 10\alpha + 10\alpha^3]^2}{r^2(1 + 100\alpha^2)^2} = 2 \times 9.901 \times 10^{-9}$$

for α, where $\alpha = \omega/\omega_0$.

This reduces to:

$$\alpha^6 - 1.9998\alpha^4 + 0.979\,70\alpha^2 + 0.009\,99 = 0,$$

a cubic equation in α^2 which may be solved, numerically, to give:

$$\alpha_1 = 0.951\,18 \quad \text{or} \quad \omega_1 = 951.18\,\text{krad/sec}$$

and

$$\alpha_2 = 1.051\,21 \quad \text{and} \quad \omega_2 = 1051.21\,\text{krad/sec}.$$

Thus, the bandwidth $(\omega_2 - \omega_1) = 100.03\,\text{krad/sec}$.

Since ω_m (and hence α_m) depends on Q, falling as Q falls, the error involved in equating eqn. (3.85) to eqn. (3.84) increases for low values of Q. It is negligible, however, down to $Q = 3$ and rises to only 0.4% for a Q of 2.

Had the coil and capacitor been connected in series, the two half-power points would be given by eqns. (3.51) and (3.50) with $a = 1$. Thus:

$$\omega_1 = 951.25\,\text{krad/sec}$$

and

$$\omega_2 = 1051.25\,\text{krad/sec},$$

giving

$$(\omega_2 - \omega_1) = 100\,\text{krad/sec}.$$

For the parallel circuit, then, the frequencies which define the bandwidth are very close to those of the corresponding series circuit, and for all but the lowest Q-factors may be calculated in the same way, i.e. by the use of eqns. (3.50) and (3.51) with $a = 1$. Some noticeable differences occur, however, for Q-values below 10, amounting, for example, to around 0.4% for $Q = 3$.

As in the case of the series circuit, tuning to resonance may be achieved by variation of L, C or ω. In the parallel circuit, conditions are dependent also on whether the circuit resistance is associated with L or C or with both. So many different cases are possible that an exhaustive treatment is beyond the scope of the present volume.[*]

---

[*] See, for example, R. S. Glasgow, *Principles of Radio Engineering*, McGraw-Hill, 1936.

3.5.3 Power-factor improvement

An alternative way of looking at the phenomenon of parallel resonance is that adopted by the power engineer, in which attention is focused on current, power and power factor rather than on resonance frequency and bandwidth.

Since power in a load is equal to $VI \cos \phi$, for constant V and I the available power becomes less as $\cos \phi$ falls. However, the power losses in the whole system from generator to load are proportional to I^2, irrespective of power factor. Hence, not only does the overall efficiency of the system fall as the power factor becomes less, but the power-handling capacity of the system is restricted, since it is determined in most cases by temperature rise (and hence by the losses). It is therefore desirable, on purely technical grounds, to keep the overall system power factor as high as possible (i.e. as near unity as possible) and, in cases where the load power factor is inherently low, some means of improving it must be found. In the vast majority of cases, loads are inductive and so a simple and effective method of achieving the required improvement in p.f. is to connect a capacitor in parallel with the load. If parallel resonance is produced, the power factor will be raised to unity, and, unlike the condition of series resonance, no dangerously high voltages can result.

PROBLEM 3.16

A certain load may be considered to be equivalent to a resistance of 35 Ω in series with an inductance of 0.1 H as shown in Fig. 3.21(a). Calculate the capacitance required in parallel with this load to raise the effective power factor to unity. The system voltage is 500 V and $f = 300/2\pi$ Hz.

Solution

The capacitance current must cancel the susceptive component of the inductive branch current.

$$\mathbf{I} = \mathbf{V}\mathbf{Y}(j\omega) \quad \text{and} \quad \mathbf{Y}(j\omega) = \frac{R}{Z^2} - j\frac{X}{Z^2},$$

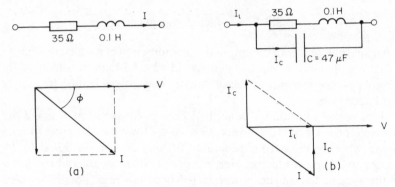

FIG. 3.21. Principle of power-factor correction. (a) Original circuit and phasor diagram. (b) Corrected circuit and phasor diagram.

where $R = 35\,\Omega$ and $X = 300 \times 0.1 = 30\,\Omega$. Hence, the magnitude of the capacitance current must be:

$$+ j\frac{X}{Z^2}\,\mathbf{V} = j\left(\frac{30}{35^2 + 30^2}\right)\mathbf{V} = j7.06\,\text{A}$$

giving

$$= j\omega C\mathbf{V},$$

$$C = \frac{7.06}{300 \times 500}\,10^6\,\mu\text{F} = 47\,\mu\text{F}, \quad \text{see Fig. 3.21(b).}$$

Note: Conductive component of current $= \dfrac{R}{Z^2}\,\mathbf{V}$

$$= 8.24\,\text{A},$$

and this component remains unchanged after p.f. correction. Thus, although the total power supplied has not changed, the current supplied by the mains has dropped from $\sqrt{8.24^2 + 7.06^2} = 10.85\,\text{A}$ to $8.24\,\text{A}$, with a corresponding reduction of power loss in the supply cables, etc.

For the load,

$$\text{power} = VI\cos\phi$$

$$= 500 \times 8.24$$

$$= 4.12\,\text{kW}$$

and volt-amperes $= VI$

$$= 500 \times 10.85$$

$$= 5.425 \text{ kVA}.$$

The product $VI \sin \phi$ is called the reactive volt-amperes (VAr). In this case

$$VI \sin \phi = 500 \times 7.06$$

$$= 3.53 \text{ kVAr}.$$

Hence,

$$VA = \sqrt{W^2 + (\text{VAr})^2}.$$

The reactive volt-amperes absorbed by the load and by the capacitor are clearly opposite in sign (since they cancel) and it is customary to assign the positive sign to the inductive circuit. The capacitor may therefore be regarded either as absorbing negative VAr from the supply or as supplying the positive VAr required by the inductive load in order to improve its power factor.

It should be noted that it is not necessarily the best economic practice to raise the p.f. to unity, since the cost of the capacitors must be balanced against the savings achieved by the improvement in efficiency. Depending on the tariffs for electric power, a final value somewhat below unity (often $0.92 - 0.97$) may be the best economic compromise.

PROBLEM 3.17

An industrial load consists of ten induction motors each absorbing 40 kW at a lagging p.f. of 0.8 and an efficiency of 88%. To improve the power factor of the plant, three of the motors are replaced by synchronous motors having a leading power factor of 0.707 and an efficiency of 92%. The mechanical loads on all motors remain unchanged. Calculate the overall power factor and the total power taken from the supply under the new conditions.

Solution

For the purpose of the problem, an induction motor is merely an inductive/resistive load and a synchronous motor is a capacitive/resistive load.

Before correction, the total load is:

$$10 \times 40 = 400 \text{ kW at } 0.8 \text{ p.f. lagging.}$$

After correction, the load is:

$$7 \times 40 = 280 \text{ kW at } 0.8 \text{ p.f. lagging, PLUS}$$

$$3 \times 40 \times \frac{88}{92} = 115 \text{ kW at } 0.707 \text{ p.f. leading.}$$

Thus, total power taken is:

$$280 + 115 = 395 \text{ kW.}$$

kVAr taken by each part of the load:

(i) Induction motors: $\text{kVA} = \dfrac{280}{0.8} = 350 \text{ kVA,}$

$$\therefore \quad \text{kVAr} = 350 \sin \phi = 350 \sin(\cos^{-1} 0.8)$$

$$= 350 \times 0.6 = 210 \text{ kVAr.}$$

(ii) Synchronous motors: $\text{kVA} = \dfrac{115}{0.707} = 163 \text{ kVA,}$

$$\therefore \quad \text{kVAr} = -163 \sin(\cos^{-1} 0.707)$$

$$= -163 \times 0.707 = -115 \text{ kVAr.}$$

$$\text{Total kVAr} = 210 - 115 = +95 \text{ kVAr.}$$

So the load is 395 kW and +95 kVAr,

$$\therefore \quad \text{kVA} = \sqrt{395^2 + 95^2}$$

$$= 406.3 \text{ kVA}$$

$$\text{and power factor} = \frac{395}{406.3} = 0.972 \text{ lagging.}$$

3.6 Z- AND Y-LOCI

If the impedance, Z, of a circuit be plotted as a point on the complex Z-plane, the line joining all such points when one or more components of Z vary is called the Z-locus. If only one component of Z is varied, the Z-locus is either a straight line or a circle. The loci of Y follow the same rule.

The use of Y- and Z-loci in the analysis of circuits frequently provides an insight not easily obtained in other ways.

CASE (i) Series circuit; variable X, constant R.

Consider the series circuit of Fig. 3.22(a) in which X is varied and R is fixed.

Then $Z = R \pm jX = Z \angle \pm \phi$, and this may be plotted on the Z-plane as a straight line parallel to the imaginary (X) axis at a distance R (measured along the real axis) from it; see Fig. 3.22(b). Any point on this line, such as A, represents Z, since $OB = R$ and $BA = X = (\omega L - 1/\omega C)$. A point, such as C, represents Z for a different value of X and the same value of R. Thus, $BC = (1/\omega C - \omega L)$, and the line CBA is the Z-locus. If X varies from $-\infty$ to $+\infty$ then the line extends also over the range $\pm\infty$.

$$Y = \frac{1}{Z},$$

$$\therefore \quad ZY = 1. \tag{3.86}$$

Hence, to plot the Y-locus, we need the reciprocal of Z.

Consider Fig. 3.22(c) which shows the Z-locus and a circle, centre F on the real axis, and of radius OF.

Then $OD \times OA = OE \cos \phi \times \dfrac{OB}{\cos \phi} = OE \times OB$. Hence, if the diameter, OE, of the circle is chosen so that

$$OE \times OB = 1,$$

then

$$OD \times OA = 1$$

also.

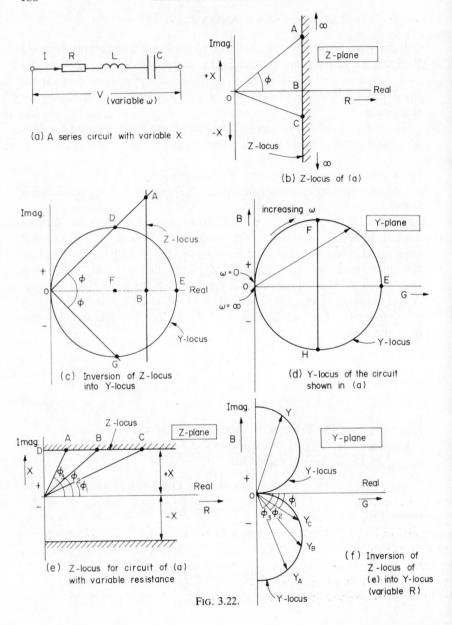

(a) A series circuit with variable X

(b) Z-locus of (a)

(c) Inversion of Z-locus into Y-locus

(d) Y-locus of the circuit shown in (a)

(e) Z-locus for circuit of (a) with variable resistance

(f) Inversion of Z-locus of (e) into Y-locus (variable R)

FIG. 3.22.

Since OA = $|\mathbf{Z}|$, then OD = $|\mathbf{Y}|$, from eqn. (3.86). But, since $\mathbf{Y}$ = $|\mathbf{Y}|\ \angle -\phi$, the point on the Y-locus corresponding to A is G.

Thus, the semicircle OGE is the part of the Y-locus corresponding to the Z-locus from B, upwards to infinity, and conversely for the semicircle EDO. Figure 3.22(d) shows the complete Y-locus corresponding to the Z-locus of Fig. 3.22(b). The point E represents the resonant value of $\mathbf{Y}$, and, if frequency is the variable, the direction of increasing ω is clockwise. Clearly, equal frequency intervals are not evenly spaced round the circle and the half-power points are F and H since B = G for these points.

CASE (ii) Series circuit; variable R, constant X.

If only R in the circuit of Fig. 3.22(a) is varied, then $\mathbf{Z} = R \pm jX$ has the straight-line locus shown in Fig. 3.22(e). The line is above the real axis for inductive X and below for capacitive X. Points such as A, B, C represent $\mathbf{Z}$ for reactance $(+X)$ and resistance DA, DB, DC, respectively. The Y-locus will, by the same arguments as those used for Case (i), be a circle—or, if R be restricted to positive values, a semicircle —passing through the origin. Figure 3.22(c) turned anti-clockwise through 90° may be used to show that the Y-locus will be a circle. Also, since

$$\mathbf{Y} = \frac{1}{\mathbf{Z}} = \frac{1}{Z}\angle -\phi$$

the admittances corresponding to $\mathbf{Z}_A, \mathbf{Z}_B, \mathbf{Z}_C$ in Fig. 3.22(e) will be $\mathbf{Y}_A, \mathbf{Y}_B, \mathbf{Y}_C$ in Fig. 3.22(f).

CASE (iii) Parallel circuit; variable B, constant G.

Consider the circuit of Fig. 3.23(a):

$$\mathbf{Y} = G \pm jB = G \pm j\left(\omega C - \frac{1}{\omega L}\right).$$

By analogy with Case (i) the locus of $\mathbf{Y}$ will be a straight line parallel to the B-axis, as shown in Fig. 3.23(b). If the variation of B is brought about by a variation of ω, then the line extends from $-\infty$ to $+\infty$ as ω is varied from 0 to ∞. The Z-locus will therefore be as shown in Fig. 3.23(c)—a circle identical with the Y-locus circle for a series circuit. The

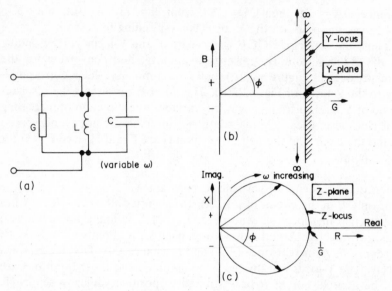

Fig.3.23. (a) A parallel circuit with constant G, variable B. (b) Y-loci of circuit of (a). (c) Inversion of Y-locus into Z-locus.

intersection of this circle with the real axis occurs when $X = 0$, i.e. at resonance.

Voltage and current loci

Since $\mathbf{V} = \mathbf{IZ}$, the locus of the $\mathbf{V}$ phasor (a complex number) for constant $\mathbf{I}$ will be identical with that of $\mathbf{Z}$. Conversely, if $\mathbf{V}$ be kept constant, the locus of current, since

$$\mathbf{I} = \mathbf{VY},$$

will be identical with the Y-locus in each case.

PROBLEM 3.18

For the parallel resonant circuit of Fig. 3.20(a) in which $L = 1\,\text{mH}$, $C = 1\,\text{nF}$ and $R = 400\,\Omega$ plot the admittance locus for variable ω, and hence determine the resonant frequency, the frequency for minimum admittance, the minimum admittance and the upper and lower frequency limits of the bandwidth.

Solution

The total admittance is obtained by adding the semicircular locus corresponding to that of Fig. 3.22(d) (lower half) to the admittance of the capacitive branch, $+j\omega C$ (when capacitance is absent from the series branch, the point $\omega = 0$ occurs at point E). This is shown in Fig. 3.24,

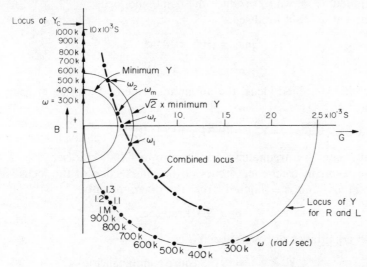

FIG. 3.24. Determination of complete **Y**-locus for parallel resonant circuit, Problem 3.18.

but to determine the values required the loci must be drawn to scale. For the inductive branch,

$$\mathbf{Y} = \frac{R}{R^2 + X^2} - j\frac{X}{R^2 + X^2} = 2.5 \times 10^{-3}\,\text{S}, \quad \text{when } \omega = 0.$$

At $\omega = 0$, **Y** for the capacitive branch $= 0$; hence one point on the combined locus is $G = 2.5 \times 10^{-3}\,\text{S}$. The semicircular locus is therefore of radius $2.5 \times 10^{-3}\,\text{S}$, and the frequency scale is marked on it by calculating $R/(R^2 + X^2)$ for various values of ω.

ECT - N

Thus, at $\omega = 800$ krad/sec,

$$G = \frac{400}{160,000 + 640,000} = 0.5 \times 10^{-3}\,\text{S}.$$

Hence, the point for $\omega = 800$ krad/sec is on the semicircle at a distance 0.5×10^{-3} S measured horizontally from the B-axis. Proceeding in this way for several frequencies enables the frequency scale to be marked on the circular locus. Then, at each frequency, $j\omega C = \mathbf{Y}_C$ is calculated and added as shown to produce the combined locus.

Thus, at $\omega = 800$ krad/sec,

$$j\omega C = j800 \times 10^3.10^{-9}\,\text{S}$$

$$= j0.8 \times 10^{-3}\,\text{S}.$$

From the combined locus, the minimum value of Y can be measured, and is:

$$\mathbf{Y}_{\min} = (0.34 + j0.13)\,10^{-3}\,\text{S},$$

and it occurs at a frequency very close to $\omega = 1000$ krad/sec.

The resonant frequency occurs at the intersection of the locus with the real axis and is estimated (from the diagram) to be

$$\omega_r = 920\,\text{krad/sec}.$$

The admittance at resonance, $\mathbf{Y}_r$, is

$$\mathbf{Y}_r = 0.4 \times 10^{-3}\,\text{S (pure conductance)}.$$

The bandwidth is defined by the intersection of a circle of radius $\sqrt{2} \times \sqrt{0.34^2 + 0.13^2}$, i.e. $\sqrt{2} \times$ the minimum $\mathbf{Y}$ with the locus. The two frequencies are estimated to be:

$$\omega_1 = 805\,\text{krad/sec}$$

and

$$\omega_2 = 1205\,\text{krad/sec}.$$

PROBLEM 3.19

For the circuit of Fig. 3.25(a) in which L, C and ω are constant, determine the condition for which the supply current is independent of

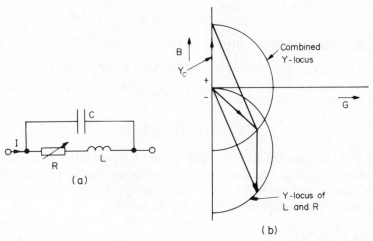

FIG. 3.25. (a) Circuit having constant $|Z|$. (b) Y-loci for circuit of (a).

the resistance. Calculate the magnitude of this current if a voltage of 25 V is applied to the circuit. $L = 1$ mH and $C = 1$ nF.

Solution

The problem is most easily solved by sketching the Y-locus. For the fixed X, variable R branch it will be the lower semicircle of Fig. 3.22(f). The admittance, Y_C, of the capacitance branch will be constant and so the combined admittance will be the semicircle raised by an amount equal to Y_C. If this is to be constant, its centre must coincide with the origin, see Fig. 3.25(b). Hence the amount by which the circle is raised is equal to its radius, or

$$Y_C = \tfrac{1}{2}\left|\frac{-j}{\omega L}\right|$$

or

$$\omega C = \frac{1}{2\omega L},$$

giving

$$\omega^2 = \frac{1}{2LC}$$

or

$$\omega = 707.1 \text{ krad/sec.}$$

The magnitude of the current $= VY_C$

$$= 25 \times 707.1 \times 10^{-9} \times 10^6 \text{ mA}$$

$$= 17.68 \text{ mA.}$$

3.7 OTHER CIRCUITS

More complicated circuits which do not fall into either the series or parallel categories must generally be solved by one of the systematic methods considered in Chapter 4. In some special cases, however, the mesh-star transformation offers a simple solution.

PROBLEM 3.20

For the circuit of Fig. 3.26(a), determine the impedance between points A and C.

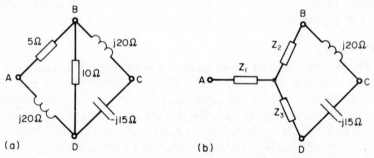

(a)

(b)

FIG. 3.26. Illustrating the use of the mesh-star transformations in the solution of a circuit: Problem 3.20. (a) Original circuit. (b) Mesh ABD transformed.

Solution

The mesh circuit ABD is first transformed to its equivalent star, giving the circuit of Fig. 3.26(b), where

$$Z_1 = \frac{Z_{AB}Z_{AD}}{Z_{AB} + Z_{BD} + Z_{AD}} = \frac{j50}{15 + j10} = \frac{j50(15 - j10)}{325}$$

$$= (1.54 + j2.31) \ \Omega.$$

Similarly,

$$Z_2 = \frac{50}{15 + j10} = \frac{50(15 - j10)}{325} = (2.31 - j1.54)\ \Omega$$

and

$$Z_3 = \frac{j100}{15 + j10} = \frac{j100(15 - j10)}{325} = (3.08 + j4.62)\ \Omega.$$

Referring to Fig. 3.26(b), let

$$Z_4 = Z_2 + j20$$

$$= (2.31 + j18.46)\ \Omega$$

and

$$Z_5 = Z_3 - j15$$

$$= (3.08 - j10.38)\ \Omega$$

and let Z_6 be equal to Z_4 and Z_5 in parallel. Then,

$$Z_6 = \frac{Z_4 Z_5}{Z_4 + Z_5} = \frac{(2.31 + j18.46)\ (3.08 - j10.38)}{5.39 + j8.08}$$

$$= (14.16 - j15.12)\ \Omega.$$

Finally,

$$Z_{AC} = Z_1 + Z_6 = (1.54 + j2.31 + 14.16 - j15.12)$$

$$= (15.7 - j12.8)\ \Omega.$$

PROBLEMS III

1. Explain the necessity for, and the uses of, the r.m.s. value of an alternating quantity. Calculate the r.m.s. value of each of the currents the waveforms of which are shown in Fig. P.III.1.
2. A current $i(t) = 25 \cos 15t$ flows in a 10-Ω resistor. Determine (a) the peak power, (b) the mean power.
3. A voltage whose waveform is triangular (such as that of Fig. P.III.1(d)) having a peak value of 240 V is applied to a 100-Ω resistor. Calculate (a) the peak power, (b) the mean power.

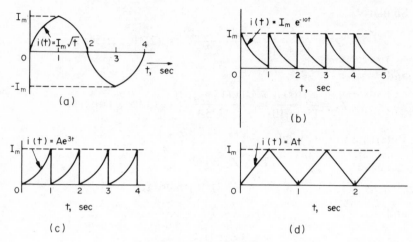

FIG. P.III.1 (Problem III.1).

4. Four voltage sources connected in series have magnitudes and phases as follows:

$$e_1(t) = 50 \cos \omega t,$$

$$e_2(t) = 100 \sin (\omega t + 30°),$$

$$e_3(t) = -20 \cos (\omega t + 60°),$$

$$e_4(t) = 150 \sin (\omega t - 90°).$$

Determine the magnitude and phase of the combined e.m.f. by (i) calculation in the time domain, (ii) phasor addition, (iii) phasor diagram.
5. Three sources of e.m.f. $e_1(t) = 80 \sin \omega t$, $e_2(t) = 120 \sin(\omega t + (\pi/6))$ and $e_3(t) = 60 \cos \omega t$ are connected in series.

Calculate the resultant e.m.f. and its phase difference from $e_1(t)$.

With $e_2(t)$ reversed, determine the new resultant.
6. A resistor having $R = 40 \Omega$ and a 10-µF capacitor are connected in series across a voltage source.

Given that the current is 2 A (r.m.s.) and leads the voltage by 40°, determine the frequency and the p.d. at the source terminals.
7. A coil and a non-reactive resistor are connected in series across a 240-V, 50-Hz supply. The current is 4 A (r.m.s.) and the voltage drops across the coil and the resistor are 120 V (r.m.s.) and 150 V (r.m.s.) respectively.

Calculate the resistance of the resistor, the resistance and inductance of the coil and the power dissipated in the coil.
8. A coil of resistance 5 Ω and inductive reactance 25 Ω is connected in series with a 50-Ω resistor to a 200-V, a.c. supply.

Calculate the total power, the power factor, the current taken from the supply and the power loss in the coil.

9. A series circuit is supplied from a 240-V, 60-Hz mains supply.
   Given that the current through the circuit is lagging and of magnitude 8 A (r.m.s.) and that the power absorbed is 500 W, calculate the inductance, resistance and power factor of the circuit.

10. Two coils are connected in parallel. When 30 V (constant) is applied the currents in the coils are 2 A and 3 A. With 50 V (r.m.s.) at 35 Hz applied the corresponding currents are 1.0 A and 1.6 A (both r.m.s. values).
    Calculate the total current, power and power factor when the coils are connected in series across a 240-V, 50-Hz supply.

11. A coil, having an inductance of 200 mH and a resistance of 4 Ω, is connected in series with a capacitor across a 50-Hz supply.
    Calculate the capacitance required to give the circuit a power factor of 0.5.

12. A coil, of resistance 10 Ω and inductance 50 mH, is connected to a 100-V, 50-Hz mains supply.
    Calculate the current, expressed in polar form, and determine the in-phase and quadrature components.
    Calculate the capacitance required to be connected in parallel to raise the overall power factor to unity, and determine the supply current in this case.

13. Sketch the frequency-domain phasors which represent the following time-domain quantities:
    (a) $8\cos 10t$, (b) $18\cos(10t + \pi/4)$, (c) $30\sin 314t$,
    (d) $-5\cos(5000t - \pi/6)$, (e) $12\cos(242t + 180°)$.

14. Express the following frequency-domain phasors in (i) rectangular form, (ii) exponential form:
    (a) $12 \angle 0$, (b) $10 \angle \pi/4$, (c) $10 \angle 36°52'$, (d) $5 \angle 135°$, (e) $15 \angle -90°$.

15. Convert the following phasors to time-domain expressions:
    (a) $12 \angle 0$, $\omega = 10$, (b) $15 \angle 53°$, $\omega = 5000$, (c) $5 \angle -60°$, $\omega = 314$,
    (d) $3 - j4$, $\omega = 280$, (e) j, $\omega = 1000$, (f) $20e^{j(\pi/4)}$, $\omega = 3$,
    (g) $5e^{(-2+j(\pi/4))}$, $\omega = 500$.

16. Convert to the exponential form:

$$\text{(a) } (3 + j4)(-4 - j3), \text{ (b) } \frac{2}{-0.6 + j0.8}, \text{ (c) } \frac{-1 + j2}{-1 - j2}.$$

17. Two impedances, $\mathbf{Z}_1 = 8 + j12 \, \Omega$ and $\mathbf{Z}_2 = 15 \, e^{j(\pi/4)} \, \Omega$ are connected in parallel and the combination connected in series with $\mathbf{Z}_3 = 20 \angle -\pi/6 \, \Omega$.
    Determine the total impedance.

18. Three impedances, $\mathbf{Z}_1 = 20 \, e^{j(\pi/4)} \, \Omega$, $\mathbf{Z}_2 = 25 \, e^{j0.2} \, \Omega$ and $\mathbf{Z}_3 = 10 \, e^{-j0.4} \, \Omega$ are connected in parallel, and a current $\mathbf{I} = 20 \, e^{j1.2} \, A$ is supplied by the source to which they are connected.
    Calculate (a) the p.d. of the source, (b) the power supplied, (c) the reactive volt-amperes supplied.

19. Four loads, as follows, are connected in parallel to a 440-V mains supply.
    Load 1: 10 kW at 0.8 p.f., lagging.
    Load 2: 25 kW at unit power factor.
    Load 3: 30 kVA at 0.6 power factor, leading.
    Load 4: A current of $20 - j80$ A.
    Determine the total load on the supply (a) in kW, (b) in kVA, (c) in kVAr, and calculate the overall power factor.

20. Two a.c. supplies, generating at the same frequency, work in parallel, the total output power being 2.5 kW at 0.85 p.f., lagging.

Given that one supply delivers 1 kW at 0.95 p.f., leading, determine the power output and power factor of the other.

21. Determine the impedance between the terminals A and B of the circuit represented by Fig. P.III.2.

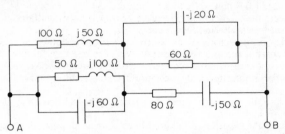

FIG. P.III.2 (Problem III.21).

22. A 100-μF capacitor and a 60-Ω resistor in series are connected in parallel with a coil, of inductance L and resistance R, a 100-μF capacitor and a 60-Ω resistor all in series.

Given that $\omega = 100$ rad/sec, calculate L and R so that the currents in the two parallel branches are equal in magnitude but out of phase by $\pi/4$.

23. The equivalent circuit of a certain capacitor is a capacitance of 0.3 μF shunted by a conductance of 3 μS, at $\omega = 10,000$ rad/sec.

Determine the power factor of the capacitor and its equivalent series resistance and capacitance.

24. Determine the admittance between terminals A and B of the circuit represented by Fig. P.III.3, and calculate the current and power supplied by the source.

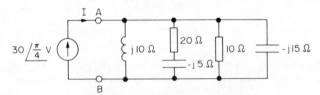

FIG. P.III.3 (Problem III.24).

25. A coil having an inductance of 80 mH is connected in series with a loss-free capacitor, C, across a 60-V a.c. supply. Resonance occurs at $\omega = 1000$ rad/sec and the power absorbed is then 100 W.

Determine the resistance of the coil and the capacitance of C.

Given that the capacitance can be varied, calculate the values of capacitance for which the total power absorbed from the supply is 50 W.

26. Two coils are connected in parallel to a 400-V a.c. supply. Coil A has a resistance of 10 Ω and a reactance of 20 Ω and the corresponding values for coil B are 15 Ω and 15 Ω.

Calculate (a) the conductance, susceptance and admittance of each branch and of the whole circuit, (b) the total current, power and power factor, (c) the capacitance to be connected across the whole circuit to raise the power factor to unity. $\omega =$ 300 rad/sec.

27. A coil of inductance 50 µH is to be tuned by series-connected capacitance to resonate at 1000 kHz, and the bandwidth to the half-power points is to be 20 kHz.

Calculate the capacitance required and the necessary Q-factor of the coil. Determine also the frequencies of the half-power points. Assume the capacitor to be loss-free.

28. Show that, for a series resonant circuit in which the inductance and the frequency are fixed, the values of capacitance at the half-power points are given by:

$$C = \frac{QC_0}{Q \pm 1}$$

where C_0 is the capacitance for resonance and Q is the Q-factor of the circuit.

Such a circuit, having a coil of inductance 100 µH and a Q-factor of 10, is tuned to resonance at 1000 kHz.

Calculate the required tuning capacitance and the two values at the half-power points.

29. For the circuit of Problem 28, determine the capacitance for maximum voltage (a) across the coil, (b) across the capacitor. Assume that the circuit is supplied from a constant-voltage source and, in case (b), determine the ratio of voltage across the capacitor to the voltage applied to the circuit.

30. A coil of inductance 120 mH and Q-factor 8 is connected in parallel with a 60-µF capacitor to a constant-voltage, variable-frequency supply.

Calculate the frequency of resonance and the dynamic impedance, R_D, at resonance.

31. A coil of inductance L and resistance R_L is connected in parallel with a capacitor of capacitance C and equivalent series loss resistance R_C.

Show that the frequency of resonance is given by:

$$f_r = \frac{\omega_0}{2\pi} \sqrt{\frac{L - CR_L^2}{L - CR_C^2}},$$

where $\omega_0^2 LC = 1$, and that if $R_L = R_C = \sqrt{L/C}$, the circuit is non-resonant.

32. A fixed inductive reactance of 10 Ω is connected in series with a resistance R, variable over the range $0 \to \infty$. The two are connected in parallel with a resistance of 10 Ω to a 200-V, fixed frequency supply.

Draw the locus of the supply current phasor and hence show that the total range of its phase angle variation relative to the applied voltage, as R is varied, is $0 \to -\pi/4$.

Determine (a) the maximum power, (b) the maximum and minimum kVA, supplied to the circuit.

33. For the circuit of Problem 31 in which L, C and R_C are fixed and $\omega^2 = 1/LC$, derive the magnitude of R_C for which the supply current phasor swings through $\pm \pi/4$ (relative to the voltage) as R_L is varied from 0 to ∞. (*Hint:* sketch the locus diagram.)

CHAPTER 4

CIRCUIT ANALYSIS

4.0 INTRODUCTION

The process of circuit analysis consists of determining the currents in, and potential differences across, all branches of a network or circuit. The data normally comprise all source voltages and/or currents and all branch resistances/impedances.

Ohm's and Kirchhoff's Laws form the basis of all methods of analysis, either directly or in modified form, according to circumstances. Thus, in circuits containing only voltage sources, mesh or loop analysis is generally to be preferred to Kirchhoff's Laws themselves since fewer simultaneous equations result and, when only current sources are present, nodal analysis is generally best.

In addition, many network theorems exist which, although not strictly falling within the above definition of circuit analysis, are nevertheless useful aids in the process. A few of these will be dealt with in this chapter.

4.1 NETWORK TERMINOLOGY

First a few definitions.
(a) A branch of a circuit is that part of the circuit containing a single active or passive element.
(b) A node is the point of interconnection of two or more branches. The junction of three or more branches is referred to as a principal node; a secondary node is the junction of two branches.

(c) A planar network is one whose schematic may be drawn on a plane surface without branch crossings.

(d) A non-planar network is one whose schematic may not be so drawn.

(e) A loop is any closed path in a network which does not pass through any branch or node more than once.

(f) A mesh is a loop which contains no other loops. It is defined only for planar networks.

4.2 KIRCHHOFF'S LAWS

The reader is referred to section 1.3 for a statement of the laws, which are valid for both planar and non-planar networks.

An unknown current is assigned to every branch and the first law applied at as many nodes as will provide independent equations. The second law is then applied to as many independent loops as are necessary to form, in total, the same number of simultaneous equations as there are unknowns. They are solved for the branch currents by substitution, determinants or matrix methods. All branch voltages are then easily found by applying Ohm's Law.

With simple circuits it is relatively easy to choose nodes and loops which yield independent equations. A rule of thumb, satisfactory in simple cases, is to choose each new node or loop so as to involve at least one branch current not already involved, either explicitly or implicitly. For more complicated circuits some care is needed and for guaranteed independence of the equations, the methods of section 4.5 must be used.

The method of application of the laws is most readily understood by dealing initially with steady (direct current) conditions.

PROBLEM 4.1

Calculate, using Kirchhoff's Laws, all the branch currents and voltages in the network represented by Fig. 4.1.

Solution

The circuit has six branches and four nodes and we begin by assigning six unknown currents, one to each branch (Fig. 4.1(a)).

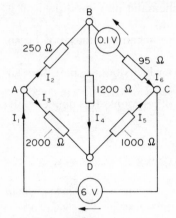

FIG. 4.1. (a) Diagram of the network for Problem 4.1.

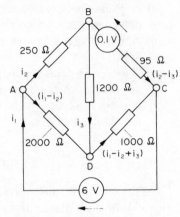

FIG. 4.1. (b) The network for Fig. 4.1(a) with the number of unknowns reduced to three.

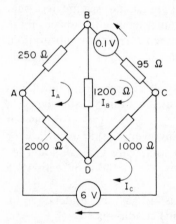

FIG. 4.1. (c) Analysing the circuit of Fig. 4.1(a) using the loop-current method.

Applying the first Law at node A:

$$I_1 = I_2 + I_3. \tag{4.1}$$

At node B:

$$I_2 - I_4 = I_6. \tag{4.2}$$

At node D:

$$I_3 + I_4 = I_5. \tag{4.3}$$

This is the limit of independent equations obtainable from the first Law since, at node C, the equation would be:

$$I_5 + I_6 = I_1 \tag{4.4}$$

which is already obtainable from eqns. (4.1), (4.2) and (4.3).

Applying the second Law to loop (or mesh) ABD, taking the clockwise direction as positive:

$$250I_2 + 1200I_4 - 2000I_3 = 0. \tag{4.5}$$

I_2 and I_4 flow clockwise round the loop and I_3, anticlockwise (and hence is negative in eqn. (4.5)) whilst the total e.m.f. in the loop is zero.

Similarly, in loop (or mesh) BCD:

$$95I_6 - 1000I_5 - 1200I_4 = -0.1. \tag{4.6}$$

In the loop containing ADC and the 6-V source:

$$2000I_3 + 1000I_5 = 6. \tag{4.7}$$

Solving eqns. (4.1), (4.2), (4.3), (4.5), (4.6) and (4.7) gives:

$$I_1 = 19.11 \, \text{mA}, \qquad I_4 = -0.14 \, \text{mA},$$

$$I_2 = 17.06 \, \text{mA}, \qquad I_5 = 1.91 \, \text{mA},$$

$$I_3 = 2.05 \, \text{mA}, \qquad I_6 = 17.20 \, \text{mA}.$$

Ohm's Law is used to calculate the potential differences for all branches. Thus:

$$V_{AB} = 250I_2 \qquad = 4.265 \, \text{V},$$

$$V_{AD} = 2000I_3 \qquad = 4.100 \, \text{V},$$

$$V_{BD} = 1200I_4 \qquad = -0.168 \, \text{V},$$

$$V_{DC} = 1000I_5 \qquad = 1.91 \, \text{V},$$

$$V_{BC} = 95I_6 + 0.1 = 1.734 \, \text{V}.$$

4.2.1 Reducing the number of unknowns

The computational work may be reduced considerably, for this problem, by a more skilful application of the two Laws at the outset. Thus, referring to Fig. 4.1(b), if at node A, i_1 is made to divide into i_2 and $(i_1 - i_2)$, three branches have been covered with the introduction of only two unknown currents. Similarly at node B, if i_3 flows along BD, then $(i_2 - i_3)$ flows along BC, and $(i_1 - i_2 + i_3)$ flows along DC. Node C adds no further information (as before) since $(i_2 - i_3)$ and $(i_1 - i_2 + i_3)$ combine to give i_1. A total of only three unknown currents has been introduced for the whole circuit and only three independent equations are required for their solution. Using the same loops as before:

$$250i_2 + 1200i_3 - 2000(i_1 - i_2) = 0, \qquad (4.8)$$

$$95(i_2 - i_3) - 1000(i_1 - i_2 + i_3) - 1200i_3 = -0.1 \qquad (4.9)$$

and

$$2000(i_1 - i_2) + 1000(i_1 - i_2 + i_3) = 6 \qquad (4.10)$$

which may be rearranged as follows:

$$2000i_1 - 2250i_2 - 1200i_3 = 0, \qquad (4.8a)$$

$$1000i_1 - 1095i_2 + 2295i_3 = 0.1, \qquad (4.9a)$$

$$3000i_1 - 3000i_2 + 1000i_3 = 6 \qquad (4.10a)$$

and subsequently solved for i_1, i_2 and i_3. The current in any branch may be found by combining, as appropriate, the values for i_1, i_2 and i_3.

4.3 THE LOOP- AND MESH-CURRENT METHODS

Either of these methods replaces both of Kirchhoff's Laws by one rule, and is therefore generally simpler to apply in practice. The two methods differ only in the choice of closed path in a network round which the total voltage drop is equated to the e.m.f. In the mesh-current method the paths are the obvious simple meshes and the method is therefore restricted to planar networks. The loop-current method is more general in that it applies to both planar and non-planar networks, but, as with the loops chosen for Kirchhoff's second Law, care must be taken to ensure a sufficient number of independent equations in order to solve for all the unknown currents.

In either method a circulating current is associated with each selected closed path. One particular direction is arbitrarily chosen as positive and the total voltage drop round each path is calculated by taking the *algebraic* sum of the products of (a) the path circulating current and the total path resistance, and (b) such other circulating currents (from adjoining paths) as impinge upon the chosen path and the resistances through which they flow. The result is equal to the total e.m.f. acting round the path.

Referring to Fig. 4.1(c), three possible loops (which in this case are meshes) are chosen, as shown, and the currents I_A, I_B and I_C associated with them.

Round loop A:

$$I_A(250 + 1200 + 2000) - 1200I_B - 2000I_C = 0$$

or

$$3450I_A - 1200I_B - 2000I_C = 0. \qquad (4.11)$$

Comparing Figs. 4.1 (b) and (c), clearly for the method to be valid, $I_A = i_2$, $I_B = (i_2 - i_3)$ and $I_C = i_1$. Substituting these into eqn. (4.11) gives:

$$3450i_2 - 1200i_2 + 1200i_3 - 2000i_1 = 0$$

or

$$2000i_1 - 2250i_2 - 1200i_3 = 0 \qquad (4.12)$$

which is seen to be identical with eqn. (4.8a), and the method is therefore justified by Kirchhoff's Laws.

Round loop B:

$$2295I_B - 1200I_A - 1000I_C = -0.1. \qquad (4.13)$$

Round loop C:

$$3000I_C - 2000I_A - 1000I_B = 6. \qquad (4.14)$$

The three loop equations (4.11), (4.13) and (4.14) are solved to give:

$$I_A = 17.06 \text{ mA},$$

$$I_B = 17.20 \text{ mA},$$

$$I_C = 19.11 \text{ mA}$$

and the branch currents calculated as appropriate. Thus:

$$I_{AB} = 17.06 \text{ mA}, \quad I_{BC} = 17.20 \text{ mA},$$

$$I_{BD} = (I_A - I_B) = -0.14 \text{ mA},$$

$$I_{AD} = (I_C - I_A) = 2.05 \text{ mA},$$

$$I_{DC} = (I_C - I_B) = 1.91 \text{ mA},$$

$$I_{CA} = 19.11 \text{ mA},$$

i.e. the same result as for Kirchhoff's Laws.

Other loops might have been chosen—for the network of Fig. 4.1 there are seven such possible. They cannot all be independent as there are only three unknown currents, but in a circuit as simple as that of Fig. 4.1 the most obvious choices are the three mesh currents.

4.4 THE NODE-VOLTAGE METHOD

One principal node in the given network is chosen as a reference node and an unknown p.d. (with respect to the reference node) is assigned to every other principal node. Kirchhoff's first Law is applied to each node in turn, each branch current meeting at a node being written as the product of the branch voltage and the branch conductance. If a current source feeds the node it must, of course, be included in the Kirchhoff Law summation.

The method is the exact dual of the loop-current method and is valid for both planar and non-planar networks.

PROBLEM 4.2

Calculate, by the node-voltage method, all branch currents and node potential differences for the circuit represented by Fig. 4.1.

Solution

The circuit diagram is redrawn in Fig. 4.2, and it will be seen that node C has been chosen as the reference node. Since V_A (with respect to the reference) is 6 V, as determined by the voltage source, this leaves only two node voltages to be determined.

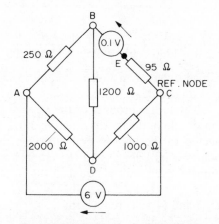

FIG. 4.2. Analysing the circuit of Fig.4.1(a) using the node-voltage method (see Problem 4.2).

Designating these V_B and V_D, we apply Kirchhoff's first Law to node D:

$$\left(\frac{V_D - 6}{2000}\right) + \left(\frac{V_D - V_B}{1200}\right) + \frac{V_D - 0}{1000} = 0. \qquad (4.15)$$

Each term in the equation is a current flowing away from the node —calculated by multiplying a branch conductance by the potential difference between the ends of the branch. Since there is no current source connected to the node, their sum is equal to zero. Similarly, at node B:

$$\left(\frac{V_B - 6}{250}\right) + \left(\frac{V_B - V_D}{1200}\right) + \left(\frac{V_B - 0.1}{95}\right) = 0. \qquad (4.16)$$

There is no need to include the secondary node E in the analysis since

$(V_B - V_E)$ is uniquely determined by the 0.1 V source, and, as soon as V_B is found from (4.15) and (4.16), V_E follows.

Rearranging (4.15) and (4.16) gives:

$$V_D\left(\frac{1}{2000} + \frac{1}{1200} + \frac{1}{1000}\right) - \frac{6}{2000} - \frac{V_B}{1200} = 0 \qquad (4.15a)$$

and

$$V_B\left(\frac{1}{250} + \frac{1}{1200} + \frac{1}{95}\right) - \frac{6}{250} - \frac{V_D}{1200} - \frac{0.1}{95} = 0 \qquad (4.16a)$$

an arrangement which suggests an alternative, more easily remembered form of the node-voltage rule.

At each node, calculate the product of the voltage (to the reference node) and the sum of all conductances meeting at the node. For every other node connected to the chosen node through one conductance, calculate the product of its voltage and the conductance and subtract from the first product. The result is equal to the total current flowing into the node.

Equations (4.15a) and (4.16a) reduce to:

$$23.333V_D - 8.333V_B = 30 \qquad (4.15b)$$

and

$$-8.333V_D + 153.597V_B = 250.526 \qquad (4.16b)$$

which may be solved to give:

$$V_D = 1.905 \text{ volts} \quad \text{and} \quad V_B = 1.734 \text{ volts.}$$

The other potential differences follow:

$$V_{AB} = 6 - 1.734 = 4.266 \text{ V}; \qquad V_{AD} = 6 - 1.905 = 4.095 \text{ V},$$

$$V_{BD} = 1.734 - 1.905 = -0.171 \text{ V}; \quad V_{EC} = 1.734 - 0.1 = 1.634 \text{ V.}$$

And the current in each branch calculated by Ohm's Law:

$$I_{AB} = \frac{4.266}{250} = \underline{17.064 \text{ mA}},$$

$$I_{AD} = \frac{4.095}{2000} = \underline{2.0475 \text{ mA}},$$

$$I_{BC} = \frac{1.734 - 0.1}{95} = \underline{17.20 \text{ mA}},$$

$$I_{DC} = \underline{1.905 \text{ mA}},$$

$$I_{BD} = \frac{-0.171}{1200} = \underline{-0.143 \text{ mA}}.$$

The network of Fig. 4.2 has four nodes, one being chosen as the reference. In general, therefore, three node voltages would be unknown and three equations would be required for their determination. This would have been the case if the 6-V source had been a current source. However, in cases where a voltage source is connected between two principal nodes, one of these nodes is chosen as the reference and this immediately determines the voltage of the other, thus reducing the number of unknown voltages by one. If more than one pair of principal nodes are connected to voltage sources, a solution by the node-voltage method, directly, is not possible. Source transformation or mesh (or loop) analysis must be used.

4.5 NETWORK TOPOLOGY

A method of determining the correct number of independent loops in a network consists of first drawing the network graph. This is a line diagram showing all principal nodes and branches of the original network but omitting the character of each branch. As an example, the diagram of Fig. 4.3(a) shows the graph of Fig. 4.2. Branches are then removed from the graph so that all nodes remain interconnected but no loops remain. The remaining diagram is called a TREE. For the graph of Fig. 4.3(a) there are several possible trees, three of which are shown by the full lines in 4.3 (b), (c) and (d). The full lines are referred to as TREE BRANCHES and the dotted lines (which convert the tree to the original graph) as LINKS.

Clearly, no loop current can flow in a tree, but for each link added (in the process of reforming the graph from the tree) an extra loop current can flow. Thus, in the tree of Fig. 4.3(b) the reinsertion of link BC would allow the loop ABCD to be formed; link BD would allow the loop ABD and link AC allows the loop ADCF. Each of these loops

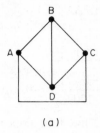

FIG. 4.3. (a) Graph of the network of Fig. 4.1.

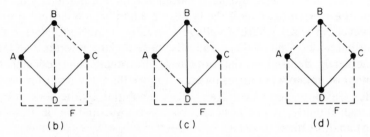

FIG. 4.3. (b–d) Three possible trees of the graph of Fig. 4.3(a).

is the path of an independent loop current. Obviously, as soon as each link current is known, all branch currents can be calculated from various linear combinations of the link currents.

If a network has N principal nodes, then the tree must have $(N-1)$ branches, since the first branch connects two nodes and each subsequent branch adds one node. If there are B branches altogether then L, the number of links, must be:

$$L = B - (N-1) = B - N + 1 \qquad (4.17)$$

and this is the minimum number of independent loop equations for solution of the original network.

For the network represented by Fig. 4.3(a) $B = 6$ and $N = 4$. Hence:

$$L = 6 - 4 + 1 = 3$$

so that three equations are required. However, the trees of Fig. 4.3 (b), (c) and (d) show that at least three different sets of three equations are possible. In (b), the three loops containing the link currents are ABDA (which includes the link BD), ABCDA (link BC) and ADCFA (link AC). In (c) the three loops are ABDA, BCDB and ABDCFA; and in (d) the three loops correspond to the three meshes chosen for Fig. 4.1(c). Several others are possible.

The choice of suitable loops can also depend on the type and number of energy sources in the network.

Thus, for a network containing current sources the tree should be chosen so that, as far as possible, the current sources appear as links, so reducing the number of unknown currents to less than that given by eqn. (4.17).

PROBLEM 4.3

Calculate, by both the node-voltage and the loop-current methods, all branch currents and node potential differences for the non-planar network represented in Fig. 4.4(a).

Solution

(a) *Node-voltage method.* For the given network $N = 4$, hence a sufficient number of equations to solve for the unknown voltages is three. Choosing node C as the reference, the three equations are set up as follows:

For node A:

$$(1 + \tfrac{1}{2} + \tfrac{1}{4}) V_A - V_B - \tfrac{1}{2} V_D = 5. \tag{4.18}$$

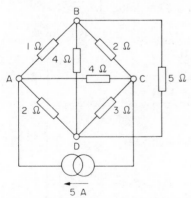

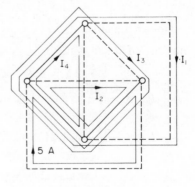

FIG. 4.4. (a) Diagram of the network for Problem 4.3.

FIG. 4.4. (b) Tree for the network of Fig. 4.4(a).

At node B:

$$(1 + \tfrac{1}{2} + \tfrac{1}{4}) V_B - V_A - (\tfrac{1}{4} + \tfrac{1}{5}) V_D = 0. \tag{4.19}$$

At node D:

$$(\tfrac{1}{2} + \tfrac{1}{4} + \tfrac{1}{3} + \tfrac{1}{5}) V_D - \tfrac{1}{2}V_A - (\tfrac{1}{4} + \tfrac{1}{5}) V_B = 0. \tag{4.20}$$

These may be rearranged as follows:

$$7V_A - 4V_B - 2V_D = 20, \tag{4.18a}$$

$$-20V_A + 39V_B - 9V_D = 0, \tag{4.19a}$$

$$-30V_A - 27V_B + 77V_D = 0 \tag{4.20a}$$

and solved by substitution, determinants or matrix methods to give

$$V_A = 6.3741 \text{ volts}, \tag{4.21}$$

$$V_B = 4.1801 \text{ volts}, \tag{4.22}$$

and $\qquad\qquad V_D = 3.9492 \text{ volts}. \tag{4.23}$

Thus, the voltages between nodes are:

and $\qquad \left. \begin{aligned} V_{AB} &= V_A - V_B = 2.1940 \text{ volts,} \\ V_{AD} &= V_A - V_D = 2.4249 \text{ volts,} \\ V_{BD} &= V_B - V_D = 0.2309 \text{ volts,} \end{aligned} \right\} \tag{4.24}$

enabling the currents to be calculated, by Ohm's Law, as follows:

$$\left. \begin{aligned} I_{AB} &= \frac{2.194}{1} = 2.194 \text{ A,} \quad & I_{BD} &= \frac{0.2309}{4} = 0.0577 \text{ A,} \\ I_{BC} &= \frac{4.1801}{2} = 2.0901 \text{ A,} \quad & I_{AC} &= \frac{6.3741}{4} = 1.5935 \text{ A,} \\ I_{AD} &= \frac{2.4249}{2} = 1.2125 \text{ A,} \quad & I_{BD} \text{ (through 5 } \Omega\text{)} &= \frac{0.2309}{5} \\ & & &= 0.0462 \text{ A,} \\ I_{DC} &= \frac{3.9492}{3} = 1.3164 \text{ A.} \end{aligned} \right\} \tag{4.25}$$

(b) *Loop-current method.* The number of branches, B, is 8, and since $N = 4$,

$$L = 8 - 4 + 1$$

$$= 5.$$

Hence five loop currents are needed, requiring five equations.

We begin by drawing the line graph of the network, and proceed by reducing to a tree as shown in Fig. 4.4(b). The links are shown dotted, as before, and, by making the current source one of the links, we can reduce the unknown currents to four.

The loop currents are chosen, as shown, and the equations are set up as follows:

$$\left.\begin{aligned}
\text{Round loop } I_1 \quad & 8I_1 + 2I_2 + 3I_3 + 3I_4 - 2 \times 5 = 0, \\
\text{Round loop } I_2 \quad & 2I_1 + 9I_2 + 5I_3 + 2I_4 - 5 \times 5 = 0, \\
\text{Round loop } I_3 \quad & 3I_1 + 5I_2 + 8I_3 + 3I_4 - 5 \times 5 = 0, \\
\text{Round loop } I_4 \quad & 3I_1 + 2I_2 + 3I_3 + 7I_4 - 2 \times 5 = 0.
\end{aligned}\right\} \quad (4.26)$$

The unknowns are best found by matrix methods, and the result is:

$$I_1 = 0.04619 \text{ A},$$

$$I_2 = 1.5935 \text{ A},$$

$$I_3 = 2.0901 \text{ A},$$

$$I_4 = 0.05774 \text{ A}.$$

By combining these currents in the manners indicated in Fig. 4.4(b), the current in any branch may be calculated. For example,

$$I_{AB} = I_1 + I_3 + I_4 = 0.04619 + 2.0901 + 0.05774 = 2.194 \text{ A}$$

which agrees with I_{AB} in eqns. (4.25). The other currents may be found similarly. The node potential differences can be found using Ohm's Law. For example,

$$V_{AC} = 4 \times I_2$$

$$= 4 \times 1.5935$$

$$= \underline{6.374 \text{ volts.}}$$

In general, the method chosen to solve a particular network should be that which gives the smaller number of unknowns, as calculated from:

$$L = B - N + 1 \quad \text{for the loop-current method,}$$
$$\text{and} \quad N - 1 \qquad \text{for the node-voltage method.}$$

However, as Problem 4.3 shows, the number of unknowns may be reduced by a judicious choice of links (or reference node).

4.6 STEADY-STATE SINUSOIDAL CONDITIONS

The application of source voltages and/or currents which are sinusoidal functions of time to a network composed of linear elements will always result in sinusoidal steady-state responses at every point in the network. Hence the methods of analysis discussed in the present chapter are applicable to such networks providing complex phasors are substituted for the constant values hitherto used.

PROBLEM 4.4

For the circuit of Fig. 4.5 determine the power delivered by the source.

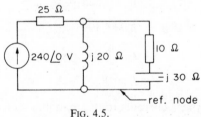

FIG. 4.5.

Solution

There are two principal nodes and three branches, hence $B = 3$, $N = 2$. For the loop-current method, $L = 3 - 2 + 1 = 2$ (unknowns). For the node-voltage method, unknowns $= N - 1 = 1$. Hence, choose the latter. All data are frequency-domain quantities, hence the frequency is not required (it is implicit in the reactances).

The reference node is indicated in the diagram. Let **V** be the voltage at the other node.

Then

$$\mathbf{V}\left(\frac{1}{25} + \frac{1}{j20} + \frac{1}{10 - j30}\right) - \frac{1}{25} \cdot 240 \angle 0° = 0$$

or

$$\mathbf{V}(0.04 - j0.05 + 0.01 + j0.03) = 9.6 \angle 0°$$

or

$$\mathbf{V} = \frac{9.6 \angle 0°}{0.05 - j0.02} = \frac{9.6 \angle 0°}{0.05385 \angle -21°48'} = \underline{178.273 \angle 21°48'}$$

$$= \underline{(165.522 + j66.209)} \text{ volts.}$$

The current in the 25-Ω branch is:

$$\frac{240 - 165.522 - j66.209}{25} = (2.979 - j2.648) \text{ A.}$$

So that the power delivered by the source, which is:

$$P = \mathcal{R}e[\mathbf{VI}^*] = 240 \times 2.979$$

$$= \underline{714.989 \text{ W.}}$$

PROBLEM 4.5

For the circuit of Fig. 4.6, determine the current in each branch and the power delivered to the circuit by each source.

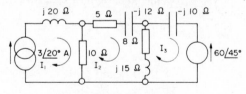

FIG. 4.6.

Solution

In this circuit, $B = 5$ and $N = 3$, hence $L = 5 - 3 + 1 = 3$. However, if the three loops (meshes in this case) are chosen as shown, the current I_1 is already known—thus reducing the unknowns to 2. The node-voltage method would also produce two unknowns (and two equations) but since we require the branch currents we choose the loop-current method.

Let I_1, I_2 and I_3 be the three loop currents, as shown in Fig. 4.6.
Then,

$$I_2(23 + j15 - j12) - 30 \angle 20° - I_3(8 + j15) = 0 \qquad (4.27)$$

and

$$-I_2(8 + j15) + I_3(8 + j5) = -60 \angle 45° \qquad (4.28)$$

since

$$I_1 = 3 \angle 20°.$$

Solving for I_2 by Cramer's Rule:

$$I_2 = \frac{\begin{vmatrix} 30 \angle 20° & -(8 + j15) \\ -60 \angle 45° & (8 + j5) \end{vmatrix}}{\begin{vmatrix} 23 + j3 & -(8 + j15) \\ -(8 + j15) & (8 + j5) \end{vmatrix}}$$

$$= \frac{\begin{vmatrix} 30 \angle 20° & -17 \angle 61° 56' \\ -60 \angle 45° & 9.434 \angle 32° \end{vmatrix}}{\begin{vmatrix} 23.195 \angle 7° 26' & -17 \angle 61° 56' \\ -17 \angle 61° 56' & 9.434 \angle 32° \end{vmatrix}}$$

$$= \frac{283.019 \angle 52° - 1020 \angle 106° 56'}{218.819 \angle 39° 26' - 289 \angle 123° 52'}$$

$$= 2.573 \angle -40° 56' \text{ A} = (1.944 - j1.686) \text{ A}.$$

Likewise for I_3:

$$I_3 = \frac{\begin{vmatrix} (23 + j3) & 30 \angle 20° \\ -(8 + j15) & -60 \angle 45° \end{vmatrix}}{\begin{vmatrix} (23 + j3) & -(8 + j15) \\ -(8 + j15) & (8 + j5) \end{vmatrix}}$$

$$= \frac{\begin{vmatrix} 23.195 \angle 7° 26' & 30 \angle 20° \\ -17 \angle 61° 56' & -60 \angle 45° \end{vmatrix}}{\begin{vmatrix} 23.195 \angle 7° 26' & -17 \angle 61° 56' \\ -17 \angle 61° 56' & 9.434 \angle 32° \end{vmatrix}}$$

$$= \frac{-1391.689 \angle 52°26' + 510 \angle 81°56'}{218.819 \angle 39°26' - 289 \angle 123°52'}$$

$$= 2.841 \angle -125°23' \text{ A}$$

$$= (-1.645 - j2.316) \text{ A}.$$

Current in the 10-Ω resistor = $\mathbf{I}_1 - \mathbf{I}_2$

$$= 3 \angle 20° - 1.944 + j1.686 \text{ A}$$

$$= 2.819 + j1.026 - 1.944 - j1.686 \text{ A}$$

$$= (0.875 + j2.712) \text{ A}.$$

Current in the $(8 + j15)$-Ω impedance = $\mathbf{I}_2 - \mathbf{I}_3$

$$= 1.944 - j1.686 + 1.645$$

$$+ j2.316 \text{ A}$$

$$= 3.589 + j0.630 \text{ A}.$$

Current in the j20-Ω impedance = $3 \angle 20°$ A.

Current in the $(5 - j12)$-Ω impedance = $\mathbf{I}_2 = 2.573 \angle -40°56'$ A.

Current in the $-j10$-Ω impedance = $\mathbf{I}_3 = 2.841 \angle -125°23'$ A.

Power from each source

(a) *Current source.* We first calculate the voltage across the source.
Voltage drop across the 10-Ω resistor

$$= 10(0.875 + j2.712) \text{ volts}$$
$$= 8.75 + j27.12 \text{ volts}.$$

Voltage drop across the j20-Ω reactor

$$= 3 \angle 20°.20 \angle 90° \text{ volts}$$
$$= 60 \angle 110° \text{ volts}$$
$$= -20.521 + j56.382 \text{ volts}.$$

∴ Voltage across the source

$$= (8.75 - 20.521) + j(56.382 + 27.12) \text{ volts}$$
$$= -11.771 + j83.502 \text{ volts}$$
$$= 84.328 \angle 90° 1' \text{ volts.}$$

And power delivered

$$= \Re e[\mathbf{VI}^*]$$
$$= \Re e[84.328 \angle 98° 1'.3 \angle -20°] \text{ W}$$
$$= \Re e[252.984 \angle 78° 1'] = \underline{52.529 \text{ W.}}$$

(b) *Voltage source*. The current through the source in the same sense as its e.m.f. is $(-\mathbf{I}_3)$.
Hence, power

$$= \Re e[\mathbf{VI}^*] = \Re e[\mathbf{V}(-\mathbf{I}_3)^*]$$

$$= \Re e[60 \angle 45° (-2.841) \angle 125° 23'] \text{ W}$$

$$= \Re e[-170.460 \angle 170° 23'] = \underline{168.065 \text{ W.}}$$

4.7 MUTUAL INDUCTANCE

Mutual inductance is said to exist between two circuits when a changing current in one induces, by electromagnetic induction, an e.m.f. in the

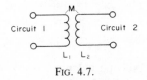

FIG. 4.7.

other. Since this implies mutual magnetic flux, which is a fraction of the self-flux set up by each circuit, each circuit must also possess self-inductance. The idealised equivalent circuit of a mutual inductor is therefore as shown in Fig. 4.7. L_1 and L_2 are the self-inductances of the two circuits and M the mutual inductance between them. The mutual inductance M is defined by the relationships:

$$e_2(t) = M_{12}\frac{di_1(t)}{dt} \tag{4.29}$$

or

$$e_1(t) = M_{21} \frac{di_2(t)}{dt} \qquad (4.30)$$

where e_2 is the e.m.f. in circuit 2 due to i_1 in circuit 1, and e_1 that in circuit 1 due to i_2 in circuit 2. As in eqn. (1.11), when the units of i and v are amperes and volts, respectively, the units of M_{12} and M_{21} are henrys.

It may be shown* that $M_{12} = M_{21}$.

4.7.1 The dot notation

The polarity of the induced e.m.f. due to mutual inductance is identified by placing a dot, on the diagram, adjacent to that end of each equivalent winding which bears the same relationship to the magnetic flux. Thus, if a current in one winding changes so as to induce an e.m.f. positive at the dot end of that winding, an e.m.f. will be induced in the other winding which is also positive at its dot end. Using this notation, the mesh- or loop-current method may be applied to circuits having separate parts coupled by mutual inductance.

For steady-state sinusoidal conditions eqns. (4.29) and (4.30) may be transformed, in the manner used to derive eqn. (3.11), into

$$\mathbf{E}_2 = j\omega M \mathbf{I}_1 \qquad (4.29a)$$

and

$$\mathbf{E}_1 = j\omega M \mathbf{I}_2. \qquad (4.30a)$$

PROBLEM 4.6

A mutual inductor is used to couple a 10-Ω resistive load to a 100-V generator, as shown in Fig. 4.8. The generator has an internal resistance

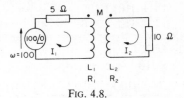

FIG. 4.8.

---

* See, for example, E. G. Cullwick, *The Fundamentals of Electromagnetism,* C.U.P.

of 5 Ω and the parameters of the mutual inductor are: $L_1 = 0.1$ H, $R_1 =10$ Ω, $L_2 =0.2$ H, $R_2 =15$ Ω and $M =0.1$ H. Calculate the generator and load currents for (a) the two windings having the same sense (as shown by the position of the dots in Fig. 4.8) and (b) the windings having the opposite sense. Given $\omega = 100$ rad/sec.

Solution

(a) Referring to the diagram there are two clear mesh currents, as shown. Then, for mesh 1:

$$\mathbf{I}_1(R_1 + j\omega L_1) - j\omega M \mathbf{I}_2 = 100 \angle 0°$$

or

$$\mathbf{I}_1(15 + j10) - j10\mathbf{I}_2 = 100 \angle 0° \qquad (4.31a)$$

and for mesh 2:

$$-j\omega M \mathbf{I}_1 + \mathbf{I}_2(R_2 + 10 + j\omega L_2) = 0$$

or

$$-j10\mathbf{I}_1 + \mathbf{I}_2(25 + j20) = 0. \qquad (4.32a)$$

In eqn. (4.31a) the term $j\omega M \mathbf{I}_2$ is negative in mesh 1, since the flux produced by $\mathbf{I}_2$ induces an e.m.f. in L_2 *away* from the dot, which means that it induces an e.m.f. in L_1 also away from the dot—i.e. in the same direction as $\mathbf{I}_1$. This is in the same sense as the 100-V source and is therefore positive on the R.H.S. of eqn. (4.31a) or negative on the L.H.S. Similarly, in eqn. (4.32a) the $j\omega M \mathbf{I}_1$ term can be thought of as being the sole e.m.f. in mesh 2 and hence responsible for the current. It is therefore positive on the R.H.S. of eqn. (4.32a) or negative on the L.H.S.

Solving eqns. (4.31a) and (4.32a) by Cramer's Rule:

$$\mathbf{I}_2 = \frac{\begin{vmatrix} (15 + j10) & 100 \\ - j10 & 0 \end{vmatrix}}{\begin{vmatrix} (15 + j10) & - j10 \\ - j10 & (25 + j20) \end{vmatrix}}$$

$$= \frac{j1000}{(15 + j10)(25 + j20) + 100} = \frac{j1000}{275 + j550} \text{ A}$$

$$= \underline{1.626 \angle 26°34' \text{ A}.}$$

And

$$I_1 = \frac{\begin{vmatrix} 100 & -j10 \\ 0 & (25 + j20) \end{vmatrix}}{275 + j550} = \frac{2500 + j2000}{275 + j550}$$

$$= \frac{3201.562 \angle 38° 40'}{614.919 \angle 63° 26'} A$$

$$= 5.206 \angle -24° 46' A.$$

(b) If the secondary winding (that feeding mesh 2) is reversed, so that the dots appear at opposite ends of the windings, the two mesh currents can still be applied clockwise. Then, eqns. (4.31a) and (4.32a) become:

$$I_1(15 + j10) + j10I_2 = 100 \qquad (4.31b)$$

and

$$+j10I_1 + I_2(25 + j20) = 0, \qquad (4.32b)$$

giving the solutions:

$$I_1 = 5.206 \angle -24° 46' A$$

and

$$I_2 = 1.626 \angle -153° 26' A.$$

I_2 is 180° out of phase with the solution for part (a) since the winding has been reversed. However, I_1 is unchanged, since I_2 always flows in that direction which opposes the flux set up by I_1. Hence, the winding direction is immaterial.

However, if a mutual inductor forms one of several common imped-ances between two meshes of a circuit, reversal of either winding will affect both primary and secondary currents.

PROBLEM 4.7
The mutual inductor of Problem 4.6 is connected in the circuit of Fig. 4.9. Calculate the source and load currents for (a) the windings as shown (dots adjacent), (b) one winding reversed (dots at opposite ends). $\omega = 100$ rad/sec.

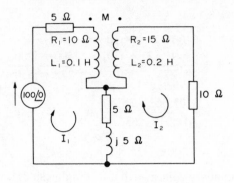

FIG. 4.9.

Solution

(a) Using the two mesh currents, as shown, the mesh equations are:
Mesh 1

$$I_1(20 + j15) - j10I_2 - I_2(5 + j5) = 100 \angle 0° \qquad (4.33a)$$

or

$$I_1(20 + j15) - I_2(5 + j15) = 100. \qquad (4.33b)$$

Mesh 2

$$-j10I_1 - I_1(5 + j5) + I_2(30 + j25) = 0 \qquad (4.34a)$$

or

$$-I_1(5 + j15) + I_2(30 + j25) = 0. \qquad (4.34b)$$

Solving eqns. (4.33b) and (4.34b) by Cramer's Rule:

$$I_1 = \frac{\begin{vmatrix} 100 & -(5 + j15) \\ 0 & (30 + j25) \end{vmatrix}}{\begin{vmatrix} (20 + j15) & -(5 + j15) \\ -(5 + j15) & (30 + j25) \end{vmatrix}} = \frac{3000 + j2500}{425 + j800}$$

$$= 4.311 \angle -22° 13' \text{ A}$$

and

$$\mathbf{I}_2 = \frac{\begin{vmatrix} (20 + j15) & 100 \\ -(5 + j15) & 0 \end{vmatrix}}{425 + j800} = \frac{500 + j1500}{425 + j800}$$

$$= 1.745 \angle 9° 33' \text{ A}.$$

(b) When one of the windings of the mutual inductor is reversed, the $j\omega M\mathbf{I}$ term in eqns. (4.33a) and (4.34a) changes sign but not those due to the voltage drop in the $(5 + j5)$-Ω impedance. Hence, the two equations become:

$$\mathbf{I}_1(20 + j15) - \mathbf{I}_2(5 - j5) = 100 \angle 0° \tag{4.35}$$

and

$$-\mathbf{I}_1(5 - j5) + \mathbf{I}_2(30 + j25) = 0, \tag{4.36}$$

whence

$$\mathbf{I}_1 = 3.810 \angle -37° 31' \text{ A}$$

and

$$\mathbf{I}_2 = 0.690 \angle -122° 19' \text{ A}.$$

4.8 CIRCUIT THEOREMS

4.8.1 The superposition theorem

The theorem is the most general expression of the linearity of a circuit or network. It states that the current in or voltage across any branch of a linear network containing more than one source is the algebraic sum of the separate currents or voltages (as the case may be) due to each source acting alone, all other sources being temporarily set to zero.

The theorem is useful in comparatively simple circuits, but containing several sources, and in which one branch is of particular interest. It enables the contribution of each source to the current or voltage in the branch to be assessed readily.

PROBLEM 4.8

For the circuit of Fig. 4.10 determine, using the superposition theorem, the current **I** and the component of **I** due to each source.

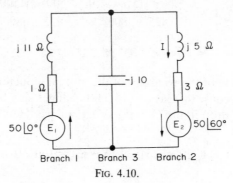

Branch I   Branch 3   Branch 2

FIG. 4.10.

Solution

Consider the circuit with E_1 acting alone, source E_2 being replaced by a short circuit. Then E_1 acts upon the impedance of branch 1 in series with a parallel combination of branches 2 and 3.

Thus, the current through Z_2 due to E_1 is:

$$I_1 = \frac{50}{(1 + j11) + [(-j10)(3 + j5)/(3 - j5)]} \cdot \left(\frac{-j10}{3 - j5}\right) \text{ A}$$

$$= \frac{-j500}{(1 + j11)(3 - j5) - j10(3 + j5)} = \frac{-j500}{108 - j2} \text{ A}$$

$$= 4.629 \angle -88° 56' \text{ A}.$$

Now consider E_2 acting alone with E_1 replaced by a short circuit. E_2 acts upon Z_2 in series with a parallel combination of Z_1 and Z_3. Hence, the current through Z_2 due to E_2 is:

$$I_2 = \frac{50 \angle 60°}{3 + j5 + [(-j10)(1 + j11)/(1 + j1)]}$$

$$= \frac{50 \angle 60°}{3 + j5 + \frac{1}{2}(110 - j10)(1 - j)}$$

$$= \frac{100 \angle 60°}{106 - j110} = 0.655 \angle 106° 4' \text{ A}.$$

Or the current through Z_2 due to E_1 is more than 7 times greater than that due to E_2.

$$I = (I_1 + I_2) = 0.0862 - j4.628 - 0.181 + j0.629 \text{ A}$$
$$= 4.000 \angle -91°22' \text{ A}.$$

4.8.2 Thévenin's and Norton's theorems

When interest is focused on one particular branch of a circuit or network containing active and passive elements, the theorems of Thévenin and Norton can often provide a much simpler solution than either loop-current or node-voltage analysis.

The theorems achieve this by replacing the whole of the rest of the network—viewed from the branch—by a voltage source in series with an impedance (Thévenin's theorem) or by a current source in parallel with an impedance (Norton's theorem).

The e.m.f. of the voltage source is equal to the open circuit p.d. at the terminals of the network to which the branch was connected, and the series impedance is equal to the impedance looking into the open-circuited terminals with all voltage sources in the network replaced by short circuits and all current sources replaced by open circuits. The result is called the Thévenin Equivalent Generator.

For Norton's theorem, the current of the current source is equal to the short-circuit current which would flow from the network at the terminals to which the branch was connected and the shunting impedance is defined in exactly the same way as for Thévenin's theorem. The result is called the Norton Equivalent Generator.

The theorems are therefore duals of each other and either could be deduced from the other by the source transformation process.

PROBLEM 4.9

A 600/150-V volt-ratio box having a total resistance of 30 kΩ is used in the measurement of the voltage of a d.c. source. The whole box is connected across the source and a voltmeter is applied to the 150-V tapping.

Using Thévenin's theorem, calculate the lowest resistance which the voltmeter may have so that the measurement error shall not exceed 0.1%.

Solution

The volt-ratio box is a 30,000-Ω resistor with a tapping at:

$$30,000 \times \frac{150}{600} = 7500 \ \Omega \quad \text{(see Fig. 4.11(a))}.$$

The Thévenin equivalent of the circuit seen from the voltmeter terminals is as shown in Fig. 4.11(b), where R' is given by:

$$R' = \frac{7500 \times 22,500}{30,000} = \underline{5625 \ \Omega}.$$

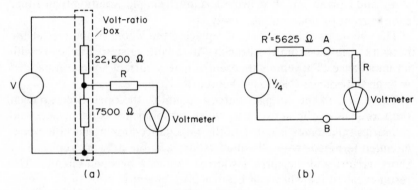

(a)   (b)

FIG. 4.11.

If R were infinite, no error would result, but for finite R a current is drawn through R' and the voltage at terminals AB falls. Hence, for 0.1% error:

$$\frac{R}{R + 5625} = \frac{(V/4) - (1/1000) \cdot (V/4)}{(V/4)} = 1 - \frac{1}{1000} = \frac{999}{1000}$$

$$\therefore \quad \frac{5625}{R} = \frac{1}{999}, \text{ giving } R = 5,619,375 \ \Omega.$$

PROBLEM 4.10

A simple d.c. slide-wire potentiometer is used to measure the voltage of a source, the circuit arrangement being as shown in Fig. 4.12(a). The slide wire current is 50 mA and its 100-cm length, ABC, has a volt-drop across it of 1.5 V. Balance (indicated by zero galvanometer current) is

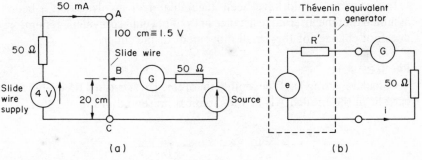

FIG. 4.12.

achieved when the slider at B is 20 cm from C. Using Thévenin's theorem calculate the galvanometer current when the slider is moved 1 mm, towards C.

Solution

A movement of the slider by 1 mm, to B', represents an out-of-balance voltage of 1.5 mV (since 100 cm represents 1.5 V).

Hence, from the viewpoint of the galvanometer circuit, the e.m.f. of the Thévenin equivalent generator is 1.5 mV and its internal resistance is the resistance of B'C shunted by 50 Ω and AB' in series.

The resistance of B'C is:

$$\frac{19.9}{100} \cdot \frac{1.5}{0.05} = 5.97 \ \Omega$$

and that of AB' is:

$$\frac{1.5}{0.05} - 5.97 = 24.03 \ \Omega$$

so that R' (see Fig. 4.12(b)) is given by:

$$R' = \frac{5.97 \times 24.03}{5.97 + 24.03} = 5.524 \ \Omega.$$

Hence

$$i = \frac{0.0015}{50 + 5.524} = 0.027 \ \text{mA}.$$

In fact there would have been negligible error involved had it been assumed that the internal resistance of the Thévenin equivalent generator does not change for this small movement of the slider.

PROBLEM 4.11

Calculate, using (a) Thévenin's theorem, (b) Norton's theorem, the current in the branch AB of the circuit represented in Fig. 4.13(a).

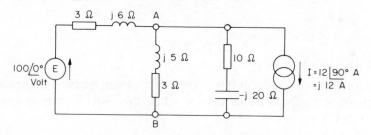

FIG. 4.13. (a) Diagram of the circuit for Problem 4.11.

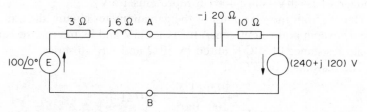

FIG. 4.13. (b) The branch AB removed and the current source replaced by its equivalent voltage source.

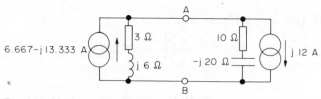

FIG. 4.13. (c) The branch AB removed and the voltage source replaced by its equivalent current source.

Solution

Remove the branch AB, short-circuit the voltage source and open-circuit the current source. The internal impedance of the circuit viewed from AB is that of $(3 + j6)$ Ω and $(10 - j20)$ Ω in parallel, or

$$\mathbf{Z} = \frac{(3 + j6)(10 - j20)}{13 - j14} = \frac{30 + 120}{13 - j14} \, \Omega$$

$$= (5.342 + j5.753) \, \Omega$$

$$= 7.851 \angle 47° 7' \, \Omega.$$

(a) *By Thévenin's theorem*

First change the current source shunted by $(10 - j20)$ Ω into a voltage source of e.m.f.:

$$\mathbf{E} = j12(10 - j20) = (240 + j120) \, V$$

in series with $(10 - j20)$ Ω. The circuit is now as shown in Fig. 4.13(b). The circulating current is:

$$\mathbf{I}_1 = \frac{340 + j120}{13 - j14} = (7.507 + j17.315) \, A.$$

And the open-circuit voltage at AB is:

$$100 \angle 0° - (7.507 + j17.315)(3 + j6) \, V = (181.370 - j96.986) \, V.$$

Hence, the current through the branch AB, on replacing it, is:

$$\mathbf{I} = \frac{181.370 - j96.986}{3 + j5 + 5.342 + j5.753} = 15.112 \angle -80° 20' \, A.$$

(b) *By Norton's theorem*

First change the voltage source in series with $(3 + j6)$ Ω to a current source of generated current $\mathbf{I}_N$ shunted by $(3 + j6)$ Ω, as shown in Fig. 4.13(c),

$$\mathbf{I}_N = \frac{100}{3 + j6} = (6.667 - j13.333) \, A.$$

If terminals AB are short-circuited, the current which flows, which is also the generated current of the Norton equivalent source, is:

$$(6.667 - j13.333) - j12 = (6.667 - j25.333) \text{ A}$$

and this is shunted by the impedance looking into AB—which is:

$$(5.342 + j5.753) \ \Omega.$$

Hence, the current through the branch AB, when replaced, is:

$$\frac{5.342 + j5.753}{8.342 + j10.753} (6.667 - j25.333) \text{ A} = 15.112 \ \angle -80°20' \text{ A},$$

the same result as was obtained using Thévenin's theorem.

PROBLEMS IV

1. A Wheatstone-bridge circuit whose four arms have resistances of 3, 4, 5 and 6 Ω (when taken in cyclic order) is fed by a 5-A current source connected between opposite corners.

   Calculate (a) the voltage across the other opposite corners, (b) the current taken by a 10-Ω resistor connected to these corners.

2. For the circuit represented by Fig. P.IV.1, calculate the current through and the power absorbed by the 10-Ω resistor.

3. Calculate the voltage appearing between the terminals A and B in the circuit represented by Fig. P.IV.2. Use the node-voltage rule.

4. For the circuit of Fig. P.IV.3, calculate the current in the 6-Ω resistor by (a) Kirchhoff's Laws, (b) the superposition theorem.

5. Using Thévenin's theorem, calculate the current through the 10-Ω resistor in the circuit of Fig. P.IV.4.

6. Deduce the conditions under which maximum power is delivered to a load of resistance R_L by a generator of e.m.f. E and internal resistance r.

   For the circuit of Fig. P.IV.5, calculate the resistance R for which maximum power is absorbed and the magnitude of this power.

7. For the circuit of Fig. P.IV.6, containing current-controlled voltage sources, calculate the mesh currents i_1, i_2 and i_3.

8. Use the node-voltage rule to obtain the currents in all the branches of the circuit of Fig. P.IV.7.

9. In the circuit represented by Fig. P.IV.8, the switch S is arranged to short-circuit half the 12-Ω resistor. When S is closed the current through its contacts is 2 A.

   Calculate the current through the 12-Ω resistor when S is open.

10. Define the terms *graph*, *tree*, *link-branch* in network topology. For the circuit of Fig. P.IV.9, draw the graph and choose a tree which allows all branch currents to be evaluated with just one equation.

    Calculate the branch currents and the power delivered by each source.

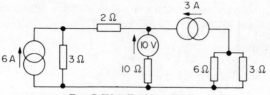

FIG. P.IV.1 (Problem IV.2).

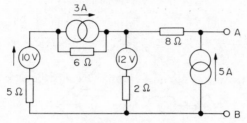

FIG. P.IV.2 (Problem IV.3).

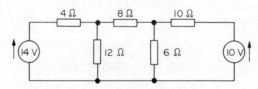

FIG. P.IV.3 (Problem IV.4).

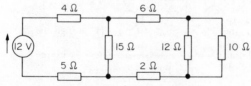

FIG. P.IV.4 (Problem IV.5).

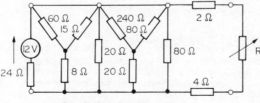

FIG. P.IV.5 (Problem IV.6).

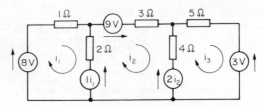

F IG. P.IV.6 (Problem IV.7).

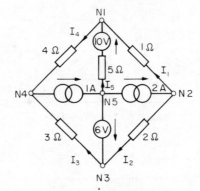

F IG. P.IV.7 (Problem IV.8).

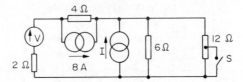

F IG. P.IV.8 (Problem IV.9).

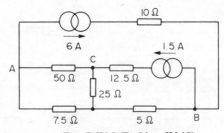

F IG. P.IV.9 (Problem IV.10).

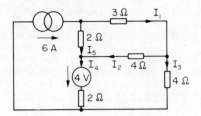

FIG. P.IV.10 (Problem IV.11).

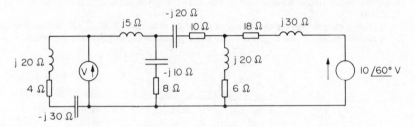

FIG. P.IV.11 (Problem IV.12).

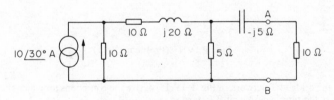

FIG. P.IV.12 (Problem IV.13).

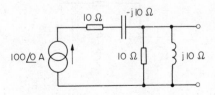

FIG. P.IV.13 (Problem IV.14).

11. For the circuit of Fig. P.IV.10, draw the graph and choose a suitable tree for evaluating all branch currents.

    Calculate each branch current and hence determine the power delivered by the 6-A source.

12. For the frequency-domain circuit of Fig. P.IV.11, determine the voltage V (magnitude and phase) such that no current flows through the 18-Ω resistor.

13. Determine the voltage—in polar form—across the source and the power delivered by the source in the circuit of Fig. P.IV.12.

    Determine the Thévenin equivalent generator at the terminals AB and hence the current in the 10-Ω resistor.

14. Determine the Thévenin equivalent generator for the network represented by Fig. P.IV.13. Then apply a source-transformation to obtain the Norton equivalent generator.

15. In the bridge circuit represented by Fig. P.IV.14, a voltage source is connected to D and B.

    Derive expressions for the values of R and L, in terms of r, C, C_1, R_1 and ω, which cause the points A and C to be at the same potential (i.e. to balance the bridge).

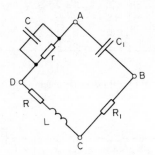

FIG. P.IV.14 (Problem IV.15).

16. For the bridged-T network of Fig. P.IV.15, derive the conditions for which the voltage across the terminals A and B is zero.

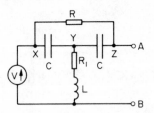

FIG. P.IV.15 (Problem IV.16).

17. The circuit represented by Fig. P.IV.16 is supplied by the voltage source for which
$V = 100 \angle 0$ at $\omega = 1000$ rad/sec.

Calculate the current I_1, in polar form.

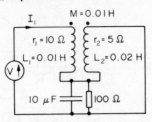

FIG. P.IV.16 (Problem IV.17).

CHAPTER 5

FREQUENCY RESPONSE OF NETWORKS

5.0 INTRODUCTION

In this chapter we bring together many of the principles used in previous sections, and extend the results in order to derive the steady-state properties of circuits in relation to variable-frequency forcing signals. Only sinusoidal currents and voltages will be considered.

Thus, for example, we may wish to find the dependence on frequency of the impedance, admittance or transfer functions of a circuit and the result, when determined, is often most clearly presented in graphical form.

5.1 IMMITTANCE FUNCTION MAPPING

It has been shown in Chapter 3 (section 3.6 and Figs. 3.22 and 3.23) that the **Z**- and **Y**-loci for simple series and parallel circuits, as the frequency is varied, are either straight lines or circular arcs. This mode of presentation is valuable in some cases because both magnitude and phase information are given in a single diagram. Thus, a series resonant circuit has a **Z**-locus which (plotted on the **Z**-plane) is a straight line parallel to the reactance axis and a distance R from it. The corresponding **Y**-locus is a circle, of diameter $G = 1/R$, with centre on the real (conductance) axis at a distance $G/2$ from the imaginary (susceptance) axis. For a parallel circuit the **Z**- and **Y**-loci are interchanged. If, in either case, L or C is absent the locus is confined to half the complete locus. Both **Z**- and **Y**-loci may be plotted on the same diagram (with suitable additional axis scales) and the location of points on one locus by reference

236

to corresponding points on the other locus is referred to as *mapping*. Thus, although the complete loci may be easily inverted from one to the other (by inverting the point of intersection with the real axis, i.e. R on the impedance locus inverts to $G = 1/R$ on the admittance locus) the identification of a frequency scale with points on the inverted locus may be determined only by mapping, or by calculation.

PROBLEM 5.1

A constant (r.m.s.) voltage source feeds a series circuit consisting of $L = 0.1$ H and $R = 10 \, \Omega$. Draw the impedance and admittance loci, marking a frequency scale on both.

Determine the frequency at which the conductance is 70% of its maximum value, the conductance at $\omega = 30$ rad/sec, the maximum susceptance and the frequency at which it occurs.

Solution

Referring to Fig. 5.1, the Z-locus is drawn first, to scale, by marking OP = 10 Ω along the real axis and erecting the perpendicular PQ to represent the Z-locus. Both ω and X $(=\omega L)$ scales are marked on PQ—extending in this case to $\omega = 100$ rad/sec. The semicircle representing the Y-locus is next drawn with diameter $G_{max} = 1/R = 0.1$ S and centre on the real axis at a distance 0.05 S from 0. Thus, a linear scale of conductance must be marked along the real axis. The Y-locus lies in the fourth quadrant, but to find the points on it which correspond to the equally spaced frequency scale on PQ the circle is completed into the first quadrant. The intersections, with the circle, of lines drawn from 0 to the line PQ locate the corresponding frequencies on the mirror image of the Y-locus. Strictly speaking, these points should now be transferred to the Y-locus (in the fourth quadrant) but we can save work by considering the semicircle in the first quadrant to be the Y-locus. We need only remember that susceptances measured upwards to the circle from the real axis are negative.

Making OT = 70% of 0.1 S = 0.07 S the vertical TU is erected to cut the Y-locus in U, the frequency corresponding to U being estimated either from the frequency scale on the Y-locus (which is clearly not linear) or by producing OU to cut the linear frequency scale on PQ in W. This frequency is 65 rad/sec. The conductance at $\omega = 30$ rad/sec is

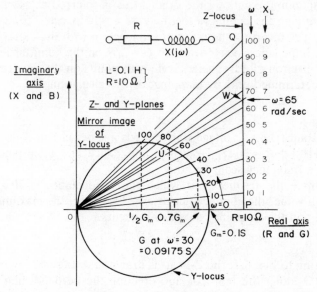

FIG. 5.1. **Z**- and **Y**-loci for series R, L circuit with variable ω. See Problem 5.1.

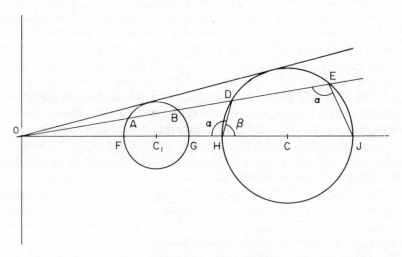

FIG. 5.2. The inversion of a circular locus.

found by dropping the perpendicular from the point $\omega = 30$ on the Y-locus to cut the real axis in V. Then $OV = 0.091\,75$ S. Finally, the maximum susceptance is obviously equal to the radius of the Y-locus, erected at the point $\frac{1}{2}G_{max}$ on the real axis. It is 0.05 S and passes through the $\omega = 100$ point on the Y-locus.

5.1.1 Inversion of any circular locus

When either the Z- or Y-locus is a circle not passing through the origin (which is the case, for example, when the frequency-dependent circuit is shunted by—in the case of the Y-locus—or in series with—in the case of the Z-locus—a frequency-independent circuit) an extension of the inversion procedure may still be used.

In Fig. 5.2 let the circle HDEJ be drawn with centre C on the real axis and diameter such that the origin, O, does not lie on it. Let any straight line from O be drawn to cut the circle in D and E. Then, since the four corners of the quadrilateral lie on the circle,

$$\alpha + \beta = 180°$$

so that the supplementary angle at H is also equal to α. Hence, the triangles ODH and OJE are similar, or

$$\frac{OD}{OH} = \frac{OJ}{OE}.$$

Now let another curve, FABG, be drawn such that $OA \cdot OE = K$ and $OB \cdot OD = K$, where K is some constant. Clearly, also, since E may move to J, $OG \cdot OH = K$. Hence

$$OA \cdot OE = OB \cdot OD = OG \cdot OH$$

or

$$\frac{OD}{OH} = \frac{OG}{OB}.$$

so that the triangles ODH and OGB are similar and so are the triangles OJE and OGB. Hence B always moves in proportion to E and the curve FABG is also a circle. When the points O and F coincide, the circle HDEJ expands to an infinite size: i.e. the circumference is a straight line, so that the loci of Fig. 5.1 represent a special case of those of Fig. 5.2.

ECT - Q

PROBLEM 5.2

By a process of mapping, determine the locus of **Z**, as ω varies, at the terminals AB of the circuit of Fig. 5.3(a). Show that the maximum phase angle of **Z** and maximum X occur at different frequencies.

Solution

The **Z**- and **Y**-plane axes are drawn first and suitable scales are chosen for R and X, G and B, as shown in Fig. 5.3(b). The range of the scales can be estimated by inspection of the circuit, since (i) the maximum impedance at AB will occur at $\omega = 0$ and is $0.5 + 2.5 = 3\,\Omega$, and (ii) the maximum admittance of the two branches in parallel occurs at the resonant frequency of the series *LCR* circuit and is $(0.4 + 0.5) = 0.9\,\text{S}$. The perpendicular, CDE, is erected at D where $OD = 2\,\Omega$. The line CDE represents the impedance locus (for variable ω) of the resonant branch. The point D corresponds to resonance. The circle OFGH is then the locus of **Y**, corresponding to this **Z**-locus, where $OG = 1/OD = 0.5\,\text{S}$. The point G corresponds to resonance. This admittance locus is then shifted to the right by an amount $0.4\,\text{S}$ which is the admittance of the parallel branch of $2.5\,\Omega$ resistance. This produces the circle MJKL, the **Y**-locus of the two parallel branches. From this locus the locus of **Z** for these branches is obtained—which, by the previous result, is another circle with centre on the real axis but not passing through O. Hence, the circle NPQT is drawn, making $ON = 1/OK$ and $OQ = 1/OM$. Finally, this circle is shifted to the right by $0.5\,\Omega$, representing the addition of the $0.5\,\Omega$ series resistance. The circle UVWX is thus the required locus. OW represents the maximum **Z**, $3\,\Omega$, and OU the minimum **Z**, $1.611\,\Omega$. The maximum reactance point is thus the point V, the height above the real axis being $0.7\,\Omega$ and the maximum phase angle point is the point Y' (both points have their images in the fourth quadrant). Clearly these do not occur at the same frequency, but to evaluate the frequencies involves retracing the path back to the line CDE which carries a scale of frequency. Thus, starting from V we pass to P, then to T and C' (N.B. NOT to L which is the reciprocal of point F') and on to B' and D' and finally E' which gives the frequency for maximum reactance as 98 rad/sec. Similarly, the frequency for maximum phase angle of $\mathbf{Z}_{AB}$ (the point Y', where OY' is the tangent to the **Z**-locus from O) is found by retracing, via G', H', A', J' to K' which cuts

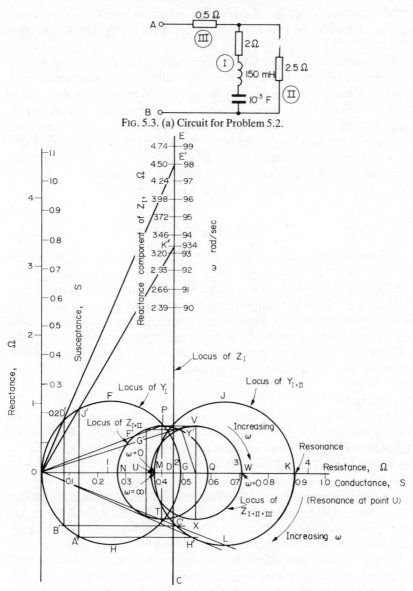

FIG. 5.3. (a) Circuit for Problem 5.2.

FIG. 5.3. (b) **Z**- and **Y**-loci for the circuit of Fig. 5.3(a).

CDE at $\omega = 93.4$ rad/sec. Two further points lie on EDC in the fourth quadrant which are mirror images of K' and E' ($\omega = 68.05$ and $\omega = 71.4$).

It is worth noting that: (i) the diameters of the Z and Y circles and the lengths of DK' and DE' are independent of the magnitudes of L and C—though the frequency scales marked on these loci would change as L or C (or both) were changed; (ii) the frequency for maximum reactive component of Z (corresponding to the point V) is not the same as that for the maximum susceptive component of Y (point L).

It should, in addition, be remembered that whenever a Z-locus is inverted into a Y-locus (and vice versa) there is an associated movement from the first to the fourth quadrant (or vice versa).

5.1.2 More complicated circuits

When more than one branch of a circuit contains reactance, the overall Z- and Y-loci are no longer (in general) circular. The principles of adding graphically impedances in series and admittances in parallel may still be used; however, the process must be done point by point. It is usually possible to start from either a straight line or a circular locus and, for each of a number of selected frequencies, progressively add the effect of each part of the circuit (by addition and/or inversion) until the effect of the whole circuit is synthesised.

PROBLEM 5.3

Derive the locus of the input impedance as the frequency is varied for the circuit of Fig. 5.4(a). From the locus determine the resonant frequencies and the input resistance at each one.

Solution

The circuit is divided, as for Problem 5.3, into three parts by the dotted lines in the diagram. For the loci, Fig. 5.4(b), Z- and Y-axes are first drawn and suitable scales in ohms and siemens marked. Dealing first with circuit I, the impedance locus will be the straight line ABC drawn perpendicular to the real axis and at a distance representing 10 Ω from the origin. The Y-locus is then the circle ODEF, where the diameter OE = 0.1 S. In this case a scale of frequency must be marked on the

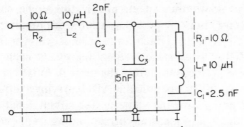

FIG. 5.4. (a) A circuit having several resonance frequencies.

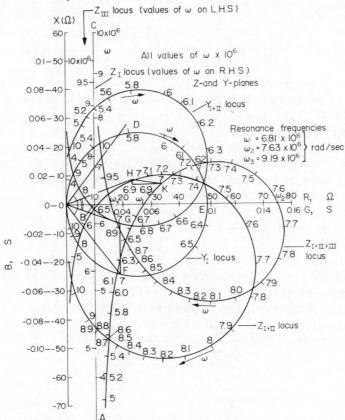

FIG. 5.4. (b) **Z**- and **Y**-loci used to determine the resonance frequencies of the circuit of Fig. 5.4(a).

circle since the admittance of circuit II (the single capacitor of 5×10^{-9} F capacitance) must be added at a sufficient number of frequencies to define the $\mathbf{Y}_{(I+II)}$ locus, which, in turn, must carry a frequency scale.

Next, the $\mathbf{Z}_{(I+II)}$ locus is derived by taking, at each frequency, the reciprocal of $\mathbf{Y}_{(I+II)}$ (measured from the origin). Finally, points are taken from the $\mathbf{Z}_{III}$ locus (the perpendicular ABC carrying a different frequency scale, since R and L are the same as for circuit I but C is different) and added to the $\mathbf{Z}_{(I+II)}$ locus at corresponding frequencies to produce the $\mathbf{Z}_{(I+II+III)}$ locus. We may trace the path for one frequency, say $\omega = 7 \times 10^6$ rad/sec, as follows:

For circuit I,

$$j\left(\omega L - \frac{1}{\omega C}\right) = j\left(7 \times 10^6 \times 10^{-5} - \frac{10^9}{2.5 \times 7 \times 10^6}\right) = j12.9 \ \Omega$$

so the point for $\omega = 7 \times 10^6$ is marked a distance of 12.9 Ω above the real axis. The line OF is drawn at the same angle below the real axis to cut the circle (the $\mathbf{Y}_I$ locus, of radius OE = 0.1 S) in F. Then FG is drawn vertically of length $\omega C_3 = 7 \times 10^6 \times 5 \times 10^{-9} = 0.035$ S and G is a point on the $\mathbf{Y}_{(I+II)}$ locus. OH is drawn, of length 1/OG, making a positive angle with the real axis equal to the negative angle which OG makes with the real axis, and H is a point on the $\mathbf{Z}_{(I+II)}$ locus. Finally, the vector HK is drawn to represent:

$$R_2 + j\left(\omega L_2 - \frac{1}{\omega C_2}\right) = 10 + j\left(7 \times 10^6 \cdot 10^{-5} - \frac{10^9}{2 \times 7 \times 10^6}\right)$$
$$= (10 - j1.428) \ \Omega,$$

giving the point K on the required $\mathbf{Z}_{(I+II+III)}$ locus. There are three resonant frequencies, corresponding to the three intersections with the real axis of this locus. The following table gives the frequencies and the effective resistance of the circuit at each one:

Resonant frequency (rad/sec)	Effective resistance (Ω)
6.81×10^6	27.2
7.63×10^6	75.1
9.19×10^6	15.8

To derive the whole locus in the manner described is a laborious process but, unless a computer or programmable calculator is available, even the determination of the resonant frequencies, and the corresponding resistances, by analytical or numerical methods, is likely to prove more time-consuming.

The alternative method of displaying the same information is to plot the modulus and the phase of Z (or Y) as functions of frequency on separate graphs. Although the data for such plots can be obtained from the polar diagrams of Figs. 5.1, 5.3(b) and 5.4(b), a better approach, because it is more direct, is to make use of the s-plane concept introduced in Chapter 2.

5.2 THE s-PLANE

5.2.1 Poles and zeros

It will be recalled that the impedance or admittance of any circuit may be expressed as an algebraic function of s, the complex frequency (see Chapter 2). The poles and zeros of the function occur at the values of s which cause that function to increase to infinity (poles) or decrease to zero (zeros). The s-plane is a Cartesian plot, having the real part of s, σ, as the x-axis and the imaginary part, ω, as the y-axis, on which the poles and zeros are plotted as crosses and circles, respectively.

PROBLEM 5.4

(a) For the circuit of Fig. 5.5(a) determine the impedance function and plot the poles and zeros on the s-plane. (b) For the P–Z plot of Fig. 5.5(c) deduce the admittance function, given that $Y(1) = 5$ S.

Solution

(a) The impedance, Z_C, of the branch containing the capacitance is:

$$Z_C = R + \frac{1}{sC}$$

$$= 2 + \frac{2}{s}.$$

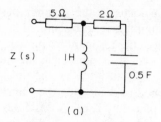

FIG. 5.5. (a) Circuit for Problem 5.4(a).

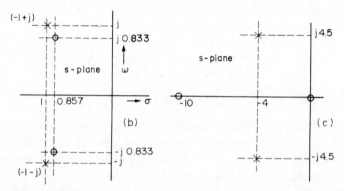

FIG. 5.5. (b) Poles and zeros in the s-plane of circuit of Fig. 5.5(a).

FIG. 5.5. (c) See Problem 5.4(b).

For the inductor, $Z_L = s$, and for the two in parallel:

$$Z' = \frac{Z_C Z_L}{Z_C + Z_L} = \frac{s[2 + (2/s)]}{s + 2 + (2/s)} = \frac{s^2[2 + (2/s)]}{s^2 + 2s + 2}.$$

Hence, for the whole circuit:

$$Z(s) = 5 + \frac{s^2[2 + (2/s)]}{s^2 + 2s + 2} = \frac{5s^2 + 10s + 10 + 2s^2 + 2s}{s^2 + 2s + 2},$$

$$\therefore \quad Z(s) = \frac{7s^2 + 12s + 10}{s^2 + 2s + 2}. \qquad (5.1)$$

To determine the zeros, we find the roots of:

$$7s^2 + 12s + 10 = 0$$

or

$$s_{1,3} = \frac{-12 \pm \sqrt{144 - 280}}{14}$$

$$= \frac{-12 \pm j11.662}{14} = \underline{-0.857 \pm j0.833}.$$

To determine the poles, we find the roots of:

$$s^2 + 2s + 2 = 0$$

or

$$s_{2,4} = \frac{-2 \pm \sqrt{4 - 8}}{2} = \underline{-1 \pm j}.$$

Hence, eqn. (5.1) may be written:

$$Z(s) = \frac{(s + 0.857 - j0.833)\,(s + 0.857 + j0.833)}{(s + 1 - j)\,(s + 1 + j)}.$$

The poles and zeros are shown plotted in Fig. 5.5(b).
(b) The zeros are: $s_1 = -10$ and $s_3 = 0$ and the poles are:

$$s_2 = -4 + j4.5 \quad \text{and} \quad s_4 = -4 - j4.5.$$

Assuming that the admittance function is the ratio of two polynomials in s (or may be converted to such a form), the numerator must equate to zero when $s = s_1$ and $s = s_3$. Hence it must be of the form:

$$k_1 s(s - s_1),$$

or

$$k_1 s(s + 10).$$

Similarly, the denominator must be of the form:

$$k_2(s + 4 - j4.5)\,(s + 4 + j4.5)$$

since it must equate to infinity when $s = -4 \pm j4.5$.

Hence,

$$Y(s) = \frac{Ks(s + 10)}{(s + 4 - j4.5)(s + 4 + j4.5)} = \frac{Ks(s + 10)}{s^2 + 8s + 36.25}.$$

The constant, K, can have any value without affecting the location of the poles and zeros, and can be evaluated only when $Y(s)$ is known for some value of s. In this case $Y(s) = 5$ S when $s = 1$.

$$\therefore \quad 5 = \frac{11K}{45.25} \text{ or } K = 20.568,$$

$$\therefore \quad Y(s) = \frac{20.568\, s(s + 10)}{s^2 + 8s + 36.25}.$$

5.2.2 Frequency response from the P–Z constellation

In general, then, the system function $G(s)$ may be expressed in the form:

$$G(s) = K \cdot \frac{f(s)}{f_1(s)} \tag{5.2}$$

where $f(s)$ and $f_1(s)$ are polynomials in s, not necessarily of the same order, and K is a constant.

Since we are confining our attention to sinusoidal variations with time, we can evaluate $G(s) = \mathbf{G}(j\omega)$ in magnitude and phase by direct calculation from eqn. (5.2). Thus, s is replaced by $j\omega$, ω being the radian frequency at which $G \angle \phi$ is required, and the frequency response of the system function determined by allowing ω to vary over the frequency range required.

Alternatively, $f(s)$ and $f_1(s)$ in eqn. (5.2) may be factorised to determine the poles and zeros of $G(s)$, which are then plotted on the s-plane. The magnitude and phase of $\mathbf{G}(j\omega)$ may then be determined graphically from the P–Z plot.

Let

$$f(s) = (s - s_1)(s - s_3)(s - s_5)\ldots, \text{ etc.,} \tag{5.3}$$

and

$$f_1(s) = (s - s_2)(s - s_4)(s - s_6)\ldots, \text{ etc.} \tag{5.4}$$

Then

$$G(s) = K \frac{(s - s_1)(s - s_3)(s - s_5) \ldots}{(s - s_2)(s - s_4)(s - s_6) \ldots}. \tag{5.5}$$

Clearly, when $s = s_1$, $s = s_3$, etc., $G(s) = 0$ so that s_1, s_3, s_5, etc., are the zeros of $G(s)$; when $s = s_2$, $s = s_4$, etc., $G(s) = \infty$ so that s_2, s_4, s_6, etc., are the poles of $F(s)$.

If these poles and zeros are plotted on the s-plane, as shown in Fig. 5.6(a), and, taking any one of the factors in eqn. (5.5), say $(s - s_1)$, we

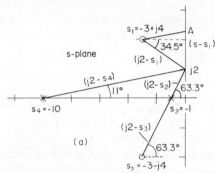

FIG. 5.6. (a) Pole–zero plot for Problem 5.5.

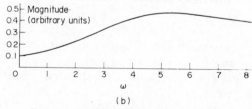

FIG. 5.6. (b) Magnitude/frequency response.

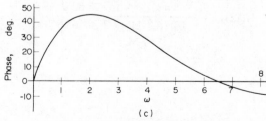

FIG. 5.6. (c) Phase/frequency response.

see that it is a complex number which gives the distance (on the plane) between the zero s_1 and any frequency s. For, let $s = j\omega$ (the point A on the ω-axis, Fig. 5.6(a)) and let the distance between s_1 and A be s'. Then:

$$s_1 + s' = s,$$

$$\therefore \quad s' = s - s_1 \text{ where } s, s_1 \text{ and } s' \text{ are all complex numbers.}$$

Similarly, every other factor in eqn. (5.5) may be represented, in magnitude and phase, by the distance drawn from the pole—or zero—to the point $s = j\omega$ (the phase being measured as the angle between the line vector and the real axis), and $G(j\omega)$ calculated, except for the factor K.

PROBLEM 5.5

Suppose that, in Fig. 5.6(a), $s_1, s_3 = -3 \pm j4$, $s_2 = -1$ and $s_4 = -10$. Evaluate $G(j\omega)$ at $\omega = 0, 2, 4$ and 8, and check the values by direct calculation. If the P–Z plot is taken to represent the impedance, $Z(j\omega)$, of a circuit, sketch the magnitude and phase of the current response against ω over the range 0 to 8 rad/sec, given that $Z(0) = 10 \angle 0\,\Omega$ and that the circuit is driven by a voltage source.

Solution

At $\omega = 2$, $s = j\omega = j2$ in Fig. 5.6(a). The four line vectors $(s - s_1)$, $(s - s_2)$, $(s - s_3)$ and $(s - s_4)$ are measured and so are the angles they make with the real axis. Their values are shown on the diagram.

Thus, at $\omega = 2$ rad/sec

$$G(j2) = \frac{K \times 3.6 \angle -34.5° \times 6.62 \angle 63.3°}{10.16 \angle 11° \times 2.2 \angle 63.3°}$$

$$= \underline{1.07K \angle -45.5°}.$$

By calculation:

$$G(j\omega) = \frac{K(s - s_1)\,(s - s_3)}{(s - s_2)\,(s - s_4)}$$

at $\omega = 2$,

$$G(j2) = \frac{K(j2 + 3 - j4)\,(j2 + 3 + j4)}{(j2 + 1)\,(j2 + 10)}$$

$$= \frac{K(21 + j12)}{6 + j22} = \frac{K \times 24.186 \angle 29.745°}{22.804 \angle 74.745°}$$

$$= \underline{1.061K \angle -45°}.$$

$G(j\omega)$ at each of the other frequencies is determined in the same way; the values are as follows:

At $\omega = 0$, $G(j0) = 2.5K$ (ϕ has no meaning).

At $\omega = 4$, $G(j4) = 0.577K\angle -28°\,19'$.

At $\omega = 8$, $G(j8) = 0.599K\angle 7°\,34'$.

In this case $G(0) = Z(0) = 10\ \Omega$. Hence,

$$10 = 2.5K \text{ or } \underline{K = 4}$$

and

$$Z(j2) = 4.244 \angle -45°,$$

$$Z(j4) = 2.308 \angle -28°\,19',$$

$$Z(j8) = 2.396 \angle 7°\,34'.$$

If the circuit were driven by a voltage source, the actual current response would be proportional to the reciprocal of these values of $Z(j\omega)$ and this response is shown plotted in Fig. 5.6(b), together with the phase response, Fig. 5.6(c).

PROBLEM 5.6

(i) Determine the transfer function for the four-terminal transmission network represented in Fig. 5.7(a). (ii) Plot the poles and zeros of the function on the s-plane and determine, graphically or by calculation, the transmission and phase responses at (a) $\omega = 2$ rad/sec and (b) $\omega = 20$ rad/sec. (iii) For $v_1(t) = 30 \cos(10t - \pi/6)$, determine $v_2(t)$.

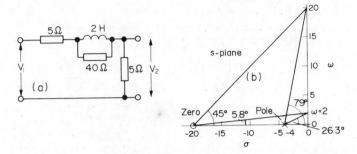

FIG. 5.7. (a) A 4-terminal transmission network. (b) Pole–zero plot for the network of Fig. 5.7(a).

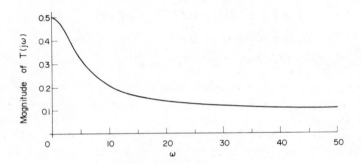

FIG. 5.7. (c) Magnitude/frequency for the circuit of Fig. 5.7(a).

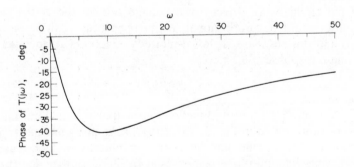

FIG. 5.7. (d) Phase/frequency for the circuit of Fig. 5.7(a).

Solution

(i) $T(s) = \dfrac{V_2(s)}{V_1(s)} = \dfrac{5}{5 + 5 + (40 \times 2s/(40 + 2s))} = \dfrac{20 + s}{40 + 10s}$. (5.6)

(ii) Zero occurs when $20 + s = 0$ or $s = -20$.

Pole occurs when $40 + 10s = 0$ or $s = -4$.

These are shown plotted in Fig. 5.7(b) together with the vectors from the pole and zero to the two points on the ω-axis representing $\omega = 2$ and $\omega = 20$. The magnitudes and angles are also shown on the diagram and we see that:

$$\mathbf{T}(j2) = K\frac{5.01 \angle 5.8°}{1.12 \angle 26.3°} = K \times 4.47 \angle -20.5°$$

and

$$\mathbf{T}(j20) = K\frac{7.04 \angle 45°}{5.08 \angle 79°} = K \times 1.39 \angle -34°.$$

Also, $\mathbf{T}(0) = K \times (20/4) = 5K$, but from eqn. (5.6) we see that $T(s) = 0.5$ when $s = 0$. Hence, $K = 0.1$, giving:

$$\mathbf{T}(j2) = 0.447 \angle -20.5°$$

and

$$\mathbf{T}(j20) = 0.139 \angle -34°.$$

By calculation:

$$\mathbf{T}(j2) = \frac{20 + j2}{40 + j20} = \frac{20.10 \angle 5.71°}{44.72 \angle 26.565°}$$

$$= \underline{0.45 \angle -20° 51'}.$$

$$\mathbf{T}(j20) = \frac{20 + j20}{40 + j200} = \frac{28.284 \angle 45°}{203.96 \angle 78.69°}$$

$$= \underline{0.1387 \angle -33° 41'}.$$

The amplitude—and phase—against frequency plots, over the range $\omega = 0$ to 50 rad/sec, are shown in Fig. 5.7 (c) and (d).

(iii) $v_1(t) = 30 \cos(10t - \pi/6)$

or

$$V_1 = \frac{30}{\sqrt{2}} \angle -\pi/6 \quad \text{and} \quad \omega = 10,$$

$$\therefore \quad T(j\omega) = \frac{20 + j10}{40 + j100} = 0.2076 \angle -41°38'$$

and

$$V_2 = V_1 \cdot T(j\omega) = \frac{30}{\sqrt{2}} \times 0.2076 \angle (-\pi/6 - 41°38')$$

$$= \frac{6.228}{\sqrt{2}} \angle -71°38'.$$

$$\therefore \quad \underline{v_2(t) = 6.228 \cos(10t - 71°38')}.$$

5.2.3 Manipulation of poles and zeros

Occasionally, we may wish to make the impedance, admittance or transfer function of a network independent of frequency—even though the network contains reactance. This apparent paradox can be realised by adding elements to the original network until the overall system function—expressed in the form of eqn. (5.5)—has pairs of poles and zeros which cancel. Thus, when $s_1 = s_2$, $s_3 = s_4$, $s_5 = s_6$, etc., the vectors $(j\omega - s_1)$ and $(j\omega - s_2)$ are equal, so are $(j\omega - s_3)$ and $(j\omega - s_4)$, etc., so that $G(j\omega) = K$.

PROBLEM 5.7

A circuit consists of two parallel branches, one having a coil of resistance 20 Ω and inductance 0.5 H and the other, capacitance C in series with resistance R.

Determine C and R so that the combined impedance shall be independent of frequency and have zero phase angle.

Solution

$$Z_L(s) = 20 + \frac{s}{2}, \quad Z_C(s) = R + \frac{1}{sC},$$

$$\therefore \quad Z(s) = \frac{Z_L(s)Z_C(s)}{Z_L(s) + Z_C(s)} = \frac{[20 + (s/2)][R + (1/sC)]}{(20 + R) + (s/2) + (1/sC)}$$

$$= \frac{20R + (20/sC) + (sR/2) + (1/2C)}{20 + R + (s/2) + (1/sC)}$$

$$= \frac{s^2 + [40 + (1/CR)]s + (40/CR)}{s^2 + (2R + 40)s + (2/C)}. \tag{5.7}$$

Both numerator and denominator may be factorised, giving two poles and two zeros for $Z(s)$. For these poles and zeros to cancel in pairs the coefficients in eqn. (5.7) must be equal. Hence:

$$\frac{40}{CR} = \frac{2}{C}, \text{ giving } \underline{R = 20 \, \Omega}$$

and

$$40 + \frac{1}{CR} = 2R + 40,$$

$$\therefore C = \frac{1}{2R^2} = \frac{1}{800} F = \underline{1250 \, \mu F}.$$

5.3 LOGARITHMIC PLOTTING: BODE PLOTS

For four-terminal transmission networks, e.g. the circuit of Fig. 5.7(a), the transfer—or gain—and phase functions may be plotted on a logarithmic basis instead of on a linear one, as in Fig. 5.7 (c) and (d). The practice originated in the communications field and it has several advantages, three of which particularly concern us here. Firstly, a much wider range of variation of both the function and the frequency may be accommodated on one plot, whilst preserving clearly the information at the lower ends of the ranges. Secondly, the process of plotting the functions is much simplified because, over large parts of the frequency range they approximate closely to straight lines. Finally, the combined effect of separate factors appearing as products in the function may be obtained by addition of their separate effects—those appearing as quotients being obtained by subtraction.

The plots thus drawn are known as Bode plots, and can often be sketched simply by inspection of the functions, thus saving much computational labour.

5.3.1 The scales

(a) *Frequency*

Logarithms to base 10 are used, so equal subdivisions of the ω-axis represent tenfold changes of frequency. Such a change is referred to as a DECADE. Thus, a frequency axis divided into, say, five decades could be taken to represent 0.1, 1, 10, 100, 1000, 10^4 rad/sec. Clearly, zero frequency cannot appear since $\log_{10} 0 = -\infty$, but it may be approached as closely as desired by increasing the number of decades downwards in frequency. Any two-fold change of frequency (a ratio also much used) is called an OCTAVE.

(b) *Amplitude: the deciBel scale*

Again logarithms to base 10 are most commonly used, but the unit, the Bel, is defined in terms of a power ratio. Thus, two powers, P_1 and P_2, are in the ratio of 1 Bel when:

$$\log_{10} \frac{P_1}{P_2} = 1$$

or

$$P_1 = 10P_2.$$

Thus, the level of P_1 is said to be 1 Bel (1 B) or 10 dB above that of P_2. Since the voltages V_1 and V_2 (or the currents I_1 and I_2) associated, respectively, with P_1 and P_2 are proportional to $\sqrt{P_1/P_2}$ only if the two impedances in which P_1 and P_2 are dissipated are equal, the Bel and deciBel scale cannot strictly be used for voltage and current ratios unless this condition is met. However, the scales *are* so commonly used in this way, even though the stated condition is not satisfied, that it seems pedantic to insist on the correct usage.

Hence, since

$$10 \log \frac{P_1}{P_2} = \text{ratio in dB},$$

then

$$10 \log \left(\frac{V_1}{V_2}\right)^2 = 20 \log \frac{V_1}{V_2} = \text{ratio in dB}.$$

Thus, for example, a voltage $V_1 = 100V_2$ is said to be $20 \log 100 = 40 \, \text{dB}$ greater than V_2. Or, when $V_1 = 0.02V_2$ then V_1 is $20 \log 0.02 = 2.3010 \times 20 = -33.98 \simeq -34 \, \text{dB}$ greater than V_2 (or $+34 \, \text{dB}$ below V_2).

5.3.2 Logarithm of a complex function

Let

$$\mathbf{G}(j\omega) = |\mathbf{G}(j\omega)| e^{j\phi(\omega)}.$$

Taking natural logarithms of $\mathbf{G}(j\omega)$:

$$\ln \mathbf{G}(j\omega) = \ln |\mathbf{G}(j\omega)| + j\phi(\omega),$$

we obtain another complex number in which the magnitude and phase-shift terms of $\mathbf{G}(j\omega)$ appear separately.

Converting to logarithms to base 10,

$$\log_{10} \mathbf{G}(j\omega) = \log_{10} |\mathbf{G}(j\omega)| + j0.4343 \phi(\omega). \tag{5.8}$$

5.3.3 The plots

Now consider a response function $G(s)$ having the form of one of the numerator factors of eqn. (5.5). Dealing first with the gain:

$$G(s) = K(s - s_1)$$

with s_1 real and negative, i.e. the function has a zero on the negative real axis. The response to a sinusoidal forcing function is:

$$\mathbf{G}(j\omega) = K(j\omega - s_1) = Ks_1\left(j\frac{\omega}{s_1} - 1\right)$$

$$= Ks_1 \sqrt{\left(\frac{\omega}{s_1}\right)^2 + 1} \cdot e^{j\phi(\omega)} \quad \text{where} \quad \tan \phi = -\frac{\omega}{s_1}.$$

Taking logarithms to base 10

$$\log \mathbf{G}(j\omega) = \log Ks_1 + \tfrac{1}{2}\log\left[\left(\frac{\omega}{s_1}\right)^2 + 1\right] + j0.4343\tan^{-1}\left(\frac{-\omega}{s_1}\right).$$

Comparing this with eqn. (5.8) we see that the phase shift

$$\phi(\omega) = \tan^{-1}\frac{-\omega}{s_1},$$

and

$$\log|\mathbf{G}(j\omega)| = \log Ks_1 + \tfrac{1}{2}\log\left[\left(\frac{\omega}{s_1}\right)^2 + 1\right]. \tag{5.9}$$

Logarithms to base 10 have been chosen so that the dB scale can be used for the log Gain axis. Plotting the gain on a linear scale of dB automatically plots log Gain.

Hence, expressed in dB, eqn. (5.9) becomes:

$$\text{Gain in dB} = 20\log Ks_1 + 10\log\left[\left(\frac{\omega}{s_1}\right)^2 + 1\right] \tag{5.10}$$

and the approximate form of this equation can be assessed by taking three particular cases:

(i) When $(\omega/s_1) \ll 1$, the second term becomes $10\log 1 = 0\,\text{dB}$.

(ii) When $(\omega/s_1) \gg 1$, the second term becomes $20\log(\omega/s_1)\,\text{dB}$.

Each decade increase in ω increases the magnitude of this term by 20 dB, so that, on a dB/log ω graph the term represents a straight line of slope $+20\,\text{dB/decade}$ (or 6 dB/octave). The line intersects the 0-dB horizontal line for $(\omega/s_1) \ll 1$ at $\omega = s_1$, so that the asymptotes of the true graph representing eqn. (5.10) are merely two straight-line segments. These are shown in Fig. 5.8(a), in which s_1 is chosen to be 100 rad/sec. The addition of the first, constant, term in eqn. (5.10) simply shifts the whole graph upwards by $20\log Ks_1$. In Fig. 5.8(a) this has been arbitrarily chosen to be 15 dB.

(iii) When $(\omega/s_1) = 1$, the second term of eqn. (5.10) becomes $10\log 2 = 3.01\,\text{dB}$, or 3 dB approximately. Thus, the true curve departs from the point of intersection of the asymptotes by 3 dB. The frequency $\omega = s_1$ is called the *break-point* or *corner frequency*. Figure 5.8(a) shows the true curve sketched in, taking the asymptotes as guidelines, and passing through the point 3 dB above the gain at the corner frequency.

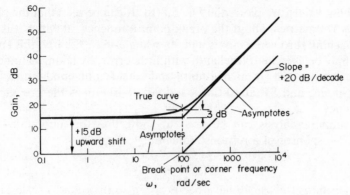

FIG. 5.8. (a) Bode plot for eqn. (5.10): Gain.

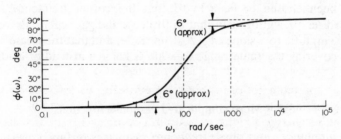

FIG. 5.8. (b) Bode plot of phase corresponding to Fig. 5.8(a).

The phase $\phi(\omega)$ given by:

$$\tan \phi = \frac{\omega}{s_1}, \text{ since } s_1 \text{ is negative.}$$

The values of ϕ may be tabulated as follows:

$\dfrac{\omega}{s_1}$	ϕ
0.01	0.6°
0.1	5.7°
1	45°
10	84.3°
100	89.4°

and these values are plotted in Fig. 5.8(b). It can be seen that the phase shift is symmetrical about the break-point frequency, at which it is 45°, approaching zero when $\omega \ll s_1$ and 90° when $\omega \gg s_1$. Clearly, this curve, also, may be sketched, freehand, with little error, by taking ϕ to be 45° at the break-point, 6° at one-tenth and zero at one-hundredth of the break-point, and 84° at 10 times and 90° at 100 times the break-point frequency.

A similar analysis can be used to show that the amplitude—and phase—responses of a response function:

$$G(s) = \frac{K}{(s - s_2)} \tag{5.11}$$

are as sketched in Fig. 5.9 (a) and (b). In these diagrams $20 \log K/s_2$ has again been chosen to be $+15 \text{ dB}$, but the corner frequency, s_2, is 1000 rad/sec. It will be seen that in this case the gain curve above $\omega = s_2$ is asymptotic to a slope of -20 dB/decade, and that the phase angle, whilst covering the same range $0 \rightarrow 90°$, is lagging instead of leading.

5.3.4 More complicated response functions

The amplitude- and phase-frequency responses of functions such as eqn.(5.5) may be dealt with using a simple extension of the same technique. The amplitude response of each factor $(s - s_1)$, $(s - s_2)$, $(s - s_3)$, etc., is first plotted separately using straight-line asymptotes, the numerator factors each giving a $+20 \text{ dB/decade}$ slope and the denominator factors a slope of -20 dB/decade above their respective corner frequencies. The several responses are then added, graphically, to produce a combined response, and this is then shifted up or down by a constant derived by combining all the constants from the separate factors. Finally, the curve is rounded at each corner frequency by adding or subtracting the 3-dB discrepancy.

PROBLEM 5.8
Plot the amplitude and phase responses, using Bode's method, for the transmission circuit of Fig. 5.7(a) over the frequency range 0.1 to 1000 rad/sec, i.e. four decades of ω.

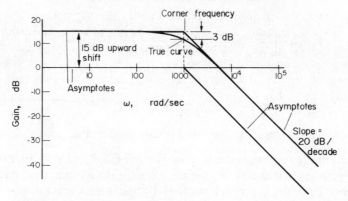

FIG. 5.9. (a) Amplitude/frequency response of the function $G(s) = K/(s - s_2)$.

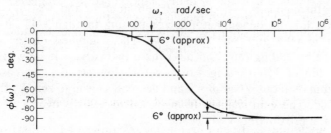

FIG. 5.9. (b) Phase/frequency response of the function $G(s) = K/(s - s_2)$.

Solution

Referring to Problem 5.6, for this circuit:

$$T(s) = \frac{20 + s}{40 + 10s}.$$

Hence, for a sinusoidal voltage input, $\mathbf{V}_1(j\omega)$,

$$\mathbf{T}(j\omega) = \frac{20 + j\omega}{40 + j10\omega} = \frac{20[1 + j(\omega/20)]}{40[1 + j(\omega/4)]}$$

$$= 0.5 \frac{[1 + j(\omega/20)]}{[1 + j(\omega/4)]}.$$

Dealing first with the numerator factor, the asymptotes are (i) a constant 0 dB extending to $\omega = 20$, and (ii) a line of slope $+20$ dB/decade starting at 0 dB at $\omega = 20$ and continuing to $\omega = 10^3$. The denominator factor gives a constant 0 dB extending from $\omega = 0.1$ to $\omega = 4$, followed by a line of slope -20 dB/decade extending from $\omega = 4$ (where it starts at 0 dB) to $\omega = 10^3$.

The constant factor 0.5, expressed in dB, is:

$$20 \log 0.5 = -6 \text{ dB independent of } \omega.$$

These three responses are sketched on the graph of Fig. 5.10, and the total response obtained by adding them. Finally, the true curve is sketched by drawing through points 3 dB below the corner at $\omega = 4$ and 3 dB above the corner at $\omega = 20$.

The two phase shift curves are sketched, that for the numerator factor passing through $\phi = +45°$ at $\omega = 20$, $+6°$ at $\omega = 2$ and $+84°$ at $\omega = 200$, and that for the denominator factor passing through $-45°$ at $\omega = 4$, $-6°$ at $\omega = 0.4$ and $-84°$ at $\omega = 40$. The combined phase curve is obtained by adding (algebraically) these two curves. It shows that the phase shift of $\mathbf{T}(j\omega)$ changes from zero below $\omega = 0.1$, increases to a maximum of about 40° at $\omega = 9$ and decreases again to zero by the time $\omega = 1000$. The gain changes from -6 dB to -20 dB over a frequency span of approximately two decades.

5.3.5 Response functions containing other factors

The Bode diagrams of any system function may be sketched in this way, provided that it takes the form of a constant times the products and quotients of simple linear factors such as $(s - s_n)$, where s_n is real and negative.

More specifically, this proviso requires that the function have poles and zeros on the negative real axis of the s-plane.

In order that the method be applicable to any system function, it is necessary to include three additional cases: (i) poles and/or zeros at the origin, (ii) one or more pairs of conjugate complex poles and/or zeros, (iii) higher order poles and/or zeros, i.e. repeated factors in the denominator or numerator.

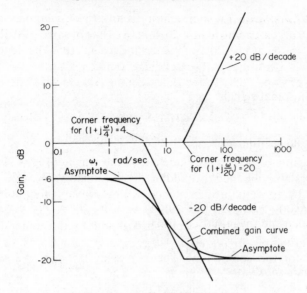

FIG. 5.10. (a) Bode plot for $T(s) = 20 + s/40 + 10s$.

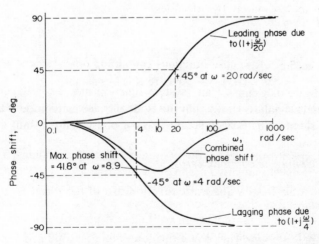

FIG. 5.10. (b) Phase response for $T(s) = 20 + s/40 + 10s$.

(i) (a) *Zero at the origin*

Let

$$G(s) = Ks \quad \text{where } K \text{ is a constant.}$$

For sinusoidal signals:

$$\mathbf{G}(j\omega) = jK\omega.$$

Taking logarithms to base 10:

$$\log \mathbf{G}(j\omega) = \log K + \log \omega + j0.4343 \frac{\pi}{2}.$$

Comparison with eqn. (5.8) shows that the phase shift is constant at $\pi/2$ and that the magnitude of the gain is:

$$\log |\mathbf{G}(j\omega)| = \log K + \log \omega$$

or, the gain in dB is:

$$\text{dB gain} = 20 \log K + 20 \log \omega,$$

i.e. a straight line of slope $+20$ dB/decade passing through the point $20 \log K$ dB at $\omega = 1$. Thus, if $K = 1$ the line passes through 0 dB at $\omega = 1$.

(b) *Pole at the origin*

Let

$$G(s) = \frac{K}{s} \quad \text{where } K \text{ is a constant.}$$

A similar analysis shows that the Bode plot for magnitude is a straight line of slope -20 dB/decade and that for phase is a constant at $-\pi/2$.

(ii) (a) *Conjugate complex zeros*

These arise from a quadratic function of s of the form:

$$G(s) = K'(as^2 + bs + c) \tag{5.12}$$

in which $b^2 < 4ac$. This equation describes a second-order circuit in which the damping is less than critical. Following the usage of Problem

2.12, Chapter 2, we let $\omega_0^2 = c/a$ and $2\alpha = b/a$. Equation (5.12) then reduces to:

$$G(s) = K(s^2 + 2\alpha s + \omega_0^2) \qquad (5.13)$$

where $K = K'a$.

For critical damping, $\alpha_c = \omega_0$, and for any value of α less than this, the roots of this equation, i.e. the zeros of $G(s)$, are complex, i.e., $s_{1,3} = -\alpha \pm j\sqrt{\omega_0^2 - \alpha^2}$. The damping ratio, defined as α/α_c, is $\alpha/\omega_0 = \zeta$.

For sinusoidal signals, eqn. (5.13) reduces to:

$$\mathbf{G}(j\omega) = K(\omega_0^2 - \omega^2 + j2\alpha\omega)$$

$$= K\omega_0^2(1 - \eta^2 + j2\zeta\eta)$$

where

$$\eta = \frac{\omega}{\omega_0}, \text{ the ratio } \frac{\text{applied frequency}}{\text{undamped natural frequency}},$$

or

$$\mathbf{G}(j\omega) = K\omega_0^2\sqrt{(1 - \eta^2)^2 + 4\zeta^2\eta^2}\, e^{j\phi} \qquad (5.14)$$

where

$$\phi = \tan^{-1}\left(\frac{2\zeta\eta}{1 - \eta^2}\right).$$

For the Bode plot we take logarithms to base 10:

$$20 \log \mathbf{G}(j\omega) = 20 \log K\omega_0^2 + \tfrac{1}{2} \cdot 20 \log[(1 - \eta^2)^2 \qquad (5.15)$$
$$+ 4\zeta^2\eta^2] + j0.4343\phi.$$

Hence, the gain function comprises two terms; a constant, $20 \log K\omega_0^2$, and a frequency-dependent term. The asymptotes may be found, as before, by considering the frequency limits:

(i) When $\eta \ll 1$ (and remembering that ζ lies within the range $0 \rightarrow 1$) the expression in the square brackets approximates to unity. Hence the second term is zero.

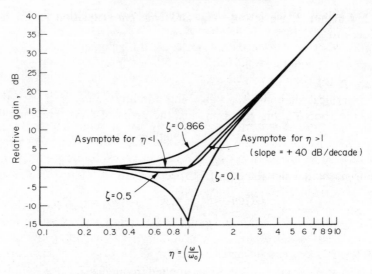

FIG. 5.11. (a) Amplitude/frequency response for gain function having a pair of complex conjugate zeros. $\zeta = 0.1$, 0.5 and 0.866.

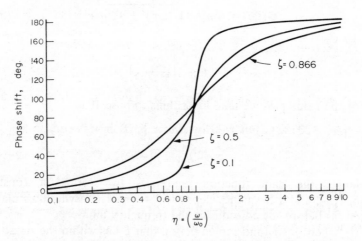

FIG. 5.11. (b) Phase/frequency response for a gain function having a pair of complex conjugate zeros. $\zeta = 0.1$, 0.5 and 0.866.

(ii) When $\eta \gg 1$, the η^4 term predominates and the slope of the asymptote is $+40$ dB/decade.

(iii) When $\eta = 1$ (the corner frequency) the magnitude of the second term is dependent wholly on ζ. Equation (5.15) shows that it is $20 \log 2\zeta$. Thus when $\zeta = 0.1$, this term becomes $20 \log 0.2 = 14$ dB below the low-frequency asymptote; and when $\zeta = 0.5$ this term becomes 0 dB. The gain curves for $K\omega_0^2 = 1$ and three values of ζ are shown in Fig. 5.11(a). It can be seen that the slope of the asymptotes and the position of the corner frequency give no clue to the gain at this frequency, so the Bode method is not quite so useful as in the previous cases, if interest is located at or near the corner frequency.

When sketching the gain curve, it is helpful to have the magnitude of the minimum gain and the frequency at which it occurs. These can be found by differentiating the magnitude term of eqn. (5.15) and equating to zero. This gives:

$$\eta = \sqrt{1 - 2\zeta^2} \quad \text{for minimum gain.}$$

Substituting this value of η gives:

$$|\mathbf{G}_{\min}(j\omega)| = 2\zeta\sqrt{1 - \zeta^2}.$$

And the gain curve passes through 0 dB when

$$(1 - \eta^2)^2 + 4\zeta^2\eta^2 = 1, \text{ or } \eta = \sqrt{2 - 4\zeta^2};$$

and this shows that the largest value of ζ for which a dip occurs in the gain curve is $\zeta = 0.707$.

The phase function of $\mathbf{G}(j\omega)$ is, by comparison with eqn. (5.8),

$$\phi = \tan^{-1}\frac{2\zeta\eta}{1 - \eta^2}.$$

At the corner frequency, $\eta = 1$ so that $\phi = \pi/2$ whatever the magnitude of ζ. At low frequencies $\phi \to 0$ and at high frequencies $\phi \to \pi$, but the rate at which the change takes place, symmetrical about $\eta = 1$, depends on ζ. Figure 5.11(b) shows the phase-shift curves for three values of ζ.

(b) *Conjugate complex poles*

A similar analysis shows that the gain and phase of a system function of the form:

$$G(s) = \frac{K}{(s - s_2)(s - s_4)}$$

where s_2 and s_4 are complex conjugates, follow curves which are the exact inverse of those of Fig. 5.11 (a) and (b), i.e. the gain rises to $20 \log 1/2\zeta$ at $\eta = 1$, and the phase is asymptotic to π at low frequencies and to zero at high frequencies.

(iii) *Repeated factors*

If any of the factors (or, in the case of conjugate complex pairs, pairs of factors) considered in sections 5.3.3 and 5.3.5 (i) and (ii) above are raised to the power n, i.e. if multiple poles and zeros occur, then the slope of the corresponding gain asymptote and the phase shift are both increased by the factor n. Thus, for example, if

$$G(s) = (s + 10)^3$$

then the Bode plot consists of a 60-dB low-frequency asymptote extending to $\omega = 10$ (the corner frequency) and a high-frequency asymptote of slope $+60$ dB/decade starting at $\omega = 10$. The true curve passes through $+9$ dB at $\omega = 10$. The phase of $G(j\omega)$ is asymptotic to 0 at low frequencies, increases to $+17.1°$ at $\omega = 1$, through $+135°$ at $\omega = 10$, to within $17.1°$ of $270°$ at $\omega = 100$ and is asymptotic to $270°$ as ω increases further.

Obviously, a quadratic function having critical damping is equivalent to such a case for $n = 2$. Then, the two complex poles or zeros converge to a double pole or zero (as the case may be) on the negative real axis.

PROBLEM 5.9

A system has a gain function $G(s)$ which has a zero at the origin and poles at $s = -5 \pm j12$. Given that the gain is -5.33 dB at $\omega = 100$ rad/sec, determine an expression for $G(s)$ and plot the gain and phase-shift on a log ω base. Determine the frequencies at which the gain is 0 dB and the phase shift at each one.

Solution

For the function to have a zero at the origin, the numerator must consist of a constant times s. The denominator is a quadratic function of s with complex roots. Hence,

$$G(s) = K \frac{s}{(s + 5 - j12)(s + 5 + j12)}. \tag{5.16}$$

K must be determined in order to achieve the required gain at the specified frequency. Given that:

$$\mathbf{G}(j100) = K \cdot \frac{j100}{(5 + j88)(5 + j112)} = -5.33 \text{ dB}$$

or

$$|\mathbf{G}(j100)| = K \cdot \frac{100}{88.14 \times 112.11} = 0.010\,12K,$$

$$\therefore \quad 0.010\,12K = -5.33 \text{ dB} = 0.5414, \therefore K = 53.5.$$

Equating the denominator of eqn. (5.16) to the standard form $\omega_0^2 - \omega^2 + j2\alpha\omega$, we see that $\omega_0^2 = 169$ or $\omega_0 = 13$ and $\alpha = 5$, giving $\zeta = 5/13 = 0.3846$.

The asymptotes of the Bode plot may now be drawn:

(i) A constant term $20 \log 53.5/169 = -10 \text{ dB}$.

(ii) A straight line through $\omega = 1$ of slope $+20 \text{ dB/decade}$ due to the single s in the numerator.

(iii) A line with two straight segments due to the quadratic term:

    (a) a constant at 0 dB, extending to 13 rad/sec, and

    (b) a slope of -40 dB/decade from 13 rad/sec upwards.

These are shown plotted in Fig. 5.12(a) and the overall gain asymptote is the sum of the three. It rises at $+20 \text{ dB/decade}$ to $\omega = 13 \text{ rad/sec}$ and then falls at 20 dB/decade (the addition of $+20 \text{ dB/decade}$ and -40 dB/decade above $\omega = 13$). If it is desired to sketch the true gain curve, the adjustment at the corner frequency is simplified by the following corrections to the quadratic term asymptotes.

(a) the gain at $\eta = 1 = -20 \log 2\zeta = +2.28 \text{ dB}$,

(b) the peak gain is $1/2\zeta\sqrt{1 - \zeta^2} = +2.97 \text{ dB}$,

(c) this peak occurs at $\eta = \sqrt{1 - 2\zeta^2} = 0.84 = 10.9 \text{ rad/sec}$,

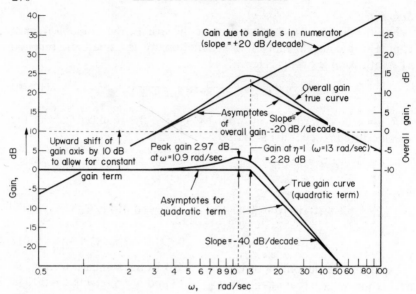

FIG. 5.12. (a) Method of building up the overall gain curve of given function by summing its separate components (see Problem 5.9).

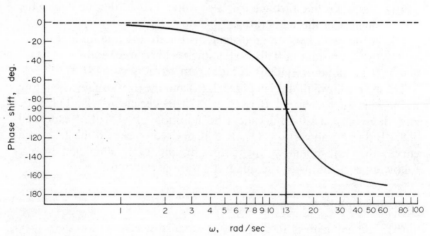

FIG. 5.12. (b) Phase shift as a function of ω for the gain function of Fig. 5.12(a) (see Problem 5.9).

(d) the curve passes through 0 dB at $\eta = \sqrt{2 - 4\zeta^2} = 1.1867$ or at 15.4 rad/sec.

The addition of the -10-dB constant term is effected in Fig. 5.12(a) by shifting the 0-dB line upward by 10 dB. It can be seen that the overall gain passes through 0 dB at $\omega = 3$ and 55 rad/sec.

The phase-shift graph is simpler to sketch, though probably not so accurate. It consists of just two components:

(i) a constant lead of $\pi/2$, due to the single s in the numerator,
(ii) a symmetrical curve similar to those of Fig. 5.11(b) changing from zero at low frequencies through $-\pi/2$ at 13 rad/sec to $-\pi$ at high frequencies, see Fig. 5.12(b). Again, addition of these can be affected by shifting the zero phase-shift line downward by $\pi/2$ so that the overall phase shift changes from $+\pi/2$ at l.f. to $-\pi/2$ at h.f.

The phase shift at 3 rad/sec is seen to be $+79°$ (approx.) and that at 55 rad/sec to be $-79°$ (approx.).

PROBLEM 5.10

An amplifier has a gain function

$$G(s) = \frac{1.4 \times 10^5 s^2 (s + 10)}{(s + 20)^2 (s + 50) (s^2 + 150s + 22,500)}. \tag{5.17}$$

Plot the approximate gain (in dB) and phase-shift graphs on a base of log ω by Bode's method and determine (i) the mid-band gain,* (ii) the frequencies at which the gain falls to unity (0 dB) and (iii) the phase shift at each of these frequencies.

Solution

The gain curve is approximated by its asymptotes, as in Problem 5.9, and in order for the asymptote intersections to occur on the 0-dB line, the constant in each term of eqn. (5.17) is first reduced to unity:

$$
\begin{aligned}
G(s) &= \frac{1.4 \times 10^5 \, s^2 10 [1 + (s/10)]}{20^2 [1 + (s/20)]^2 \, 50 [1 + (s/50)] \, 22,500 [1 + (s/150) + (s^2/22,500)]} \\
&= \frac{3.111 \times 10^{-3} s^2 [1 + (s/10)]}{[1 + (s/20)]^2 \, [1 + (s/50)] \, [1 + (s/150) + (s^2/22,500)]}.
\end{aligned}
$$

---

* i.e. the gain approximately in the middle of the useful operating bandwidth.

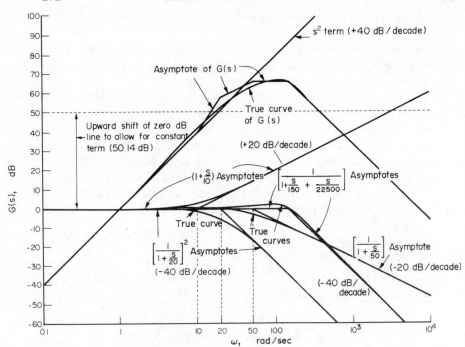

FIG. 5.13. (a) Plot of $G(s)$ against ω for the gain function of Problem 5.10, obtained by summing the asymptotes of the separate terms.

Hence, the constant term is $20 \log 3.111 \times 10^{-3} = -50.14 \, \text{dB}$. The s^2 term contributes $+40 \, \text{dB/decade}$ passing through $\omega = 1$ and $[1 + (s/10)]$ is represented by a horizontal line at $0 \, \text{dB}$ up to $\omega = 10$ joined to a line of slope $20 \, \text{dB/decade}$ thereafter. The $[1 + (s/20)]^2$ term is a quadratic with $\zeta = 1$ and therefore contributes $0 \, \text{dB}$ up to $\omega = 20$ joined to a line of slope $-40 \, \text{dB/decade}$ thereafter. The $[1 + (s/50)]$ term contributes $0 \, \text{dB}$ up to $\omega = 50$ and $-20 \, \text{dB/decade}$ from $\omega = 50$ upward.

We next investigate the nature of the second quadratic term, i.e. whether it has real or complex roots. Clearly, in this case the roots are complex and $\omega_0^2 = 22{,}500$, giving $\omega_0 = 150 \, \text{rad/sec}$. The damping ratio, $\zeta = \alpha/\omega_0 = 75/150 = 0.5$. The asymptotes for this term are, therefore, a constant at $0 \, \text{dB}$ up to $\omega = 150$ joined to a line of slope $-40 \, \text{dB/decade}$ for $\omega \geqslant 150$.

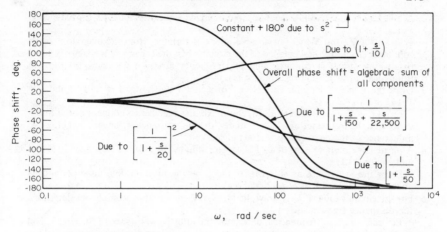

FIG. 5.13. (b) Plot of phase shift against ω of the components of $G(s)$, Problem 5.10, and of the overall phase shift.

These five sets of asymptotes are shown in Fig. 5.13(a), together with their sum. As in the previous problem, the -50.14-dB line is added by repositioning the zero dB line at $+50.14$ dB. It can be seen that (i) the mid-band gain is $+16$ dB, (ii) the gain falls to 0 dB at $\omega = 17$ and $\omega = 380$. (iii) Phase shift. Figure 5.13(b) shows the different components of phase shift and their algebraic sum. The diagram shows the origin of each, the contribution of the second quadratic term (change from 0 to $-\pi$ over a little more than two decades of ω) being lifted from the appropriate curve in Fig. 5.11(b). The overall phase shift is seen to change from $+180°$ to $-180°$ over a frequency range of about four decades. It can be seen that at $\omega = 17$, $\phi \simeq +133°$ and at $\omega = 380$, $\phi \simeq -143°$.

PROBLEMS V

1. A voltage source generating 100 V (r.m.s.), and for which ω is variable, is applied to a coil of inductance 0.4 H and resistance 50 Ω.

   Draw the **Z**- and **Y**-loci for variable ω and determine, from the diagram, (a) the conductance and susceptance at $\omega = 50$ rad/sec, (b) the maximum values of G and B and the corresponding frequencies. Suggested scales are: $1'' \equiv 10 \, \Omega$ and $1'' \equiv 0.005$ S.

   By re-scaling the admittance locus from units of **Y** to units of current, determine (c) the magnitude and phase angle of the current at $\omega = 80$ rad/sec.

2. A constant (r.m.s.) voltage source supplies 100 Ω resistance and 1 μF capacitance in series.

   Draw the **Z**- and **Y**-loci for variable ω and determine, from the diagram, (a) the conductance and the susceptance of the circuit when the capacitive reactance is 50 Ω, (b) the maximum susceptance and the frequency at which it occurs, (c) the two frequencies at which the susceptance is 0.004375 S.

3. Draw the **Y**- and **Z**-loci, for variable ω, for a circuit consisting of $R = 100$ Ω and $L = 0.1$ H in parallel.

   From the diagram, determine (a) the maximum reactive component of the impedance and the frequency at which it occurs, (b) the resistance, reactance and effective inductance of the circuit at $\omega = 1500$ rad/sec.

4. A particular circuit consists of a 20-Ω resistor shunted by a coil of resistance 10 Ω and inductance 0.1 H.

   Draw the locus of **Z** as ω is varied and from the diagram determine $|Z|$ and its phase angle, R and X at $\omega = 120$ rad/sec.

5. For the circuit of Fig. P.V.1, draw the locus of **Z** for variable ω and hence determine the resonance frequencies.

   For each of these frequencies, determine the effective resistance of the circuit, and evaluate the maximum capacitive reactance, the frequency at which it occurs and the resistive component of the impedance at this frequency.

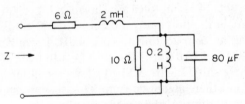

FIG. P.V.1 (Problem V.5).

6. For each of the circuits represented in Fig. P.V.2, locate the poles and zeros of the system function indicated.

7. The impedance of a particular circuit has poles at -5 and -2 and zeros at $-3 \pm j6$, and its magnitude at $s = -1$ is 15 Ω.

   Derive the impedance function and evaluate **Z**(j3).

8. The transfer function, $T(s)$, of a particular network has a zero at the origin and poles at -4 and -1. At $s = 1$, $T(s) = 5$.

   Derive the transfer function and evaluate the output voltage when the input voltage is 10 ∠30° V at $\omega = 5$ rad/sec.

9. The gain function, $G(s)$, of a particular network has a pole at $s = -4$, and a zero at $s = 0$.

   Given that $|G(s)| = 12$ at $s = j3$, determine, graphically and by calculation, the magnitude and phase of $G(s)$ over the frequency range $\omega = 0 \rightarrow 8$ rad/sec.

10. For the pole–zero plot of Fig. P.V.3, evaluate $Y(s)$ over the range $\omega = 0 \rightarrow 10$ rad/sec, given that $Y(s) = 1$ at $s = 0$.

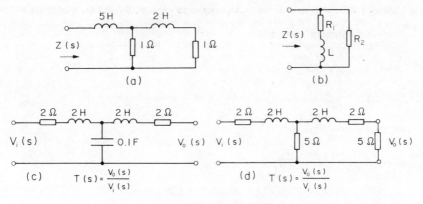

FIG. P.V.2 (Problem V.6).

Given that the plot refers to the admittance of a circuit, calculate the current for an applied voltage of 2 ∠60° V at $\omega = 5$ rad/sec.

Plot a graph of $|Y(s)|$ against ω and determine the frequency of resonance.

11. A four-terminal transmission network delivers 5 W to a load at frequency ω_1 and 1 W to the same load at ω_2.

Express, in dB, the change in gain of the network between ω_1 and ω_2.

12. A certain transmission network absorbs 50 mW at 10 V from a voltage source and delivers 10 mA to a load resistance of 200 Ω.

Determine the gain—or loss—of the network in dB.

13. The input signal of an amplifier is 10 ∠0° V into $10^5 \angle 0$ Ω and the output voltage is 10 ∠20° V into a load impedance of 15 ∠30° Ω.

Determine the gain of the amplifier in dB.

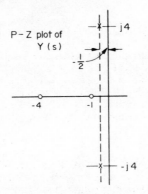

FIG. P.V.3 (Problem V.10).

14. Sketch the Bode plots (i.e. the asymptotes of the gain in dB, and the phase, against log ω) for each of the following functions and determine the actual gain and phase shift at the frequencies specified:

(i) $T(s) = \dfrac{1}{s+5}$ $\omega = 10$,

(ii) $T(s) = \dfrac{s}{s+5}$ $\omega = 2$,

(iii) $G(s) = \dfrac{s+2}{s+5}$ $\omega = 8$,

(iv) $G(s) = \dfrac{2s-6}{s+5}$ $\omega = 10$,

(v) $G(s) = \dfrac{1}{s^2 + 7s + 10}$ $\omega = 100$,

(vi) $G(s) = \dfrac{s}{s^2 + 25}$ $\omega = 5, 50$.

15. The transfer function of a certain amplifier has a zero at the origin and poles at $s = -10$ and $s = -10^4$, and the gain at $\omega = 1$ is 30 dB.

Plot the gain and phase shift of the amplifier by Bode's method and determine (i) the half-power-point frequencies, (ii) the mid-band gain, i.e. the gain at, say, $\omega = 100$.

16. A particular system has a gain function:

$$G(s) = \frac{3 \times 10^4 s \, (s + 20)}{(s - 100) \, (s^2 + 700s + 2.5 \times 10^5)}.$$

Plot the gain/frequency and the phase/frequency graphs by Bode's method and hence estimate the frequencies at which the gain is 0 dB and the phase shift at each of these frequencies.

CHAPTER 6

POLYPHASE SYSTEMS

6.1 PRINCIPLES: STAR AND MESH CONNECTIONS

We shall deal exclusively with sinusoidal voltages and currents in the steady state.

A polyphase system is a generator-load pair in which the generator, instead of producing a single (phasor) voltage between one pair of terminals, produces two or more voltages* of the same magnitude and frequency but differing from one another in phase. With the exception of the two-phase system, in which the two voltages differ in phase by only $\pi/2$ radian, the generated voltages in an n-phase system form a symmetrical array of phasors $2\pi/n$ radian apart.

Each equivalent source of the generator feeds the corresponding branch of the load—as shown in Fig. 6.1(a)—so that, in general, $2n$ connecting wires are needed to supply the load. However, by commoning one of each terminal pair of both generator and load into one terminal,

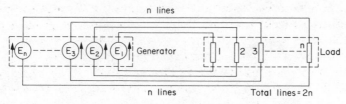

FIG. 6.1. (a) An n-phase generator supplying a load.

---

* Polyphase current sources are not considered here.

277

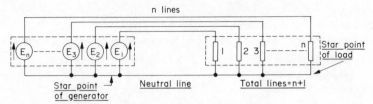

FIG. 6.1. (b) An *n*-phase star-connected system.

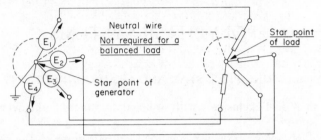

FIG. 6.1. (c) Conventional diagrammatic representation of the star-connected system.

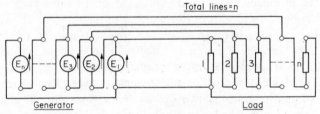

FIG. 6.1. (d) An *n*-phase mesh-connected system.

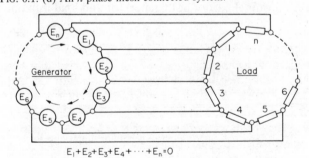

$$E_1 + E_2 + E_3 + E_4 + \cdots + E_n = 0$$

FIG. 6.1. (e) Alternative representation of mesh-connected system.

as shown in Fig. 6.1(b), only $(n + 1)$ wires are needed, and this can be reduced to n in the special case of a balanced load, i.e. a load in which all branches (or "phases") have the same impedance. A minimum of three wires is, however, needed for a two-phase system.

This is the so-called STAR system, the common terminal being referred to as the star point or neutral point, see Fig. 6.1(c).

An alternative arrangement of the generator and load phases—except for two-phase systems—is to connect them end to end in cyclic order to form a closed mesh, as shown in Fig. 6.1(d). The wires connecting load to generator are then taken to the n junctions of the n sources so that here, also, n wires are needed. There is no node corresponding to the star point and hence the mesh system on its own cannot be symmetrically located with respect to earth.

6.2 LINE AND PHASE QUANTITIES

There is no rule stipulating that the supply and the load must be connected in the same way (i.e. both star or both mesh). Indeed the commonest arrangement is with a star-connected supply and a mesh-connected load—allowing the system to be located with respect to earth, by earthing the star point.

The wires connecting the supply to the load are called the lines, and those lines other than the neutral are also sometimes called the outers. Each branch of the generator or load is called a "phase", so that the words "line" and "phase" may be used to describe the voltages and currents, as appropriate.

Referring to Fig. 6.1(c), it is clear that in the star system, the line current is equal to the corresponding phase current (since each line is connected to only one phase), whereas, in general, the line voltages (measured between any adjacent pair of outers) are not equal to the phase voltages (measured across a phase). The single exception to this rule occurs when $n = 6$; the line and phase voltages, defined as above, are equal in magnitude. On the other hand, in the mesh-connected systems, the line voltages (measured between two adjacent lines) and the corresponding phase voltages *are* equal, whereas the line and phase currents are not (since each line feeds two phases). Again an exception occurs when $n = 6$, with magnitude equality between line and phase currents.

6.3 ADVANTAGES OF POLYPHASE SYSTEMS

The choice of a polyphase, rather than a single-phase system, for the generation, transmission and utilisation of electric power may be justified on several important grounds.

   (i) In rotating machines, the space available for the windings is used more efficiently, with the result that, for a given size, the polyphase machine output power is greater. The increase amounts to 41% when $n = 2$, 50% when $n = 3$ and rises to a limiting value of 57% as n increases.

  (ii) For the same overall cross-sectional area of conductors, and the same voltage to earth, the transmission efficiency for the same power is greater. If the neutral conductor is absent the efficiency is independent of n (for $n > 2$). Including the effect of the neutral, the efficiency is only slightly less. For $n = 2$, the neutral, or third wire, cannot be ignored and the transmission efficiency is lower (see Problem 6.1).

 (iii) The total power transmitted by an n-phase supply to a balanced load is constant, and so the machine losses associated with the large time-dependent power component in a single-phase system are avoided. The polyphase machine is therefore more efficient. The effect is independent of n (see Problem 6.2).

 (iv) It is relatively easy to produce, in rotating machines, a rotating magnetic field, so rendering the polyphase induction motor inherently self-starting. This effect, also, is independent of n though some reduction of efficiency of the resulting machine occurs when $n = 2$.

  (v) On the comparatively few occasions when direct current is required, rectification produces less ripple than with a single-phase supply particularly when n is large.

PROBLEM 6.1

  (a) A single-phase transmission line delivers power P to a load at a voltage V with a 10% voltage drop from supply to load.

Assuming that this is all due to resistance in the line calculate the transmission efficiency.

(b) For the same overall conductor cross-section and the same transmitted power, calculate the transmission efficiency for a symmetrical n-phase system having a voltage V to earth on each line.

Solution

Since the loss of efficiency is due entirely to I^2R losses in the lines, we begin by calculating these.

(a) Assuming, for simplicity, a unity power factor load; if R is the load resistance, and r the resistance of each line, then:

$$P = I^2 . R \quad \text{where } I \text{ is the line current,}$$

Line loss $= I^2 . 2r$,

$$\text{Efficiency} = \frac{\text{received power}}{\text{transmitted power}} = \frac{\text{received power}}{\text{received power} + \text{line loss}}$$

$$= \frac{I^2R}{I^2R + 2I^2r} = \frac{R}{R + 2r}.$$

Total voltage drop in the line $= I . 2r$,

Voltage drop across the load $= V = IR$,

$$\text{Ratio} \; \frac{\text{voltage drop}}{\text{sending end voltage}} = \frac{2Ir}{IR + 2Ir} = \frac{2r}{R + 2r} = 10\%,$$

$$\therefore \quad r = \frac{R}{18}.$$

Hence, efficiency $= \dfrac{R}{R + R/9} = 90\%.$

(b) For a symmetrical n-phase system the same amount of conductor material must be divided amongst n line conductors, plus the neutral line (of half the cross-sectional area of each line). Hence, the effective number of conductors is:

$$(n + \tfrac{1}{2}).$$

Since the resistance is inversely proportional to the sectional area, the resistance of each line is:

$$r' = \left(\frac{n + \frac{1}{2}}{2}\right) r.$$

The same total power is transmitted by n phases, hence the current in each line is I/n (the voltage at the load being the same). Hence:

$$\text{Power loss per line} = \left(\frac{I}{n}\right)^2 \left(\frac{n + \frac{1}{2}}{2}\right) r,$$

$$\therefore \text{ Total loss for } n \text{ lines} = n\left(\frac{I}{n}\right)^2 \left(\frac{n + \frac{1}{2}}{2}\right) r = I^2 r\left(\frac{n + \frac{1}{2}}{2n}\right),$$

$$\text{Power transmitted} = I^2 R + I^2 r\left(\frac{n + \frac{1}{2}}{2n}\right).$$

Hence,

$$\text{Transmission efficiency} = \frac{I^2 R}{I^2 R + I^2 r\,(n + \frac{1}{2})/2n}$$

and, since $r = R/18$,

$$\text{Efficiency} = \frac{R}{R + (R/18)(n + \frac{1}{2})/2n}$$

$$= \frac{36n}{37n + \frac{1}{2}}, \tag{6.1}$$

$$\therefore \text{ Maximum possible efficiency} = \frac{36}{37} = 97.30\%.$$

The efficiencies for various values of n may be tabulated as shown in Table 6.1.

TABLE 6.1

n	Efficiency (%)
1	90
2	92.31*
3	96.86
4	96.97
5	97.04
6	97.08
∞	97.30

* Value included for comparison. Equation (6.1) is not valid for two-phase since the third wire carries more current than the outers, for a balanced load.

If the neutral wire were to be disregarded, the efficiency of transmission would remain at 97.30% for all $n > 2$.

PROBLEM 6.2

Prove that the power transmitted by a symmetrical n-phase supply to a balanced load is constant.

Solution

Let the n voltages be:

$$v_1(t) = \sqrt{2}V \cos \omega t,$$

$$v_2(t) = \sqrt{2}V \cos\left(\omega t - \frac{2\pi}{n}\right),$$

$$v_3(t) = \sqrt{2}V \cos\left(\omega t - \frac{4\pi}{n}\right), \text{ etc., or, in general:}$$

$$v_m(t) = \sqrt{2}V \cos\left[\omega t - \frac{2(m-1)\pi}{n}\right] \qquad m = 1, 2, 3, \ldots, n.$$

For a unity p.f. load:

$$i_m(t) = \sqrt{2}I \cos\left[\omega t - \frac{2(m-1)\pi}{n}\right] \qquad m = 1, 2, 3, \ldots, n.$$

Instantaneous power

$$p(t) = \sum_{m=1}^{m=n} v_m(t)\, i_m(t)$$

or

$$p(t) = 2 \sum_{m=1}^{m=n} VI \cos^2\left[\omega t - \frac{2(m-1)\pi}{n}\right]$$

$$= nVI + \sum_{m=1}^{m=n} VI \cos 2\left[\omega t - \frac{2(m-1)\pi}{n}\right] \qquad (6.2)$$

$$= nVI, \qquad (6.3)$$

since the second term of eqn. (6.2) represents a symmetrical set of phasors, which sums to zero. By coincidence eqn. (6.3) is valid also for a balanced two-phase system.

Since eqn. (6.3) is independent of time the instantaneous power is equal to the mean power, and, when the voltage and current are out of phase by angle ϕ, the result is:

$$P = nVI \cos \phi. \tag{6.4}$$

6.4 TWO- AND THREE-PHASE SYSTEMS

In consideration of the factors listed in section 6.3 and Problems 6.1 and 6.2, it will be clear that a choice of $n = 3$ offers most of the advantages associated with polyphase systems whilst retaining relatively simple circuitry. The increase in complexity and cost of power system equipment cannot be justified by the trivial improvement in machine output afforded by increasing n beyond 3, and, as a consequence, all large-scale power systems today are three-phase.

Although a two-phase system, needing only three connecting wires, might appear to offer a possible alternative, Table 6.1 shows that the transmission efficiency is appreciably lower than that of a three-phase system. So also is the power output of a machine of a given size. So that although this system was extensively used in the early years of this century, its use today is confined to small, special applications, such as to control systems.

When a d.c. supply is needed, it is most often derived, by a process of rectification, from the a.c. mains. The ripple content of such a supply falls as n is increased, and large values of n may easily be achieved, starting with a three-phase supply, by means of special transformer connections.

6.4.1 Relationships between line and phase values of voltage and current

(a) *Two-phase star-connected system*

For $n = 2$, the circuit of Fig. 6.1(c) reduces to that of Fig. 6.2(a). The two equivalent sources are connected at the neutral point N, the positive

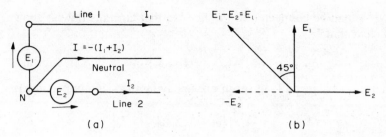

Fig. 6.2. (a) A two-phase system. (b) Phasor diagram.

directions of their e.m.f.s acting away from N. The two e.m.f.s differ in phase by $\pi/2$ radian and when $\mathbf{E}_2$ (or $\mathbf{V}_2$) lags $\mathbf{E}_1$ (or $\mathbf{V}_1$), as in the phasor diagram of Fig. 6.2(b), they are said to form a positive phase sequence system. When $\mathbf{E}_1$ lags $\mathbf{E}_2$ by $\pi/2$, this represents a negative phase sequence system.

Hence, for positive phase sequence:

$$\mathbf{V}_1 = \mathbf{V}_p \text{ (taken as the reference phasor)},$$

$$\mathbf{V}_2 = -j\mathbf{V}_p$$

and for negative phase sequence

$$\mathbf{V}_1 = \mathbf{V}_p,$$

$$\mathbf{V}_2 = j\mathbf{V}_p.$$

Clearly, the voltage between lines 1 and 2 (see Fig. 6.2(a)) is, for a positive phase sequence system,

$$\mathbf{V}_1 - \mathbf{V}_2 = \mathbf{V}_{1.2} \text{ (by the so-called double subscript notation)}$$

$$= \mathbf{V}_p - \mathbf{V}_2$$

$$= \mathbf{V}_p (1 + j)$$

$$= \sqrt{2} V_p \angle 45°.$$

This voltage is shown, derived graphically (by first reversing $\mathbf{V}_2$ and then adding it to $\mathbf{V}_1$), in Fig. 6.2(b).

If a load be connected to the lines so that currents flow as shown, it is clear that

$$\mathbf{I}_N = -(\mathbf{I}_1 + \mathbf{I}_2)$$

and for a balanced load (each phase having the same impedance),

$$|\mathbf{I}_N| = \sqrt{2}|\mathbf{I}_1|.$$

To calculate the power supplied to a balanced load in terms of the line values, we first make use of eqn. (6.4):

$$P = 2V_p I_p \cos \phi, \quad n = 2.$$

Substituting $V_l = \sqrt{2}V_p$ and $I_l = I_p$,

$$P = \sqrt{2}V_l I_l \cos \phi,$$

$\cos \phi$ is the phase p.f.

(b) *Three-phase star-connected system*

For $n = 3$, the circuit of Fig. 6.1(c) reduces to that of Fig. 6.3(a); also called the WYE system.

The positive direction of the e.m.f. in each case is from star point to line and the three e.m.f.s differ in phase by $2\pi/3$ rad, or 120°. The system has positive phase sequence when the phasors, taken clockwise, occur in the order 1—2—3, as in Fig. 6.3(b), and negative phase sequence when they occur in the order 1—3—2.

Hence, for a positive phase sequence system (P.P.S.):

$$\mathbf{V}_1 = \mathbf{V}(1 + j0) \qquad = \mathbf{V} \text{ (taken as the reference phasor)},$$

$$\mathbf{V}_2 = \mathbf{V}\left(-\tfrac{1}{2} - j\frac{\sqrt{3}}{2}\right) = \lambda^2\mathbf{V},$$

$$\mathbf{V}_3 = \mathbf{V}\left(-\tfrac{1}{2} + j\frac{\sqrt{3}}{2}\right) = \lambda\mathbf{V}$$

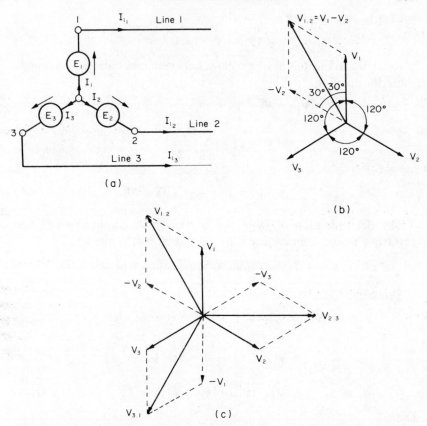

FIG. 6.3. (a) Three-phase star-connected system. (b) Phasor diagram showing derivation of line voltage. (c) Derivation of all three line voltages.

and, for a negative P.S. system:

$$\mathbf{V}_1 = \mathbf{V},$$

$$\mathbf{V}_2 = \lambda\mathbf{V},$$

$$\mathbf{V}_3 = \lambda^2\mathbf{V}.$$

The complex number $\lambda\,(=-\tfrac{1}{2}+j\,\sqrt{3}/2)$ performs a similar function to j—but rotates a phasor anticlockwise by 120° instead of 90°.

Clearly:

$$(1 + \lambda + \lambda^2) = 0. \tag{6.5}$$

Referring to Fig. 6.3(a), the voltage between lines 1 and 2 is, in double subscript notation,

$$\mathbf{V}_{1.2} = \mathbf{V}_1 - \mathbf{V}_2$$

$$= \mathbf{V} - \mathbf{V}\left(-\tfrac{1}{2} - j\frac{\sqrt{3}}{2}\right)$$

$$= \mathbf{V}\left(\frac{3}{2} + j\frac{\sqrt{3}}{2}\right) = \sqrt{3}\mathbf{V} \angle 30°. \tag{6.6}$$

The determination of $(\mathbf{V}_1 - \mathbf{V}_2)$ is performed graphically (by first reversing $\mathbf{V}_2$ and then adding it to $\mathbf{V}_1$) in Fig. 6.3(b) giving:

$$\mathbf{V}_{1.2} = 2V_1 \cos 30° = \sqrt{3}V_1, \text{ leading } \mathbf{V} \text{ by } 30°.$$

Similarly:

$$\mathbf{V}_{2.3} = \mathbf{V}_2 - \mathbf{V}_3$$

$$= \mathbf{V}\left(-\tfrac{1}{2} - j\frac{\sqrt{3}}{2}\right) - \mathbf{V}\left(-\tfrac{1}{2} + j\frac{\sqrt{3}}{2}\right)$$

$$= -j\sqrt{3}\mathbf{V} = \sqrt{3}\mathbf{V} \angle 90° \tag{6.7}$$

and

$$\mathbf{V}_{3.1} = \mathbf{V}_3 - \mathbf{V}_1$$

$$= \mathbf{V}\left(-\tfrac{1}{2} + j\frac{\sqrt{3}}{2}\right) - \mathbf{V}$$

$$= \mathbf{V}\left(-\frac{3}{2} + j\frac{\sqrt{3}}{2}\right) = \sqrt{3}\mathbf{V} \angle 150°. \tag{6.8}$$

Hence, the line voltages $\mathbf{V}_{1.2}$, $\mathbf{V}_{2.3}$ and $\mathbf{V}_{3.1}$ form a symmetrical set of phasors leading by $30°$ the set representing the phase voltages, and are $\sqrt{3} \times$ greater. These are shown, graphically derived, in Fig. 6.3(c).

If a load be connected to the generator represented in Fig. 6.3(a), currents flow as shown, and it is clear that:

$$\mathbf{I}_1 = \mathbf{I}_{l1},$$

$$\mathbf{I}_2 = \mathbf{I}_{l2},$$

$$\mathbf{I}_3 = \mathbf{I}_{l3},$$

i.e. the line and phase currents are equal.

The power supplied to a balanced load may be calculated by setting $n = 3$ in eqn. (6.4), thus:

$$P = 3V_p I_p \cos \phi,$$

$$= \sqrt{3} V_l I_l \cos \phi. \tag{6.9}$$

(c) *Three-phase mesh-connected system*

For $n = 3$, the circuit of Fig. 6.1(e) reduces to that of Fig. 6.4(a), in which the three sources are connected in cyclic order, taken clockwise. This arrangement is also called the DELTA (or Δ) -connected system.

For positive phase sequence:

$$\mathbf{V}_1 = \mathbf{V}(1 + j0) = \mathbf{V},$$

$$\mathbf{V}_2 = \mathbf{V}\left(-\tfrac{1}{2} - j\frac{\sqrt{3}}{2}\right) = \lambda^2 \mathbf{V},$$

$$\mathbf{V}_3 = \mathbf{V}\left(-\tfrac{1}{2} + j\frac{\sqrt{3}}{2}\right) = \lambda \mathbf{V}.$$

Note that, since $\mathbf{V}_1 + \mathbf{V}_2 + \mathbf{V}_3 = \mathbf{V}(1 + \lambda + \lambda^2) = 0$, the circulating current in the mesh is also zero. Clearly, the line voltages are equal to the phase voltages:

$$\mathbf{V}_{1.3} = \mathbf{V}_1,$$

$$\mathbf{V}_{2.1} = \mathbf{V}_2,$$

and

$$\mathbf{V}_{3.2} = \mathbf{V}_3.$$

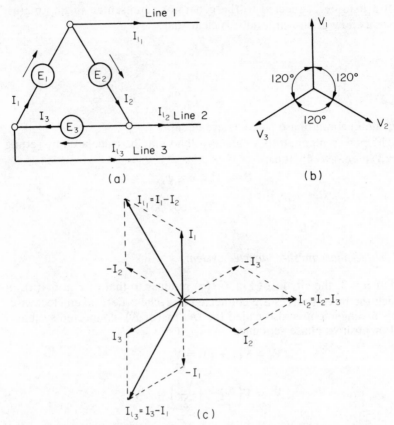

FIG. 6.4. (a) Three-phase mesh-connected system. (b) Voltage phasor diagram. (c) Derivation of line currents.

However, the line currents are not equal to the phase currents as in the star system.

Here

$$I_{l1} = I_1 - I_2,$$

$$I_{l2} = I_2 - I_3,$$

$$I_{l3} = I_3 - I_1.$$

For a balanced load, the phase currents are equal in magnitude and at 120° to one another. Hence:

$$\mathbf{I}_1 = \mathbf{I} \angle 0 = \mathbf{I}(1 + j0),$$

$$\mathbf{I}_2 = \mathbf{I}\left(-\tfrac{1}{2} - j\frac{\sqrt{3}}{2}\right) = \lambda^2\mathbf{I},$$

$$\mathbf{I}_3 = \mathbf{I}\left(-\tfrac{1}{2} + j\frac{\sqrt{3}}{2}\right) = \lambda\mathbf{I}.$$

Thus,

$$\mathbf{I}_{l1} = \mathbf{I}_1 - \mathbf{I}_2 = \mathbf{I}\left(1 + \tfrac{1}{2} + j\frac{\sqrt{3}}{2}\right) = \sqrt{3}\mathbf{I} \angle 30°,$$

$$\mathbf{I}_{l2} = \mathbf{I}_2 - \mathbf{I}_3 = \mathbf{I}\left(-\tfrac{1}{2} - j\frac{\sqrt{3}}{2} + \tfrac{1}{2} - j\frac{\sqrt{3}}{2}\right) = j\angle 3\mathbf{I}$$

$$= \sqrt{3}\mathbf{I} \angle -90°,$$

$$\mathbf{I}_{l3} = \mathbf{I}_3 - \mathbf{I}_1 = \mathbf{I}\left(-\tfrac{1}{2} + j\frac{\sqrt{3}}{2} - 1\right)$$

$$= \sqrt{3}\mathbf{I} \angle 150°.$$

So that the line currents (in a balanced system) form a symmetrical set of phasors leading by 30° the set representing the phase currents and $\sqrt{3} \times$ greater. Figure 6.4(c) shows the graphical derivation of these line currents.

The power supplied to a balanced load is, of course,

$$P = 3V_pI_p \cos \phi$$

$$= \sqrt{3}V_lI_l\cos \phi,$$

since

$$V_l = V_p$$

and

$$I_l = \sqrt{3}I_p,$$

an equation identical with eqn. (6.9).

It is important to remember that, in eqn. (6.9), the voltage and current are line values whereas the p.f. is that of each phase. In addition, it should be noted that it is immaterial whether the source e.m.f.s (in, for example, Fig. 6.4(a)) act clockwise or anticlockwise round the mesh and that the choice of numbering is purely arbitrary. It would, for example, be equally correct to select V_1 as that source across lines 1 and 2. What is important, however, is that all the e.m.f.s should act in the same direction round the mesh.

6.5 BALANCED-LOAD CALCULATIONS: THE USE OF SYMMETRY

One of the benefits of symmetry in balanced n-phase circuits is that the latter may be regarded as n single-phase circuits. This means that calculations need be made in detail on only one phase and that these results may be applied to the other phases.

PROBLEM 6.3

A 60-kW, three-phase mesh-connected induction motor has a full load power factor of 0.819 (lagging) and an efficiency of 87%. Given that the line voltage is 415 V, calculate the line and phase currents at full load.

Solution

It may be assumed that the motor presents a balanced load to the supply.

$$\text{Power output} = 60 \text{ kW},$$

$$\therefore \quad \text{Power input} \quad = \frac{60}{0.87} \text{kW} = 68,965.5 \text{ W}.$$

Using equation (6.9):

$$68,965.5 = \sqrt{3} \times 415 \times I_l \times 0.819.$$

$$\text{Giving } I_l = 117.15 \text{ A},$$

$$\therefore \quad \text{Motor phase current} = \frac{117.15}{\sqrt{3}} = 67.64 \text{ A}.$$

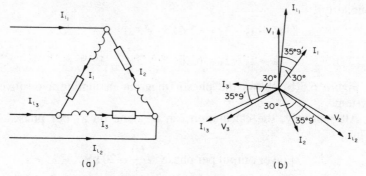

FIG. 6.5. (a) Mesh-connected load (see Problem 6.3). (b) Phasor diagram.

These are the magnitudes of the line and phase currents and each forms one of a set of phasors 120° apart. Thus, referring to Fig. 6.5(a), if V_1, the voltage across phase 1, is taken as the reference phasor,

$$V_1 = 415 \text{ V} = 415 \angle 0°,$$

$$V_2 = \lambda^2 415 = 415 \angle -120°,$$

$$V_3 = \lambda 415 = 415 \angle -240°.$$

Hence, since $\cos^{-1} 0.819 = 35° 9'$,

$$I_1 = 67.64 \angle -35° 9',$$

$$I_2 = 67.64 \angle -155° 9',$$

$$I_3 = 67.64 \angle -275° 9',$$

and the line currents are calculated, as usual, by:

$$I_{l1} = I_1 - I_2$$

$$= 67.64 (\angle -35° 9' - \angle -155° 9')$$

$$= 67.64 (\cos 35° 9' - j \sin 35° 9' - \cos 155° 9' + j \sin 155° 9')$$

$$= 67.64 [(\cos 35° 9' + \cos 24° 51') + j(\sin 24° 51' - \sin 35° 9')]$$

$$= 67.64 (1.725 - j0.1555)$$

$$= 67.64 \times \sqrt{3} \angle -5° 9' \text{ A}.$$

Similarly,

$$\mathbf{I}_{l2} = \mathbf{I}_2 - \mathbf{I}_3 = 67.64 \times \sqrt{3} \angle -125° 9' \text{ A},$$

$$\mathbf{I}_{l3} = \mathbf{I}_3 - \mathbf{I}_1 = 67.64 \times \sqrt{3} \angle -245° 9' \text{ A}.$$

Figure 6.5(b) shows the phasor diagram, assuming a positive P.S. system.

Alternatively, the calculation can be done on a "per phase" basis. Thus,

$$\text{power output per phase} = \frac{60}{3} = 20 \text{ kW}$$

and

$$\text{power input per phase} = \frac{20}{0.87} = 22{,}988 \text{ W}.$$

Since the motor is mesh-connected the voltage across each phase is 415 V, and:

$$22{,}988 = 415 I \cos \phi$$

$$= 415 \times I \times 0.819,$$

giving

$$I_p = 67.64 \text{ A}.$$

Thus,

$$\text{line current} = \sqrt{3} \times 67.64 = 117.15 \text{ A}.$$

There is no real need, in either method, to use complex numbers because we know that:

(i) each phase current lags the corresponding phase voltage by $35° 9'$,

(ii) each line current leads the corresponding phase current by $30°$.

And by symmetry, as explained above, once one phase current and one line current have been calculated, the others are the same except for phase differences.

PROBLEM 6.4

Three coils, each of resistance 5 Ω and inductive reactance 10 Ω, are connected (a) in star, (b) in mesh across a 440-V, three-phase supply. Each coil is shunted by a capacitor of reactance 20 Ω. In each case, calculate the line and phase currents and the total power absorbed.

Solution

Since the load is balanced, calculation may be on a "per phase" basis. The impedance of each phase is first calculated.

Admittance of coil,

$$Y_1(j\omega) = \frac{R}{Z^2} - j\frac{X}{Z^2} = \frac{5}{125} - j\frac{10}{125}$$

$$= (0.04 - j0.08) \text{ S.}$$

Admittance of capacitor,

$$Y_2(j\omega) = j\frac{1}{20} = j0.05 \text{ S.}$$

Total admittance $= 0.04 - j0.08 + j0.05$

$$= (0.04 - j0.03) \text{ S} = Y_p(j\omega)$$

$$= 0.05 \angle -36°\,52' \text{ S,}$$

$$\therefore \quad Z_p = \frac{1}{Y_p} = 20 \angle 36°\,52' \text{ } \Omega.$$

(a) When three such impedances are connected in star, the voltage across each is:

$$\frac{440}{\sqrt{3}} = 254 \text{ V.}$$

Taking phase 1 as the reference phase:

$$I_1 = \frac{254}{20 \angle 36°\,52'} = 12.7 \angle -36°\,52' \text{ A.}$$

This is also the line current in line 1.

$$\text{Power} = 3 \times \text{power per phase}$$

$$= 3 \times 254 \times 12.7 \cos 36°\,52'$$

$$= 7.742 \text{ kW,}$$

or

$$\text{Power} = \sqrt{3} V_l I_l \cos \phi$$

$$= \sqrt{3} \times 440 \times 12.7 \times 0.8$$

$$= 7.742 \text{ kW.}$$

(b) When mesh-connected, the reference phasor (V_1) of part (a) may be retained or a new one chosen to correspond with the line voltage across, say, lines 1 and 2.

Adopting the latter alternative, $V_{1.2} = 440$ volts,

$$I_{p1} = \frac{440}{20 \angle 36° 52'} = 22 \angle -36° 52' \text{ A},$$

where phase 1 is connected across lines 1 and 2.

The line current, I_{l1}, is:

$$I_{l1} = \sqrt{3} \times 22 \angle (-36° 52' + 30°)$$

$$= 38.105 \angle -6° 52' \text{ A}.$$

$$\text{Power} = 3 \times \text{power per phase}$$

$$= 3 \times 440 \times 22 \cos 36° 52'$$

$$= 23.232 \text{ kW}$$

or

$$\text{Power} = \sqrt{3} \times V_l I_l \cos \phi$$

$$= \sqrt{3} \times 440 \times 38.105 \times 0.8$$

$$= 23.232 \text{ kW}.$$

This result shows that the power absorbed by three equal impedances connected in mesh across a three-phase supply is 3 times that when they are star-connected across the same supply.

6.6 UNBALANCE

Unbalance is produced when the three phases of the load cease to be identical. Clearly the benefits of symmetry no longer exist and all three phases must be dealt with separately. This is still comparatively easy for a mesh-connected system and for a four-wire, star system (i.e. three lines and neutral), but when the neutral wire is removed one of the circuit-analysis methods of Chapter 4 must be used.

PROBLEM 6.5

The load of Problem 6.4 is modified, by removing one of the capacitors, and the resulting unbalanced load is connected in mesh across a 400-V, three-phase supply, the modified phase across lines 1 and 2.

Calculate the line and phase currents, the total power absorbed and the power factor. The phase sequence is 1—2—3.

Solution

Impedance of the modified phase $= 5 + j10$

$$= 11.18 \angle 63° 26' \ \Omega.$$

Figure 6.6(a) shows the three phases connected as described. Let $V_{1.3}$ be the reference phasor $= 400 \angle 0°$ volts.

Then

$$V_{2.1} = \lambda^2 400 = 400 \angle -120° \text{ volts}$$

and

$$V_{3.2} = \lambda 400 = 400 \angle -240° \text{ volts}.$$

$Z_1 = 20 \angle 36° 52' \ \Omega$, $Z_2 = 11.18 \angle 63° 26' \ \Omega$ and $Z_3 = 20 \angle 36° 52' \ \Omega$,

$$\therefore \ I_1 = \frac{400}{20 \angle 26° 52'} = 20 \angle -36° 52' \text{ A},$$

$$I_2 = \frac{400 \angle -120°}{11.18 \angle 63° 26'} = 35.78 \angle -183° \ 26' \text{ A}$$

and

$$I_3 = \frac{400 \angle -240°}{20 \angle 36° 52'} = 20 \angle -276° 52' \text{ A}.$$

Referring to the diagram, Fig. 6.6(a),

$$I_{l1} = I_1 - I_2 = 20 \angle -36° 52' - 35.78 \angle -183° 26'$$

$$= 16 - j12 + 35.716 - j2.143$$

$$= 51.716 - j14.143$$

$$= 53.614 \angle -15° 17' \text{ A}.$$

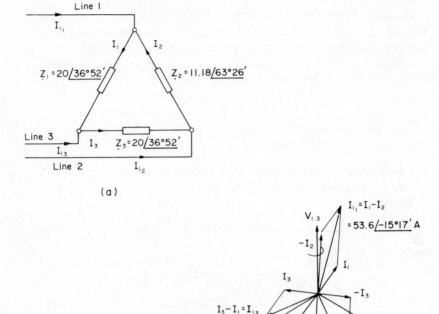

FIG. 6.6. (a) Unbalanced mesh-connected load, see Problem 6.5. (b) Corresponding phasor diagram.

Similarly:

$$\mathbf{I}_{l2} = -38.107 - j17.714$$

$$= 42.023 \angle -155° 4' \text{ A}$$

and

$$\mathbf{I}_{l3} = -13.609 + j31.857$$

$$= 34.642 \angle 113° 8' \text{ A}.$$

As a check, the line currents should sum to zero:

$$I_{l1} = 51.716 - j14.143,$$

$$I_{l2} = -38.107 - j17.714,$$

$$\underline{I_{l3} = -13.609 + j31.857.}$$

$$\text{Sum} = 0 + j0.$$

The phase power may be calculated from $P = VI \cos \phi$ or by taking the product $Re[VI^*]$, where I^* is the conjugate of I. Choosing the second alternative:

Phase 1   Complex VA $= 400 \times 20 \angle 36° 52' = 6400 + j4800.$
Phase 2   Complex VA
$$= 400 \angle -120° \times 35.78 \angle 183° 26' = 6400 + j12,800.$$
Phase 3   Complex VA $= 400 \angle -240° \times 20 \angle 276° 52' = 6400 + j4800.$

$$\text{Sum} = 19,200 + j22,400.$$

The phase powers are the same because the only difference between the phases is the shunt capacitance—which absorbs no power. Hence, the total power is 19.2 kW and the total reactive volt-amperes is 22.4 kVAr.

Now,

$$\text{kVA} = \sqrt{(\text{kW})^2 + (\text{kVAr})^2}$$

$$= \sqrt{19.2^2 + 22.4^2}$$

$$= 29.50.$$

The power factor is defined as ratio $\dfrac{\text{Total power}}{\text{Sum of phase VA}}$,

$$\therefore \quad \text{P.F.} = \frac{19.2}{29.5} = 0.651 \text{ (lagging)}.$$

The phasor diagram of Fig. 6.6(b) shows all the currents and voltages. The three line voltages, $V_{1.3}$, $V_{2.1}$ and $V_{3.2}$, are drawn first (at 120° to one another). Taking $V_{1.3}$ as the reference the three phase currents I_1, I_2 and I_3 at lagging angles of, respectively, 36° 52', 183° 26' and 276° 52'.

Finally, the three line currents are obtained by combining the phase currents in pairs, viz.

$$\mathbf{I}_{l1} = \mathbf{I}_1 - \mathbf{I}_2, \ \mathbf{I}_{l2} = \mathbf{I}_2 - \mathbf{I}_3 \text{ and } \mathbf{I}_{l3} = \mathbf{I}_3 - \mathbf{I}_1.$$

Unbalanced, star-connected loads supplied from a three-phase, four-wire supply can also be dealt with one phase at a time since the presence of the neutral ensures that the voltages across the three phases remain equal and at 120°.

PROBLEM 6.6

Three loads, $\mathbf{Z}_1 = 10 \angle 30° \ \Omega$, $\mathbf{Z}_2 = 15 \angle -45° \ \Omega$ and $\mathbf{Z}_3 = 20 \angle 60° \ \Omega$ star-connected to a 440-V, three-phase, four-wire supply. Calculate the line currents, the neutral current and the total power absorbed, and sketch the phasor diagram. The phase sequence is 1—2—3.

Solution

The diagram of Fig. 6.7(a) shows the arrangement of the loads. The voltages line-to-neutral are symmetrical and of magnitude $440/\sqrt{3} = 254 \text{ V}$.

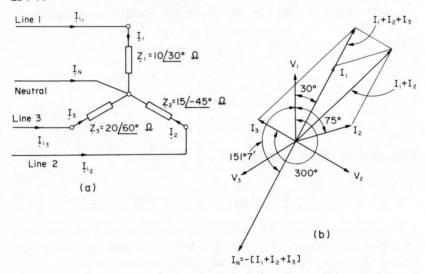

(a)

(b)

$$I_N = -[I_1 + I_2 + I_3]$$

FIG. 6.7. (a) A four-wire star-connected load, see Problem 6.6. (b) Phasor diagram.

Taking $\mathbf{V}_1$ as the reference phasor:

$$\mathbf{V}_1 = 254 \angle 0° \text{ volts,}$$

$$\mathbf{V}_2 = 254 \angle -120° \text{ volts,}$$

$$\mathbf{V}_3 = 254 \angle -240° \text{ volts,}$$

$$\mathbf{I}_1 = \mathbf{I}_{l1} = \frac{\mathbf{V}_1}{\mathbf{Z}_1} = \frac{254}{10 \angle 30°} = 25.4 \angle -30° \text{ A} = (21.997 - j12.700) \text{ A,}$$

$$\mathbf{I}_2 = \mathbf{I}_{l2} = \frac{\mathbf{V}_2}{\mathbf{Z}_2} = \frac{254 \angle -120°}{15 \angle -45°} = 16.933 \angle -75° \text{ A} = (4.383 - j16.356) \text{ A,}$$

$$\mathbf{I}_3 = \mathbf{I}_{l3} = \frac{\mathbf{V}_3}{\mathbf{Z}_3} = \frac{254 \angle -240°}{20 \angle 60°} = 12.700 \angle -300° \text{ A} = (6.350 + j10.999) \text{ A.}$$

And the neutral current,

$$\mathbf{I}_N = -[\mathbf{I}_1 + \mathbf{I}_2 + \mathbf{I}_3]$$

$$= (-32.730 + j18.058) \text{ A}$$

$$= 37.381 \angle 151° 7' \text{ A.}$$

The power into each phase is calculated separately:

Phase 1 $P_1 = 254 \times 25.4 \cos 30°\ \ \ = \ \ 5.587 \text{ kW}$

Phase 2 $P_2 = 254 \times 16.933 \cos 45° = \ \ 3.041 \text{ kW}$

Phase 3 $P_3 = 254 \times 12.700 \cos 60° = \ \ \underline{1.613 \text{ kW}}$

$$\text{Total} = \underline{\underline{10.241 \text{ kW}}}$$

The phasor diagram is shown in Fig. 6.7(b).

PROBLEM 6.7

The neutral wire is removed from the circuit of Problem 6.6. Recalculate the line currents and determine the change in potential of the star point.

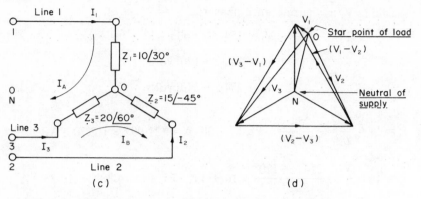

FIG. 6.7. (c) A three-wire star-connected load, see Problem 6.7. (d) Phasor diagram: determination of the star-point-to-neutral voltage.

Solution

Since the constraint imposed by the neutral wire no longer exists, the star point potential changes and the three line-to-neutral voltages are neither equal nor at 120° to one another. The three line-to-line voltages are, however, unaffected and this fact forms the basis for the solution. Referring to Fig. 6.7(c), let $\mathbf{I}_A$ and $\mathbf{I}_B$ be two mesh currents placed as shown.

The mesh-current rule gives:

$$(\mathbf{Z}_1 + \mathbf{Z}_3)\mathbf{I}_A - \mathbf{I}_B\mathbf{Z}_3 = \mathbf{V}_1 - \mathbf{V}_3 = \mathbf{V}_{1.3} \qquad (6.10)$$

and

$$(\mathbf{Z}_2 + \mathbf{Z}_3)\mathbf{I}_B - \mathbf{I}_A\mathbf{Z}_3 = \mathbf{V}_3 - \mathbf{V}_2 = \mathbf{V}_{3.2}. \qquad (6.11)$$

Now,

$$\mathbf{V}_{1.3} = \mathbf{V}_1 - \mathbf{V}_3 = 254 - \left(-\tfrac{1}{2} + j\frac{\sqrt{3}}{2}\right) 254 = 381 - j220$$

and

$$\mathbf{V}_{3.2} = \mathbf{V}_3 - \mathbf{V}_2 = 254\left(-\tfrac{1}{2} + j\frac{\sqrt{3}}{2}\right) - 254\left(-\tfrac{1}{2} - j\frac{\sqrt{3}}{2}\right) = j440.$$

Also,

$$\mathbf{Z}_1 = 10 \angle 30° = (8.66 + j5)\ \Omega,$$

$$\mathbf{Z}_2 = 15 \angle -45° = (10.61 - j10.61)\ \Omega,$$

$$\mathbf{Z}_3 = 20 \angle 60° = (10 + j17.32)\ \Omega.$$

Substituting these values into eqns. (6.10) and (6.11) gives:

$$\mathbf{I}_A(18.66 + j22.32) - \mathbf{I}_B(10 + j17.32) = 381 - j220$$

and

$$-\mathbf{I}_A(10 + j17.32 + \mathbf{I}_B(20.61 + j6.71) = j440$$

from which

$$\mathbf{I}_A = 6.01 \angle 26°15'\ A$$

and

$$\mathbf{I}_B = 25.8 \angle 71°4'\ A.$$

Referring again to Fig. 6.7(c) it is clear that:

$$\mathbf{I}_1 = \mathbf{I}_A, \mathbf{I}_2 = -\mathbf{I}_B = 25.8 \angle -108°56'\ A$$

and

$$\mathbf{I}_3 = (\mathbf{I}_B - \mathbf{I}_A) = 25.8 \angle 71°4' - 6.01 \angle 26°15'$$

$$= 21.95 \angle 82°12'\ A.$$

The star-point potential (relative to that of the neutral line) can be found by first calculating its potential relative to any one line.

Thus, choosing line 1, the voltage line 1-to-star point, $\mathbf{V}_{1.0}$, is:

$$6.01 \angle 26°15' \times 10 \angle 30° = 50.1 \angle 56°15'\ V$$

$$= 33.39 + j49.97$$

and that between load star point and neutral is, therefore,

$$254 \angle 0° - (33.39 + j49.97) = 220.61 - j49.97$$

$$= \underline{226.2 \angle -12°46'\ \text{volts}.}$$

ECT – U

The phasor diagram (Fig. 6.7(d)) shows that the star point has moved its potential by the amount NO to the point O, outside the triangle formed from the three line-voltage phasors. The latter remain fixed irrespective of the character of the load, but the individual phase voltages change with the constraint that their phasor differences must be constant. Thus

$$|\mathbf{V}_1 - \mathbf{V}_2| = |\mathbf{V}_2 - \mathbf{V}_3| = |\mathbf{V}_3 - \mathbf{V}_1| = 440 \text{ volts.}$$

Each phase voltage may be determined from the phase impedance and phase current—hence, also, the power, VAr and power factor, by the methods used in Problem 6.5.

An alternative, and perhaps more elegant, method for determining the star-point-to-neutral p.d. is to use Thévenin's theorem.

Thus, if, in the circuit of Fig. 6.7(c), the points O and N are joined (i.e. the neutral wire is replaced), the current which flows along this wire is equal to the open circuit voltage $\mathbf{V}_{ON}$ divided by the combined impedance looking into 0, i.e. $\mathbf{Z}_1$, $\mathbf{Z}_2$ and $\mathbf{Z}_3$ in parallel. This current has already been determined in Problem 6.6. Hence letting

$$\mathbf{Y}_1 = \frac{1}{\mathbf{Z}_1}, \mathbf{Y}_2 = \frac{1}{\mathbf{Z}_2} \text{ and } \mathbf{Y}_3 = \frac{1}{\mathbf{Z}_3},$$

$$\mathbf{V}_{NO} = \frac{\mathbf{I}_N}{\mathbf{Y}_1 + \mathbf{Y}_2 + \mathbf{Y}_3} = \frac{37.381}{0.1 \angle -30° + 0.0667 \angle 45° + 0.05 \angle -60°}$$

$$= 226.1 \angle 167° 15',$$

$$\therefore \quad \mathbf{V}_{ON} = 226.1 \angle -12° 45' \text{ volts.}$$

6.7 THE MEASUREMENT OF POWER AND POWER FACTOR IN THREE-PHASE CIRCUITS

6.7.1 The wattmeter

The wattmeter is an indicating instrument having both a current circuit and a voltage circuit, which are connected, respectively, in series with and in parallel with the load in which it is desired to measure the power.

The construction and operation of the instrument are such that the indication is equal to the mean power in the load. Hence:

$$\text{Indication} = VI \cos \phi \qquad (6.12)$$

where V and I are the r.m.s. values of voltage and current and ϕ is the angle of phase difference between them.

To conform fully with eqn. (6.12) the wattmeter must give a reversed indication when the connections to *either* its voltage circuit *or* its current circuit are reversed, since this corresponds to the introduction of a 180° phase shift between V and I.

Probably the most common type of wattmeter is the so-called dynamometer instrument, in which the current circuit comprises a set of fixed field coils, of very low resistance, and the voltage circuit, a single pivoted coil of high resistance (or having a resistor of high resistance connected in series with it).

One such instrument is sufficient to measure the power in a single-phase circuit, but in three-phase systems at least two are required, unless the load is balanced.

6.7.2 Connection of the wattmeter in three-phase systems

CASE 1 Four-wire system: star point available

(a) *Unbalanced load*

Each phase power is measured separately—as shown in the diagram of Fig. 6.8(a)—by connecting a wattmeter in each line with the voltage coil across the corresponding line to neutral. Figure 6.8(b) gives the phasor diagram, and it can be seen that if P_n is the power measured by W_n:

$$\left.\begin{array}{l} P_1 = I_1 V_1 \cos \phi_1 = Re[\mathbf{I}_1^* \mathbf{V}_1], \\[4pt] P_2 = I_2 V_2 \cos \phi_2 = Re[\mathbf{I}_2^* \mathbf{V}_2] \\[4pt] P_3 = I_3 V_3 \cos \phi_3 = Re[\mathbf{I}_3^* \mathbf{V}_3] \end{array}\right\} \qquad (6.13)$$

and
and

$$P = P_1 + P_2 + P_3. \qquad (6.14)$$

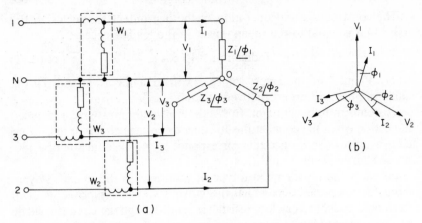

FIG. 6.8. (a) Measurement of power in four-wire load. (b) Phasor diagram.

The phase volt-amperes may be measured by including an ammeter in series with, and a voltmeter across, each phase. Then, for any phase:

$$(VAr) = \sqrt{(VA)^2 - P^2}$$

so that:

$$\text{total } (VAr) = (VAr)_1 + (VAr)_2 + (VAr)_3$$

and

$$\text{power factor} = \frac{P}{\sqrt{P^2 + (VAr)^2}}. \qquad (6.15)$$

(b) *Balanced load*

Clearly, in this case, $P_1 = P_2 = P_3$ and $P = 3P_1$, say. Hence only one wattmeter (in any phase) is needed. The overall power factor is the same as that in any one phase:

$$\text{power factor} = \frac{P_1}{V_1 I_1}.$$

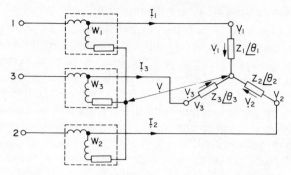

FIG. 6.9. General case of power measurement in three-wire load.

CASE 2 Three-wire system: star point not available

Considering the general case of an unbalanced star-connected load having a wattmeter in each line—as shown in Fig. 6.9. Let $\mathbf{V}$ be the potential difference between the load star point and that of the three wattmeter voltage circuits. Then:

$$\left.\begin{aligned} P_1 &= Re[\mathbf{I}_1^*(\mathbf{V}_1 - \mathbf{V})], \\ P_2 &= Re[\mathbf{I}_2^*(\mathbf{V}_2 - \mathbf{V})], \\ P_3 &= Re[\mathbf{I}_3^*(\mathbf{V}_3 - \mathbf{V})]. \end{aligned}\right\} \tag{6.16}$$

$$\therefore \quad P = P_1 + P_2 + P_3$$

$$= Re[\mathbf{I}_1^*(\mathbf{V}_1 - \mathbf{V}) + \mathbf{I}_2^*(\mathbf{V}_2 - \mathbf{V}) + \mathbf{I}_3^*(\mathbf{V}_3 - \mathbf{V})]$$

where the starred phasors represent their complex conjugates.

$$\therefore \quad P = Re[\mathbf{I}_1^*\mathbf{V}_1 + \mathbf{I}_2^*\mathbf{V}_2 + \mathbf{I}_3^*\mathbf{V}_3 - \mathbf{V}(\mathbf{I}_1^* + \mathbf{I}_2^* + \mathbf{I}_3^*)]$$

$$= Re[\mathbf{I}_1^*\mathbf{V}_1 + \mathbf{I}_2^*\mathbf{V}_2 + \mathbf{I}_3^*\mathbf{V}_3] \tag{6.17}$$

since the three currents sum to zero. Thus,

P = the sum of the powers in the phases

= total power.

This result is valid whatever the magnitude and phase of V. Hence:

(a) The load may be balanced or unbalanced.

(b) Three wattmeters having different voltage circuit resistances may be used; their readings will, in general, all be different.

(c) If the load is balanced, and the wattmeters are identical (i.e. $V = 0$) the three readings will be the same. One wattmeter could then be used, together with a Y-box (a pair of resistors both of resistance equal to that of the wattmeter voltage circuit. In use they are connected, one to each line so that, together with the voltage circuit of the wattmeter, they produce a true star point.) The total power is $3\times$ its indication.

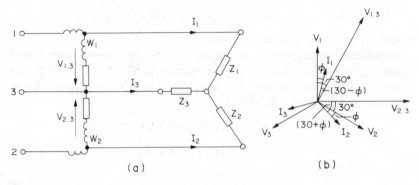

FIG. 6.10. (a) Circuit arrangement for two-wattmeter method for power measurement. (b) Phasor diagram.

(d) If, with three wattmeters, the star point of the voltage circuits is located on one of the lines, the wattmeter connected in that line will indicate zero, and the remaining two wattmeters will together indicate the total power. Figure 6.10(a) shows the circuit arrangement for the two-wattmeter method.

The mesh-star transformation can be used to show that the method is valid also for a mesh-connected load.

There is no simple method for measuring the power factor of an unbalanced three-wire load, corresponding to that of Case 1(a) above.

6.7.3 Power-factor measurement for balanced loads

Assuming a balanced load of lagging p.f. in Fig. 6.10(a), eqns. (6.16) become:

$$P_1 = Re[\mathbf{I}_1^*(\mathbf{V}_1 - \mathbf{V}_3)] = VI\cos(30° - \phi), \qquad (6.18)$$

$$P_2 = Re[\mathbf{I}_2^*(\mathbf{V}_2 - \mathbf{V}_3)] = VI\cos(30° + \phi) \qquad (6.19)$$

and

$$P_3 = 0.$$

Since

$$\mathbf{I}_1 = \mathbf{I}_2 = \mathbf{I}_3 = \mathbf{I}, \text{ say,}$$

and

$$|\mathbf{V}_1 - \mathbf{V}_3| = |\mathbf{V}_2 - \mathbf{V}_3| = \mathbf{V}, \text{ say.}$$

Hence,

$$P_1 + P_2 = VI[\cos(30° + \phi) + \cos(30° - \phi)]$$

$$= \sqrt{3}VI\cos\phi.$$

PROBLEM 6.8

The current in each line of a 440-V, three-wire supply feeding a balanced load is 25 A and two wattmeters are used for power measurement.

Show how the total power and the individual meter indications vary as the load power factor changes from zero lagging to zero leading. The phase sequence is 1—2—3.

Solution

Using eqns. (6.18) and (6.19),

$$P_1 = 25 \times 440\cos(30° - \phi) = 11\cos(30° - \phi) \text{ kW}$$

and

$$P_2 = 25 \times 440\cos(30° + \phi) = 11\cos(30° + \phi) \text{ kW}$$

and

$$P = P_1 + P_2 = \sqrt{3} \times 11 \cos \phi = 19.053 \cos \phi \, \text{kW}.$$

Selecting particular values of p.f.:

(i) when p.f. = 1, $\phi = 0$, $\therefore P_1 = P_2 = 11 \cos 30° = 9.526 \, \text{kW}$
   and $P = 2 \times 9.526 = 19.052 \, \text{kW}$;

(ii) when p.f. = 0.866 lagging, $\phi = 30°$, $P_1 = 11 \cos 0 = 11 \, \text{kW}$,
   $P_2 = 11 \cos 60° = 5.5 \, \text{kW}$
   and $P = P_1 + P_2 = 16.5 \, \text{kW}$;

(iii) when p.f. = 0.5 lagging, $\phi = 60°$, $P_1 = 11 \cos(-30°) = 9.526 \, \text{kW}$,
   $P_2 = 11 \cos 90° = 0$
   and $P = P_1 + P_2 = 9.526 \, \text{kW}$;

(iv) when p.f. = 0 lagging, $\phi = 90°$, $P_1 = 11 \cos(-60°) = 5.5 \, \text{kW}$,
   $P_2 = 11 \cos 120° = -5.5 \, \text{kW}$
   and $P = P_1 + P_2 = 0$.

Figure 6.11 shows the variation in P_1, P_2 and $(P_1 + P_2)$ over the whole

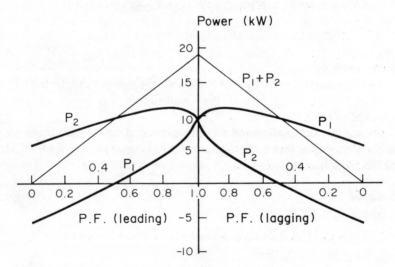

FIG. 6.11. Variation of P_1, P_2 and $(P_1 + P_2)$ with power factor for the two-wattmeter method.

range of power factor. It can be seen that, for leading power factors, the roles of W_1 and W_2 are interchanged.

From eqns. (6.18) and (6.19),

$$\frac{P_1}{P_2} = \frac{\cos(30° - \phi)}{\cos(30° + \phi)} = r, \text{ say,}$$

or

$$r = \frac{\sqrt{3} + \tan \phi}{\sqrt{3} - \tan \phi},$$

which becomes, on rearranging:

$$\cos \phi = \frac{1 + r}{2\sqrt{1 - r + r^2}}. \tag{6.20}$$

This expression, which, of course, applies only to balanced loads, shows that the power factor can be calculated from the two wattmeter readings without any knowledge of the currents or voltages in the circuit. The p.f. may be identified as leading or lagging only when connection details of the circuit and the phase sequence are known.

For practical use, a graph of $\cos \phi$ against r is usually available so that the power factor may be quickly found. For this purpose, P_1 and P_2 are chosen so that $-1 < r < +1$.

PROBLEM 6.9

Two wattmeters, connected to measure the power delivered to a three-wire, 415-V balanced load, gave readings of 48.2 kW and −32.7 kW. Calculate the total power, the line current and the power factor.

Solution

$$P = P_1 + P_2 = 48.2 - 32.7 = 15.5 \text{ kW,}$$

$$r = -\frac{48.2}{32.7} = -1.474.$$

Substituting this value into eqn. (6.20) gives:

$$\cos \phi = 0.1099.$$

[Alternatively: $r = -\dfrac{32.7}{48.2} = -0.6784$, from which eqn. (6.20) also

gives

$$\cos \phi = 0.1099.]$$

$$P = \sqrt{3}VI \cos \phi = 15,500 \text{ W}$$

or

$$I = \frac{15,500}{\sqrt{3} \times 415 \times 0.1099} = 196.2 \text{ A}.$$

PROBLEMS VI

1. Three loads are connected in star across a three-phase, four-wire, 415-V, 50-Hz mains supply. Each load consists of a coil of inductance 0.5 H and resistance 40 Ω.
   Calculate (a) the total power supplied to the load, (b) the line currents, (c) the power factor and (d) the neutral current.
2. Three 16-μF capacitors are connected in star across the load of Problem VI.1.
   Calculate the new-line currents and the power factor of the total load on the supply.
3. Given that the three capacitors of Problem VI.2 are connected in mesh instead of star, calculate the new current taken from the supply and the overall power factor.
4. Three loads of 3 kW, 4 kW and 5 kW all at unity power factor are star-connected to lines 1, 2 and 3, respectively, of a 440-V, three-phase, four-wire supply.
   Calculate the line currents and the neutral current. The phase sequence is 1, 2, 3.
5. Three impedances, 20 ∠0° Ω, 16 ∠30° Ω and 10 ∠−60° Ω are connected in mesh across lines 1 and 2, 2 and 3, and 3 and 1, respectively, of 400-V, three-phase mains supply.
   Calculate the phase currents and the line currents. The phase sequence is 1, 2, 3.
6. A 440-V, three-phase power system carries the following loads connected in mesh: across lines 1 and 2 (10 +j10) Ω, across lines 2 and 3 (20 −j15) Ω and across lines 3 and 1 (15 +j5) Ω.
   (a) Calculate the line currents and the power supplied to the load.
   (b) Given that the load between lines 2 and 3 is now disconnected, calculate the new line currents and the total power supplied.
   The phase sequence is 1, 2, 3.
7. Three equal loads of 5 kVA at 0.8 power factor (lagging) are connected in star to a 415-V, three-phase, three-wire supply system.
   Calculate the total power supplied and the line currents.
   The load connected to line 3 is then short-circuited. Calculate the total power supplied and the three line currents under these conditions. The phase sequence is 1, 2, 3.

8. Three non-reactive resistors are star-connected to a 415-V, three-phase, three-wire balanced supply and the voltages across two of them are 260 V.

   Determine the magnitude of the voltage across the third resistor and the phase relationships between all three phase voltages. (*Hint:* work from the phasor diagram.)

9. The red, yellow and blue lines of a three-phase, three-wire, 440-V supply carry resistive loads of 5 Ω, 10 Ω and 15 Ω, respectively, in star.

   Calculate the voltage between star point and neutral and the current and power in each resistor. Phase sequence *R, Y, B*.

10. Two dynamometer wattmeters are connected in the usual way to measure the power in a balanced three-phase load.

    With the aid of suitable circuit and phasor diagrams, show that

$$\tan \phi = \sqrt{3} \left(\frac{W_2 - W_1}{W_2 + W_1} \right)$$

   where W_1 and W_2 are the two wattmeter readings and ϕ is the load phase angle.

   Two wattmeters are used to measure the power input to a 10-kW, 415-V, three-phase balanced load and the ratio of their readings is +0.5.

   Calculate the line current, the power factor of the load and the two wattmeter readings.

11. An unbalanced star-connected load, as follows, is connected to a three-phase, four-wire, 415-V power supply system: $\mathbf{Z}_1 = 20 + j15 \ \Omega$, line 1 to neutral, $\mathbf{Z}_2 = 20 - j20 \ \Omega$, line 2 to neutral, $\mathbf{Z}_3 = 40 + j10 \ \Omega$, line 3 to neutral. Three wattmeters are connected, one current coil in each line with the corresponding voltage coil from that line to neutral.

    Calculate the line currents, the neutral current and the readings of the three wattmeters. The phase sequence is 1, 2, 3.

12. A balanced three-phase load having a lagging power factor of 0.6 takes a line current of 25 A from a 415-V, three-phase supply. A wattmeter is connected with its current coil in line 1 and its voltage coil across lines 2 and 3.

    Show that the reading of the wattmeter is $1/\sqrt{3} \times$ VAr of the load and calculate the reading in this case.

13. A 2-kW load and the generator supplying it are 1 km apart. A 12-core cable of the required length is available and both generator and load can be arranged for single-, three-, four-, six- or twelve-phase working. Thus, for single-phase working six cores are arranged in parallel for each line, for three-phase, four cores in parallel for each line, and so on.

    Calculate the transmission efficiency in each case, given that the voltage to earth at the load (voltage to star point in the polyphase cases) is 400 V and that the resistance of each core of the cable is 0.012 Ω/metre.

14. The power supplied to a balanced three-phase load is measured by two wattmeters connected in the usual way.

    Calculate the power and power factor of the load (a) when the readings are +3 kW and +700 W, (b) when the readings are +3 kW and −700 W.

BIBLIOGRAPHY

THE following texts may be consulted for further elucidation of material covered in the chapters of the present book identified by the numbers in parentheses.

1. ATABEKOV, G. I. *Linear Network Theory*, Pergamon Press, 1965. (1) (2) (3) (4) (5)
2. BOSE, A. G. and STEVENS, K. N. *Introductory Network Theory*, Harper & Row, 1965. (1) (2) (3) (4) (5)
3. BROOKES, A. M. P. *Basic Electric Circuits*, Pergamon Press, 1963. (1) (2) (3)
4. BROOKES, A. M. P. *Advanced Electric Circuits*, Pergamon Press, 1966. (2) (3) (4) (6)
5. CASSELL, W. L. *Linear Electric Circuits*, John Wiley & Sons Inc., 1964. (2) (3) (4) (5)
6. COX, C. W. and REUTER, W. L. *Circuits, Signals and Networks*, Collier-Macmillan Ltd., 1969. (1) (2) (3) (4) (5) (6)
7. CARSLAW, H. S. and JAEGER, J. C. *Operational Methods in Applied Mathematics*, Oxford University Press, 1941. (2) (3)
8. DAY, W. D. *Introduction to Laplace Transforms*, Iliffe & Sons Ltd., 1960. (2) (3)
9. EDMINISTER, J. A. *Electric Circuits*, McGraw-Hill Book Co., 1965. (1) (2) (3) (4) (6)
10. FIDLER, J. K. *Introductory Circuit Theory*, McGraw-Hill Book Co., 1979. (1) (2) (3) (4)
11. GUILLEMIN, E. A. *Introductory Circuit Theory*, John Wiley & Sons Inc., 1953. (1) (2) (3) (4)
12. HARMAN, W. W. and LYTLE, D. W. *Electrical and Mechanical Networks*, McGraw-Hill Book Co., 1962. (2) (3) (4) (6)
13. HAYT, W. H. and KEMMERLY, J. E. *Engineering Circuit Analysis*, McGraw-Hill Book Co., 1978. (1) (2) (3) (4) (5) (6)
14. HUGHES, E. *Electrical Technology*, Longman Group Ltd., 1972. (1) (3) (6)
15. JAEGER, J. C. *An Introduction to the Laplace Transformation*, Methuen & Co. Ltd., 1951. (2)
16. KUO, F. F. *Network Analysis and Synthesis*, John Wiley & Sons Inc., 1962. (2) (5)
17. MEADOWS, R. G. *Electric Network Analysis*, Penguin Books—Athlone Press of the University of London, 1972. (1) (2) (3) (4)
18. PFEIFFER, P. E. *Linear Systems Analysis*, McGraw-Hill Book Co., 1961. (2)
19. SCOTT, R. E. *Linear Circuits*, Addison-Wesley Publishing Co. Inc., 1964. (1) (2) (3) (4) (5)

20. SKILLING, H. H. *Electrical Engineering Circuits*, John Wiley & Sons Inc., 1965. (1) (2) (3) (4) (6)
21. STARKEY, B. J. *Laplace Transforms for Electrical Engineers*, Iliffe & Sons, 1958. (2)
22. TABER, M. R. and SIGALIS, E. *Electric Circuits,* Houghton Mifflin, London, 1979. (1) (3) (6)
23. TUCKER, D. G. *Elementary Electrical Network Theory*, Pergamon Press, 1964. (1) (3) (4)
24. VAN VALKENBURG, M. E. *Network Analysis*, Prentice-Hall Inc., 1961. (1) (2) (3) (4)
25. WARE, L. A. and TOWN, G. R. *Electrical Transients*, The Macmillan Company, 1954. (2)

ANSWERS TO PROBLEMS

ANSWERS I

1. (a) 5 A, (b) 300 W, (c) 2.16 MJ.
2. $i(t) = 20e^{-5t}$ A, $2000e^{-10t}$ W, 200 J.
3. 31.35 kW.
4. $266\frac{2}{3}\,\Omega$.
5. (a) 100-V source in series with 30 Ω,
   (b) 3.33-A source in parallel with 30 Ω.
6. (a) 20 A, (b) 2 A, (c) ∞.
7. 4.16 kJ.
8. 2.298 MJ.
9. (a) 12-V source in series with 0.2 Ω,
   (b) 60-A source in parallel with 0.2 Ω,
   (c) 180 W.
10. (a) 37,485 Ω in series,
    (b) 0.003 Ω in parallel.
11. 5000 V.
12. 100 mA, 0, -400 mA.
13. 2.5 A, 1000 V negative (in relation to the first pulse).
14. 4.242 kW, 8 kJ, 2320.8 J, 46.08 kJ.
15. 37.8 MW, 16.2 MJ.
16. 1118 V.
17. 1.866 63 Ω.
18. $r_1 = 558.258\,\Omega$, $r_2 = 280.258\,\Omega$, $r_3 = 106.462\,\Omega$, $r_4 = 55.022\,\Omega$.
19. $R_{AB} = 0.703\,88\,\Omega$, $G_{AB} = 0.2240$ S.
20. $a = 4$, $b = -\dfrac{2}{15}$, $V_{AB} = \left(4t + \dfrac{4}{15}\right)$ V, $i_2(t) = \left(4t - \dfrac{8}{15}\right)$ A, $i_3(t) = 0.4$ A.

ANSWERS II

1. (a) 27.36 mA,
   (b) 1.722 sec.
2. (a) 100 V,
   (b) 36.79 V,
   (c) 1.8316 V.
   $t = 11.513$ msec.

3. (a) $v_c(t) = 30$ V,
   (b) $v_c(t) = 30U(t) e^{-2t}$ V.

4. (a) $i(t) = 4$ A,
   (b) $i(t) = 4U(t) e^{-5t}$ A.

5. $i(t) = 3.5 + 0.4375 e^{-3.125t}$ A.

6. (a) $i(t) = 5$ A for $t < 0$ and $t > 0$,
   (b) $v_c(t) = 60$ V, $t < 0$ and $v_c(t) = 12(1 + 4e^{-5t})$, $t > 0$.

7. (a) $i_F(t) = -1.4286 e^{-3t}$ A,
   (b) $i_N(t) = A e^{-1.25t}$ A,
   (c) $i(t) = -1.571e^{-1.25t} - 1.4286e^{-3t}$ A,
   (d) $i(1) = -0.5213$ A.

8. $v_c(t) = 20(1 - e^{-500t})$ V.

9. (a) $i(0^+) = 50$ mA,
   (b) $i(\infty) = 0$,
   (c) $v_c(t) = 250(1 - e^{-50t})$ V,
   (d) $W = 0.01935$ J,
   (e) $W_\infty = 0.125$ J.

10. $i(t) = 51.653 e^{-2.5t} \sin 1.936t$ A.

11. $i(t) = 50 e^{-250t} - 40 e^{-500t}$ A.

12. $v(t) = 20 - 0.056 e^{-\alpha t} - 19.944 e^{-\beta t}$ V, where $\alpha = 18.944 \times 10^6$ and $\beta = 1.056 \times 10^6$.

13. $i(t) = 2.011 e^{-0.523t} - 0.011 e^{-4.777t}$ A.

14. Poles at $s = -22.81$ and -2.19, zeros at $s = -2$ and 0.
   (a) $Z(-3) = -0.9375 \Omega$,
   (b) $Z(j3) = 0.0554 + j0.6303 \Omega$.

15. Two poles at $s = -1.25 \pm j0.3227$, two zeros at $s = -0.75 \pm j1.392$. $Y(0) = 0.25$ S.

16. Natural response $A e^{-40t}$.
   (a) $i(t) = 13.33 e^{-10t}$ A,
   (b) $i(t) = 9.89 \cos(6t - 0.1489)$ A,
   (c) $i(t) = 12.649 e^{-10t} \cos(10t - 0.3218)$ A.

17. Forced response at $\sigma = -5$, $i_F(t) = 30 e^{-5t}$ A. Critical frequencies $\sigma = -6$ and $\sigma = -4$ (poles), $\sigma = 0$ and $\sigma = \infty$ (zeros). Natural response $i_N(t) = A e^{-6t} + B e^{-4t}$ A. Complete response $i(t) = 30 e^{-5t} - 18 e^{-6t} - 12 e^{-4t}$ A.

18. (a) $Z(j\omega) = 25 \angle 53°8' \Omega$, $Z(j\omega) = 15 + j20 \Omega$;
   (b) $I = 4.8 - j6.4$ A, $I = 8 \angle -53°8'$ A, $i(t) = 8 \cos(5000t - 53°8')$ A.

19. $i(t) = 2.891 \cos(\tfrac{1}{2}t + 16°2.6') + 0.012\,55 e^{-4.777t} - 2.7906 e^{-0.523t}$ A.

20. (a) $\dfrac{2}{s-1} - \dfrac{1}{s}$,

   (b) $\dfrac{3}{s} + \dfrac{1}{s^2} - \dfrac{3}{s-1} + \dfrac{2}{(s-1)^2}$,

   (c) $\dfrac{9}{49(s+3)} + \dfrac{40}{49(s-4)} + \dfrac{16}{7(s-4)^2}$,

   (d) $\dfrac{3}{2(s-3)} - \dfrac{3}{s-4} + \dfrac{3}{2(s-5)}$,

   (e) $\dfrac{9}{5(s-2)} - \dfrac{35}{13(2s-3)} + \dfrac{3s+11}{65(s^2+1)}$,

   (f) $\dfrac{3}{s+1} - \dfrac{1}{(s+1)^2} - \dfrac{3}{s+2} - \dfrac{2}{(s+2)^2}$.

21. (a) $f(t) = \dfrac{1}{\sqrt{6}} e^{-2t} \sin \sqrt{6}t,$

   (b) $f(t) = \dfrac{6}{40} e^{t} - \dfrac{1}{12} e^{-7t} - \dfrac{1}{15} e^{-4t},$

   (c) $f(t) = \dfrac{9}{5} e^{2t} - \dfrac{35}{26} e^{(3/2)t} + \dfrac{3}{65} \cos t + \dfrac{11}{65} \sin t,$

   (d) $f(t) = e^{-t} \cos 5t,$

   (e) $f(t) = \dfrac{1}{9} (\cos 4t - \cos 5t),$

   (f) $f(t) = 3 e^{-t} - t e^{-t} - 3 e^{-2t} - 2t e^{-2t}.$

22. (a) $i(t) = \dfrac{1}{61} (5 e^{(2/3)t} - 5 e^{-t} \cos 2t + 6 e^{-t} \sin 2t),$

   (b) $i(t) = -\dfrac{3}{4} - t + \dfrac{22}{8} e^{-(3/4)t} \cosh \dfrac{\sqrt{41}}{4} t + \dfrac{66}{8\sqrt{41}} e^{-(3/4)t} \sinh \dfrac{\sqrt{41}}{4} t,$

   (c) $i(t) = \dfrac{1}{9} (1 - 6t + e^{3t} + e^{-t}).$

23. $i_1(t) = 4t - e^{-7.5t} (4.5 \cos 9.683t + 0.955 \sin 9.683t), t > 0.$

24. $T(s) = \dfrac{s^2 + s + 10}{s^2 + 2s + 10}, v_0(t) = 10(1 - \tfrac{1}{3} e^{-t} \sin 3t) \text{ V}.$

ANSWERS III

1. (a) $I_m/\sqrt{2},$
   (b) $0.2236 I_m,$
   (c) $0.4077 I_m,$
   (d) $0.5774 I_m.$
2. Peak power = 6.25 kW; Mean power = 3.125 kW.
3. Peak power = 576 W; Mean power = 192 W.
4. (i) Sum = $120 \cos(\omega t + 240°)$, (ii) Sum = $84.85 \angle +240°$, (iii) Sum = a line of length 120 leading e_1 by 240°.
5. Sum = $219.61 \sin(\omega t + 33° 7')$; Sum = $23.923 \sin(\omega t + \pi)$.
6. $f = 474.2$ Hz; $V = 104.43$ V (r.m.s.).
7. $R = 37.5 \, \Omega$; $r = 17.25 \, \Omega$ and $L = 78.12$ mH; 276 W.
8. $P = 602.62$ W, p.f. = 0.9103 (lagging), 3.31 A, 54.78 W.
9. $L = 76.83$ mH, $R = 7.8125 \, \Omega$, p.f. = 0.2604 (lagging).
10. $I = 2.12$ A, $P = 112.32$ W, p.f. = 0.2208 (lagging).
11. 56.94 μF or 45.63 μF.
12. $5.37 \angle -57° 31'$ A, in-phase compt. = 2.884 A, quadrature compt. = -4.530 A, 60.08 μF, 2.884 A.

13.

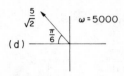

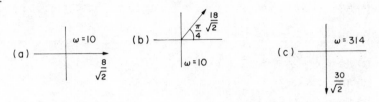

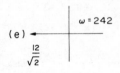

14. (a) $12 + j0 = 12 e^{j0}$,
  (b) $7.071 + j7.071 = 10 e^{j(\pi/2)}$,
  (c) $8 + j6 = 10 e^{j0.6434}$,
  (d) $-3.536 + j3.536 = 5 e^{j2.3562}$,
  (e) $0 - j15 = 15 e^{-j(\pi/2)}$.

15. (a) $12 \sqrt{2} \cos 10t$,
  (b) $15 \sqrt{2} \cos (5000t + 53°)$,
  (c) $5 \sqrt{2} \cos (314t - 60°)$,
  (d) $5 \sqrt{2} \cos (280t - 53° 7')$,
  (e) $\sqrt{2} \cos [1000t + (\pi/2)]$,
  (f) $20 \sqrt{2} \cos [3t + (\pi/4)]$,
  (g) $0.675 \sqrt{2} \cos [500t + (\pi/4)]$.

16. (a) $25 e^{-j(\pi/2)}$,
  (b) $2 e^{-j2.213}$,
  (c) $e^{j4.069}$.

17. $22.742 e^{-j0.2005} \, \Omega$ (or $22.742 \angle -0.2005 \, \Omega$).

18. (a) $119.96 e^{j1.2262} \, V$,
  (b) $2.398 \, kW$,
  (c) $62.81 \, VA$ (lagging).

19. (a) $61.8 \, kW$,
  (b) $64.57 \, kVA$,
  (c) $18.7 \, kVAr$, p.f. $= 0.957$ (lagging).

20. $1.5 \, kW$ at 0.624 p.f. (lagging).

21. $81.928 - j9.353 \, \Omega$.

22. $L = 0.71716 \, H$, $R = 53.137 \, \Omega$.

23. p.f. $= 0.001$, $R_{se} = \frac{1}{3} \, \Omega$, $C_{se} = 0.3 \, \mu F$.

24. $\mathbf{Y}_T = 0.147 - j0.02157 \, S$, $\mathbf{I} = 4.459 \angle 36° 39' \, A$, $P = 131.6 \, W$.

25. $r = 36 \, \Omega$, $C = 12.5 \, \mu F$; $C_1 = 22.727 \, \mu F$ and $C_2 = 8.621 \, \mu F$.

26. (a) $G_A = 0.02$ S, $B_A = -0.04$ S, $Y_A = (0.02 - j0.04)$ S; $G_B = 0.0333$ S,
$B_B = -0.0333$ S, $Y_B = (0.0333 - j0.0333)$ S; $G_T = 0.0533$ S, $B_T = -0.0733$ S,
$Y_T = (0.0533 - j0.0733)$ S.
(b) $I = 21.333 - j29.333$ A, $P = 8.533$ kW, p.f. $= 0.588$, lagging.
(c) $244.4\,\mu$F.

27. $C = 506.6$ pF, $Q = 50$, $\frac{1}{2}$-power points at 990.05 kHz and 1010.05 kHz.

28. $C = 253.303$ pF, $\frac{1}{2}$-power points at 281.448 pF and 230.275 pF.

29. (a) $C = 253.303$ pF,
(b) $C = 250.795$ pF, Ratio $V_c/V = 10.0498$.

30. $f_r = 58.848$ Hz, $R_D = 357.77\,\Omega$.

32. (a) $p_{max} = 6$ kW,
(b) $kVA_{max} = 6.324$ kVA, $kVA_{min} = 4$ kVA.

33. $R_c = \sqrt{L/C}$.

ANSWERS IV

1. (a) 2.5 V,
(b) 0.1724 A.

2. $I = 1.5333$ A, $P = 23.511$ W.

3. $V_{AB} = 62.924$ V.

4. $I = 0.91102$ A.

5. $I = 0.2144$ A.

6. $R_L = r$, 12 Ω, 0.1875 W.

7. $i_1 = 3$ A, $i_2 = 2$ A, $i_3 = 1$ A.

8. Taking the centre node as the reference: $V_1 = 8.521$ V, $V_2 = 9.014$ V, $V_3 = 6$ V, $V_4 = 5.366$ V, then $I_1 = 0.493$ A, $I_2 = 1.507$ A, $I_3 = 0.2113$ A, $I_4 = 0.7887$ A, $I_5 = 0.296$ A.

9. $I = 1.2$ A.

10.

Graph   Tree

$I_{25} = 0.5$ A, $I_{50} = 1$ A, $I_{7.5} = 5$ A,
$I_5 = 4.5$ A. 6-A source, $P = 720$ W;
1.5-A source, $P = 13.125$ W.

11.

$I_1 = 2.054$ A, $I_2 = 0.4325$ A,
$I_3 = 1.6216$ A, $I_4 = 4.3784$ A,
$I_5 = 3.9459$ A, $P = 75.892$ W.

Graph   Tree

12. $V = 6.823 \angle 25.374°$ V.

13. $V = 77.667 \angle 45.62°$ V, Power = 747.99 W. $E = 15.53 \angle -7.51°$ V and
$Z = 6.295 \angle -45.78°\,\Omega$, $I_{10} = 1.03 \angle 9.898°$ A.

14. Thévenin: $\mathbf{V} = 44.721\ \angle 73.435°$ in series with $(5 + j5)$;
   Norton: $\mathbf{I} = 6.325\ \angle 28.435°$ in parallel with $(5 + j5)$.

15. $R = \dfrac{\omega^2 C r^2 C_1 R_1}{1 + \omega^2 C^2 r^2}$, $\quad L = \dfrac{r C_1 R_1}{1 + \omega^2 C^2 r^2}$.

16. (i) $\omega^2 LC = 2\dfrac{R_1}{R}$, (ii) $L = \dfrac{2 C R R_1^2}{R - 4R_1}$.

17. $\mathbf{I} = 0.412\ \angle -11.746°$ A.

ANSWERS V

1.

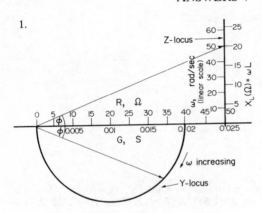

(a) $G = 0.017$ S, $B = 0.007$ S at $\omega = 50$;
(b) $G_{max} = 0.02$ S at $\omega = 0$, $B_{max} = 0.01$ S at $\omega = 125$;
(c) $\mathbf{I} = 1.685$ A at $32.6°$ lagging at $\omega = 80$.

2.

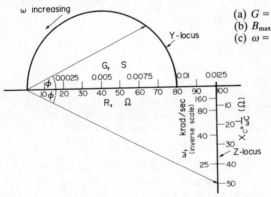

(a) $G = 0.008$ S, $B = 0.004$ S;
(b) $B_{max} = 0.005$ S at $\omega = 10^4$;
(c) $\omega = 17$ krad/sec and 5.9 krad/sec.

3.

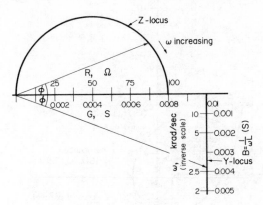

(a) $X_{max} = 50 \ \Omega$ at $\omega = 1000$ rad/sec;
(b) $R = 69.4 \ \Omega$, $X = 46 \ \Omega$, $L = 30.67$ mH at $\omega = 1500$ rad/sec.

4.

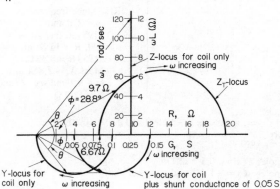

At $\omega = 120$ rad/sec,
$Z = 9.7 \ \angle 28.8 \ \Omega$,
$R = 8.7 \ \Omega$, $X = 4.7 \ \Omega$.

5.

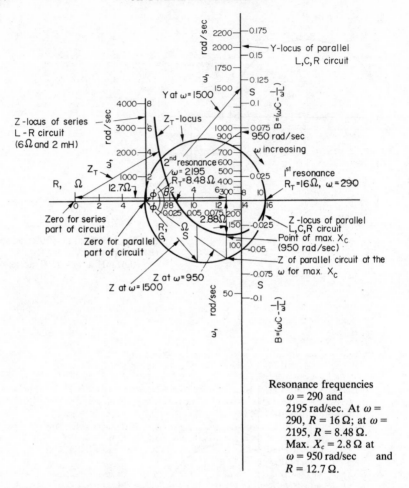

Resonance frequencies
$\omega = 290$ and
2195 rad/sec. At $\omega =$
290, $R = 16\,\Omega$; at $\omega =$
2195, $R = 8.48\,\Omega$.
Max. $X_c = 2.8\,\Omega$ at
$\omega = 950$ rad/sec and
$R = 12.7\,\Omega$.

6. (a) Poles at $s = -1$ and $s = \infty$, zeros at $s = -1.1099$ and $s = -0.0901$.

(b) Pole at $s = -\dfrac{R_1 + R_2}{L}$, zero at $s = -\dfrac{R_1}{L}$.

(c) Zero when $s = \infty$, poles at $s = -0.5 \pm j2.179$.

(d) Zero when $s = \infty$, poles at $s = -7.545$ and $s = -1.955$.

7. $Z(s) = \dfrac{3s^2 + 18s + 135}{2s^2 + 14s + 20}$, $\mathbf{Z}(j3) = 2.872\ \angle - 60°\,42'\ \Omega$.

8. $T(s) = \dfrac{50s}{s^2 + 5s + 4}$; $\mathbf{V}_o = 76.57\ \angle - 10.03°$ volts.

9.

ω	0	1	2	3	4
$G(s)$	0	4.85 $\angle 76°$	8.94 $\angle 63.4°$	12 $\angle 53.1°$	14.14 $\angle 45°$

ω	5	6	7	8
$G(s)$	15.6 $\angle 38.7°$	16.6 $\angle 33.7°$	17.4 $\angle 29.7°$	17.9 $\angle 26.6°$

10.

ω	1	2	3	4	5
$Y(s)$	1.55 $\angle 55.3°$	3.27 $\angle 80.7°$	8.18 $\angle 85.9°$	23.6 $\angle 34.5°$	13.2 $\angle -20.2°$

ω	6	7	8	9	10
$Y(s)$	8.6 $\angle -26.3°$	6.9 $\angle -25.8°$	6.05 $\angle -24.2°$	5.54 $\angle -22.4°$	5.21 $\angle -20.7°$

At $\omega = 5$ rad/sec, $\mathbf{I} = 27.26 \angle 39.8°$ A. Resonance at $\omega = 4.395$ rad/sec.

11. A drop of 7 dB between ω_1 and ω_2.

12. 4 dB loss.

13. Gain = 37.6 dB.

14. (i) Gain constant at -14 dB up to $\omega = 5$, then falls at 20 dB/decade. At $\omega = 10$, gain = -21 dB. Phase is 0 at low frequencies, $-90°$ at high frequencies, $-45°$ at $\omega = 5$. At $\omega = 10$, phase = $-63°26'$.

   (ii) Gain = -14 dB at $\omega = 1$, rising at 20 dB/decade to 0 dB at $\omega = 5$, continuing at 0 dB thereafter. Phase is $+90°$ at low frequencies, falling to 0 at high frequencies, passing through 45° at $\omega = 5$. At $\omega = 2$, $\mathbf{T}(j2) = -8.6$ dB, phase = 68.2°.

  (iii) Gain = -8 dB, constant up to $\omega = 2$ when it rises at 20 dB/decade to 0 dB at $\omega = 5$ and stays at 0 dB thereafter. Phase rises from about 1.7° at $\omega = 0.1$ to a maximum of about $+26°$ at $\omega = 3$ and falls to 1.7° again at $\omega = 100$. At $\omega = 8$, gain = -1.17 dB, phase = $+17.79°$.

  (iv) Gain = 1.58 dB constant up to $\omega = 3$ when it rises at 20 dB/decade to $+6$ dB at $\omega = 5$ and stays at this value thereafter. Phase goes from $+180°$ at $\omega = 0.1$ to 0 at $\omega = 1000$, passing through $+150.3°$ at $\omega = 1$, $+43.3°$ at $\omega = 10$, $+4.58°$ at $\omega = 100$. At $\omega = 10$ gain = 5.43 dB, phase = 43.3°.

  (v) Gain = -20 dB up to $\omega = 2$, then falls at 20 dB/decade up to $\omega = 5$, then falls at 40 dB/decade. Phase is 0 at low frequencies and goes to $-180°$ at high frequencies. At $\omega = 100$, gain = -80 dB, phase = $-176°$.

  (vi) Gain is rising at 20 dB/decade from low frequencies, passing through -28 dB at $\omega = 1$ and -14 dB at $\omega = 5$, then falls at 20 dB/decade from $\omega = 5$ upwards. Phase is constant at $+90°$ up to $\omega = 5$ and changes abruptly to $-90°$ from $\omega = 5$ upwards. Gain = ∞ at $\omega = 5$ and the phase is indeterminate. At $\omega = 50$, gain = -33.9 dB, phase is $-90°$.

15. Bode plot: gain rising at low frequencies at 20 dB/decade, passing through $+30$ dB at $\omega = 1$ to $+50$ dB at $\omega = 10$, then constant at 50 dB to $\omega = 10^4$ when it falls at 20 dB/decade for ω increasing. Phase shift changes from $+90°$ at low frequencies to $-90°$ at high frequencies, passing through $+45°$ at $\omega = 10$ and $-45°$ at $\omega = 10^4$.
   (i) Half-power points at $\omega = 10$ and $\omega = 10^4$ rad/sec.
   (ii) Mid-band gain = 50 dB.
16. Bode plot: gain rising at low frequencies at 20 dB/decade, passing through -32.4 dB at $\omega = 1$, then at $+40$ dB/decade from $\omega = 20$ to $\omega = 100$, then at 20 dB/decade from $\omega = 100$ to $\omega = 500$, then falls at 20 dB/decade for ω increasing. Gain is 0 dB at $\omega = 26$ and $\omega = 3 \times 10^4$ rad/sec. Phase is $-90°$ at low frequencies, rising to about $+17.4°$ at $\omega = 100$ and falling to $-90°$ again at high frequencies. Phase is $-27.2°$ at $\omega = 26$ and $-88.7°$ at $\omega = 3 \times 10^4$ rad/sec.

ANSWERS VI

1. (a) 262.17 W,
   (b) 1.478 A,
   (c) p.f. = 0.2468,
   (d) neutral current = 0.
2. $I_L = 0.4305$ A; power factor = 0.8474 (lagging).
3. $I_L = 2.2093$ A; power factor = 0.165 (leading).
4. $I_1 = 11.809 + j0$ A, $I_2 = -7.873 - j13.636$ A, $I_3 = -9.841 + j17.045$ A, $I_N = 5.905 - j3.409$ A.
5. Phase currents: $i_1 = 20 + j0$ A, $i_2 = -21.65 - j12.5$ A, $i_3 = -40 + j0$ A.
   Line currents: $I_1 = 60 + j0$ A, $I_2 = -41.65 - j12.5$ A, $I_3 = -18.35 + j12.5$ A.
6. (a) $I_1 = 27.578 - j49.258 = 56.453 \angle -60°45'$ A,
       $I_2 = -19.895 + j4.526 = 20.403 \angle 167°11'$,
       $I_3 = -7.683 + j44.732 = 45.387 \angle 99°45'$, 27.487 kW.
   (b) $I_1 = 27.578 - j49.258 = 56.453 \angle -60°45'$ A,
       $I_2 = -22 + j22 = 31.113 \angle 135°$ A,
       $I_3 = -5.578 + j27.258 = 27.823 \angle 101°34'$ A, 21.292 kW.
7. Load = 12 kW, $I_1 = 20.87 \angle 0$, $I_2 = -10.434 - j18.072 = 20.868 \angle -120°$,
   $I_3 = -10.434 + j18.072 = 20.868 \angle 120°$,
   Load = 24 kW, $|I_1| = |I_2| = 36.145$ A, $|I_3| = 62.604$ A.
8. V = 202.75 V; taking this as the reference phasor, V_2 lags by 127° 3' and V_3 by a further 105° 54', for phase sequence 1, 2, 3.
9. 83.27 V; taking voltage red-to-neutral as reference, $I_R = 34.87 \angle 6°35'$, $I_Y = 28.84 \angle -136°06'$, $I_B = 21.17 \angle 130°54'$; $P_5 = 6.08$ kW, $P_{10} = 8.32$ kW, $P_{15} = 6.72$ kW.
10. $I_L = 16.064$ A, p.f. = 0.866, $W_1 = 3.333$ kW, $W_2 = 6.666$ kW.
11. Line currents: $I_1 = 9.584 \angle -36°52'$ A, $I_2 = 8.471 \angle -75°$ A, $I_3 = 5.811 \angle 105°58'$ A (voltage $V_{1.2}$ taken as the reference). $I_N = 11.743 \angle 134°42\frac{1}{2}'$ A. $W_1 = 1.837$ kW, $W_2 = 1.435$ kW, $W_3 = 1.351$ kW.
12. Wattmeter reading = 8.3 kVAr.
13. Single-phase, $\eta = 95.238\%$; all other cases, $\eta = 98.765\%$.
14. (a) Power = 3700 W, p.f. = 0.6805;
    (b) Power = 2300 W, p.f. = 0.3378.

INDEX